THE MACMILLAN COMPANY
NEW YORK · BOSTON · CHICAGO
DALLAS · ATLANTA · SAN FRANCISCO

MACMILLAN AND CO., LIMITED
LONDON · BOMBAY · CALCUTTA
MADRAS · MELBOURNE

THE MACMILLAN COMPANY
OF CANADA, LIMITED
TORONTO

THE LOGIC OF THE SCIENCES
AND THE HUMANITIES

THE LOGIC OF THE SCIENCES

AND THE HUMANITIES

F. S. C. NORTHROP

STERLING PROFESSOR OF PHILOSOPHY AND LAW

IN YALE UNIVERSITY

"Those rules of old, discover'd, not devis'd,
Are nature still, but nature methodiz'd."
— POPE

THE MACMILLAN COMPANY · NEW YORK

1948

To
Douglas C. Macintosh
and
Henry M. Sheffer

PREFACE

Logic is conceived in this book in the broadest possible manner. The emphasis is upon its applications in the diverse scientific methods of the several natural and social sciences and in the humanities.

Any specific scientific method is studied in connection with some specific theory and subject matter of a specific science in which its use is appropriate. As a consequence, many of the chapters of this volume are reprints of papers written at the request of specific scientific research groups and brought together here for the first time from diverse professional journals in the field of the natural sciences, the social sciences, both factual and normative, philosophy and the humanities. This results in a certain amount of repetition of general principles and distinctions, but it has the advantage of keeping the consideration of logic and scientific method in contact (a) with the empirical materials of the specific subjects to which it applies and (b) with technical scientific theories which it has successfully verified and the diverse humanistic arts which they have influenced, both normatively and technically. It also results in a treatise on logic and scientific method which in considerable part has been called forth by the needs of experts in scientific research in different fields and has passed through the fire of their critical judgment. In each instance where this has occurred, the professional group and journal are indicated at the end of the chapter in question, with an acknowledgement of indebtedness for the permission to republish. The first seven, and several other, chapters of this volume, formulating the general principles, distinctions and sequence of analysis, appear in print here for the first time.

Deductive logic, with its use of formal logic as well as inductive logic, is emphasized. Since there are many books on formal logic proper, both traditional and modern, no section on the basic technical concepts and rules of formal logic is included.

Logic is also conceived broadly in this volume to include any form of knowing in religion and art as well as the sciences proper. Thus the Oriental method of immediate apprehension, close to aesthetic sensitivity, which the experts in Oriental ways of knowing call the method of intuition, is treated here as falling under logic. This intimately relates logic to art, to culture and to the humanities generally, including religion. It also relates logic and scientific method to the relation between the knower and what he is knowing in the subject matter in question. Thus, the book is as much a treatise on epistemology as on logic.

Most important of all perhaps is the emphasis from the very outset upon the primacy of the character of the specific type of problem in scholarly inquiry and the attendant distinction in the social sciences and the humanities between problems of fact and problems of value and between factual theory and normative theory respectively. Each has its unique method or its unique sequence of methods, for scientific verification.

Even the scientific methods for solving problems of fact are much more diverse than is usually supposed, varying in the natural sciences from one stage of inquiry to another and being different in the deductive theory of modern economic science from what they are in modern mathematical physics, as Chapters VIII and XIII show.

The emphasis upon the primacy of the character of the problem results in the relativity of scientific method to the type of problem before one and the stage of inquiry with respect to that type of problem.   It follows that there is no one scientific method and that to talk about scientific method apart from the specification of the specific stage of inquiry for a given type of problem is as meaningless as to talk about either space by itself or time by itself, apart from the specification of the frame of reference from which each is determined.

Consequently, the problem of the traditional treatises on scientific method, concerning whether Bacon, Cohen or John Dewey has the correct conception of it, turns out to be a pseudo-problem. There is no one scientific method.   John Dewey has the appropriate method for one stage of inquiry, even though he never pursued it fully.   Bacon is correct for another stage, and Cohen for still another stage.

Such are some of the fruits of cultivating an understanding of logic and scientific method as they exhibit themselves in different specific scientific investigations, as compared with its cultivation in a vacuum or in the light of its character in one specific type of science, as has happened all too often in the traditional treatises on the subject.

The approach of this volume with its emphasis upon the primacy of the problem and the attendant relativity of scientific methods, directs attention also from the very outset to the difference between problems of fact and problems of value in the social sciences and humanities with the attendant differences in scientific methods.   It thereby forces one to face the previously controversial and unresolved question concerning whether normative or ethical problems can be solved by scientific methods and if so, what the specific methods are.

This is the most difficult portion of the entire inquiry. Two things demonstrate the inadequacy of the traditional answers of social scientists and moral philosophers.   One is the inadequacy of the methods they propose as exhibited by an analysis of the difference between problems of fact and problems of value and between factual theories and normative theories. The other is the failure of the traditional methods to solve a single specific normative problem of our world, notwithstanding the fact that the proposed traditional methods have been known for decades, if not centuries. If the methods for handling problems of fact in the natural sciences could evidence in their support only talk about their adequacy, while never solving a specific scientific problem or verifying a specific theory, to remove it from the realm of controversy and debate, experts studying nature would most certainly reject them. It is time for social scientists, moral philosophers and humanists generally to do the same with the traditionally proposed methods for solving ethical and normative social questions.

The clue to the correct method is the character of problems of value and the character of normative theory. The heart of the difficulty centers in what we term the paradox of moral authority. Analysis of the character of normative problems and normative theory carried through in Chapters IV and XVII specifies the resolution of this paradox, and Chapter XXI specifies the requisite scientific method.

It happens that the complete scientific procedure for solving problems of value is complicated, combining the scientific method in the third stage of inquiry in the natural sciences with the purely analytic scientific method of the philosophy of natural science, which in turn is combined with the analytic and inductive-deductive methods of the philosophy of culture and the humanities. The manner in which such a scientifically verified normative social theory or philosophy of culture designates normative economic, political, aesthetic and religious theory which is valid for everyone is then indicated in the concluding chapters, with a sketch of the specific ideology which a contemporary application of this scientific method prescribes.

The result is a procedure which may bring scientific verification and attendant human agreement into the present demoralized world of ideological humanistic controversy. In any event, a method for the humanities as well as the technical sciences is indicated, and the harmonious relation between them is specified. Hence the title, *The Logic of the Sciences and the Humanities.*

Grateful acknowledgment is herewith given to Harcourt, Brace and Company and Henry Holt and Company for permission to quote at some length in Chapter I from *An Introduction to Logic and Scientific Method* by Morris Cohen and Ernest Nagel and from *Logic: The Theory of Inquiry* by John Dewey. Also, similar acknowledgment is given to the Princeton University Press for permission to reprint, in this volume as Chapters V and XXIV, parts of my lengthy monograph in their volume *Philosophy: East and West,* edited by Charles A. Moore, and for similar permission to reprint here, as Chapters XX and XXII, two articles in the forthcoming proceedings of the Princeton Bicentennial Celebration. Similar permission from the editors of many professional journals are also deeply appreciated. Specific acknowledgment in each instance appears at the end of the chapter in question.

Financial aid from the Viking Fund, and the devoted and efficient care of Miss Edith Burnham have made possible the preparation of the manuscript for the publisher. The attention and tireless effort of the editors of The Macmillan Company are also especially appreciated.

Of longer range is my permanent debt to my first teachers in epistemology and logic, Douglas C. Macintosh and Henry M. Sheffer. Hence, the dedication of this book to them.

F. S. C. Northrop

New Haven, Connecticut

TABLE OF CONTENTS

TABLE OF CONTENTS

CHAPTER I

THE INITIATION OF INQUIRY

The most difficult portion of any inquiry is its initiation. One may have the most rigorous of methods during the later stages of investigation, but if a false or superficial beginning has been made, rigor later on will never retrieve the situation. It is like a ship leaving port for a distant destination. A very slight erroneous deviation in taking one's bearings at the beginning may result in entirely missing one's mark at the end regardless of the sturdiness of one's craft or the excellence of one's subsequent seamanship.

Again and again investigators have plunged into a subject matter, sending out questionnaires, gathering a tremendous amount of data, even performing experiments, only to come out at the end wondering what it all proves, and realizing after years of industry and effort that the real difficulty has slipped through their fingers. Others, noting the success of a given scientific method in one field, have carried this method hastily and uncritically into their own, only to end later on in a similar disillusionment. All such experiences are a sign that the initiation of inquiry has been glossed over too hastily, without any appreciation of its importance or its difficulty.

There are many reasons for believing that perhaps more than anywhere else it is at the beginning of any investigation that the source of genius is to be found. For what characterizes a genius like Galilei, Lavoisier or Einstein is the economy of thought and effort by means of which he achieves his result. Each one of these men found the key factor in the situation and went directly to the heart of the problem which had been baffling his predecessors. The methods which all three used at later stages of their investigation are well known. It was in finding the key difficulty and in knowing precisely at what points to direct the well-known methods that their genius consists.

This capacity to find the heart of the problem to which the well-known methods are to be applied is a part of inquiry that must precede the actual understanding or application of the methods. It is what comes at the beginning which is the key to success, since it is the effectiveness with which one initiates inquiry that directs one to the key facts and designates the appropriate methods.

Notwithstanding its importance and the difficulty of handling it effectively, the initiation of inquiry has received very little attention. Scientists know the techniques for performing experiments once they know what experiments to perform. Theoretical physicists and pure mathematicians know how to carry through rigorous logical deductions and precise calculations once they know the postulates or assumptions with which they are to begin. All the methods for the later stages of inquiry are well known. Countless books about them have been written. But what to do at the very beginning in order to determine which of the possible methods is to be used for the inquiry in question and in order to find among the infinite number of facts in experience the particular ones to which the particular methods chosen are to be applied — with respect to these initial difficulties the textbooks on methodology are ominously silent, or if they say anything their authors unequivocally disagree.

The Disagreement of the Authorities

If one asks the classical experts on method in either science or philosophy what the specific procedure is to be followed at the very beginning of inquiry, one gets as many different

answers as there are authorities. Four examples will suffice
to make this clear: Francis Bacon, René Descartes, Morris
Cohen and John Dewey.

(a) Francis Bacon

In his famous *Aphorisms,* Bacon states his position as follows:

APHORISM

I

Man, being the servant and interpreter of Nature, can do and
understand so much and so much only as he has observed in fact
or in thought of the course of nature: beyond this he neither
knows anything nor can do anything.

II

Neither the naked hand nor the understanding left to itself
can effect much. It is by instruments and helps that the work is
done, which are as much wanted for the understanding as for
the hand. And as the instruments of the hand either give motion
or guide it, so the instruments of the mind supply either suggestions for the understanding or cautions.

IX

The cause and root of nearly all evils in the sciences is this —
that while we falsely admire and extol the powers of the human
mind we neglect to seek for its true helps.

XII

The logic now in use serves rather to fix and give stability to
the errors which have their foundation in commonly received
notions than to help the search after truth. So it does more
harm than good.

XIV

The syllogism consists of propositions, propositions consist of
words, words are symbols of notions. Therefore if the notions

themselves (which is the root of the matter) are confused and over-hastily abstracted from the facts, there can be no firmness in the superstructure. Our only hope therefore lies in a true induction.

XIX

There are and can be only two ways of searching into and discovering truth. The one flies from the senses and particulars to the most general axioms, and from these principles, the truth of which it takes for settled and immoveable, proceeds to judgment and to the discovery of middle axioms. And this way is now in fashion. The other derives axioms from the senses and particulars, rising by a gradual and unbroken ascent, so that it arrives at the most general axioms last of all. This is the true way, but as yet untried.

XX

The understanding left to itself takes the same course (namely, the former) which it takes in accordance with logical order. For the mind longs to spring up to positions of higher generality, that it may find rest there; and so after a little while wearies of experiment. But this evil is increased by logic, because of the order and solemnity of its disputations.

XXII

Both ways set out from the senses and particulars, and rest in the highest generalities; but the difference between them is infinite. For the one just glances at experiment and particulars in passing, the other dwells duly and orderly among them. The one, again, begins at once by establishing certain abstract and useless generalities, the other rises by gradual steps to that which is prior and better known in the order of nature.

XXIV

It cannot be that axioms established by argumentation should avail for the discovery of new works; since the subtlety of nature is greater many times over than the subtlety of argument. But axioms duly and orderly formed from particulars easily discover the way to new particulars, and thus render sciences active.

XXVI

The conclusions of human reason as ordinarily applied in matter of nature, I call for the sake of distinction *Anticipations of Nature* (as a thing rash or premature). That reason which is elicited from facts by a just and methodical process, I call *Interpretation of Nature.*

XXX

Though all the wits of all the ages should meet together and combine and transmit their labours, yet will no great progress ever be made in science by means of anticipations; because radical errors in the first concoction of the mind are not to be cured by the excellence of functions and remedies subsequent.

XXXVI

One method of delivery alone remains to us; which is simply this: we must lead men to the particulars themselves, and their series and order; while men on their side must force themselves for awhile to lay their notions by and begin to familiarize themselves with facts.

XXXVIII

The idols and false notions which are now in possession of the human understanding, and have taken deep root therein, not only so beset men's minds that truth can hardly find entrance, but even after entrance obtained, they will again in the very instauration of the sciences meet and trouble us, unless men being forewarned of the danger fortify themselves as far as may be against their assaults.

XXXIX

There are four classes of Idols which beset men's minds. To these for distinction's sake I have assigned names, — calling the first class *Idols of the Tribe;* the second, *Idols of the Cave;* the third, *Idols of the Market-place;* the fourth, *Idols of the Theatre.*

XL

The formation of ideas and axioms by true induction is no doubt the proper remedy to be applied for the keeping off and

clearing away of idols. To point them out, however, is of great
use.

Our question is, What is the first thing to do when one initiates any inquiry? To this query Bacon's answer is clear.
One must proceed purely inductively, putting all preconceived ideas, or Idols, aside. Aphorism XXVI specifies that
all *"Anticipations of Nature,"* *i.e.,* all hypotheses, are to be
rejected also as "rash or premature." Also formal logic is
to be rejected since it tends to "fix and give stability" to old
errors.

(b) René Descartes

In his *Discourse on Method* Descartes tells us of his disillusionment with respect to the traditional knowledge of his
time, notwithstanding the fact that he had been educated in
"one of the most celebrated schools in Europe." The traditional natural science of his time had broken down, even
though its founder, Aristotle, had placed an excessive emphasis upon sense awareness and constructed the empirical
sciences by means of the methods of observation, description
and classification. The humanistic studies of Descartes' time,
while cultivating the imagination, were equally unsatisfactory because of the conflicting and doubtful values which
they expressed. And in philosophy Descartes adds that "no
truth is to be found therein which is not disputed, and which
consequently is not doubtful."

Finding the teaching of the schools thus unsatisfactory,
Descartes turned to the practical judgments of the men of
the world, employing the remainder of his youth in traveling. "For it seemed to me," he writes, "that I could meet
with much more truth in the reasoning which each man
made touching the things which concerned himself, and
whose immediate consequences would soon punish him for
any errors of judgment than in those made by a scholar in
his study concerning speculations which produce no effect.

. . ." But this prospect turned out to be illusory also: "I remarked almost as much diversity among them [practical men of the world] as I had done before among the opinions of the philosophers."

But among all Descartes' theoretical and practical experiences one bit of knowledge stood out. He "took pleasure in mathematics, because of the certainty and evidence of their reasons, but I did not yet remark their true use; and thinking that they served the mechanical arts alone, I was surprised that since their foundations were so firm and solid, nothing more lofty had been built upon them." This, as we shall see, gives Descartes his clue and determines his later emphasis upon the importance of reasoning deductively, after the manner of the mathematicians, rather than upon the empirical, inductive method of Bacon.

Like Bacon, however, Descartes finds the traditional use of the syllogisms of logic to be unsatisfactory. "And although they indeed contain many very true and very good precepts, there are always so many others mingled therewith that it is almost as difficult to separate them as to extract a Diana or a Minerva from a block of marble not yet rough hewn."

Even the methods of mathematics, while trustworthy, needed supplementation: ". . . as to the analysis of the ancients and the algebra of the moderns, besides that they extend only to extremely abstract matters and appear to have no other use, the first is always so restricted to the consideration of figures that it cannot exercise the understanding without greatly fatiguing the imagination, and in the other one is so bound down to certain rules and ciphers that it has been made a confused and obscure art which embarrasses the mind, instead of a science which cultivates it. This made me think that some other method must be sought, which, while combining the advantages of these three, should be free from their defects." The third method, in addition to those of analysis and algebra, is the deductive method of formal logic.

Thus Descartes comes upon his four rules of method:

The first was, never to accept anything as true when I did not recognise it clearly to be so, that is to say, to carefully avoid precipitation and prejudice, and to include in my opinions nothing beyond that which should present itself so clearly and so distinctly to my mind that I might have no occasion to doubt it.

The second was, to divide each of the difficulties which I should examine into as many portions as were possible, and as should be required for its better solution.

The third was, to conduct my thoughts in order, by beginning with the simplest objects, and those most easy to know, so as to mount little by little, as if by steps, to the most complex knowledge, and even assuming an order among those which do not naturally precede one another.

And the last was, to make everywhere enumerations so complete, and surveys so wide that I should be sure of omitting nothing.

Upon a first reading Descartes' prescription seems similar to that of Francis Bacon. If the biographical background is kept in mind, however, and if his subsequent application of these four rules is examined, it immediately becomes evident that Descartes' prescription, apart from its negative aspect, is directly opposed to that of Bacon.

To be sure, Descartes, like Bacon, urges one to get all traditional notions out of one's mind. In the case of Bacon this is accomplished by designating the four Idols which are convenient names for different types of traditional procedure or belief. Thus Bacon gets rid of traditional beliefs by noting them empirically and by putting the empirical data given through the senses in the center of one's consciousness. Descartes, on the other hand, removes the traditional beliefs by the intellectual method of doubting. One will admit into one's knowledge only those beliefs which are so clear and so distinct that they cannot be doubted. This is the negative portion of Descartes' procedure. The positive portion begins with this bare minimum of intellectually indubitable, clear and distinct ideas and moves step by step to the remainder of all trustworthy knowledge. This step by step procedure is not, as it was for Bacon, that of inductively piling up observable empirical data, but the deductive, formal method of the mathematicians. Descartes writes, ". . . it is the mathematicians alone who have been able to find demonstrations, . . . I did not doubt that I must start with the same things that they have considered. . . ." Thus immediately after specifying his four rules, Descartes writes:

The long chains of perfectly simple and easy reasons which geometers are accustomed to employ in order to arrive at their most difficult demonstrations, had given me reason to believe that all things which can fall under the knowledge of man succeed each other in the same way, and that provided only we abstain from receiving as true any opinions which are not true, and always observe the necessary order in *deducing* one from the other, there can be none so remote that they may not be reached, or so hidden that they may not be discovered.

Descartes' answer to our question concerning the method to be used in initiating inquiry is now clear. One's procedure is purely rationalistic. One intellectually doubts everything which can possibly be doubted and then, from the indubitable minimum which remains, one *deduces* the remainder of one's knowledge.

The reasons for Descartes' prescriptions are easy to understand. All his traditional knowledge except that in mathematics had failed him. We need hardly wonder, therefore, that he began with doubting. The one branch of his traditional knowledge which did stand up was mathematics. Its method is the deductive one of formal logic rather than the empirical procedure of the natural sciences. Hence Descartes' confidence in deductive reasoning.

(c) Morris Cohen

Morris Cohen appreciates both the empirical inductive method of Bacon and the deductive method of mathematical logic, mathematics and mathematical physics. Like both

Bacon and Descartes there is a negative portion to his prescription. It consists in designating, after the manner of Bacon's *Idols,* three frequently used methods which are untrustworthy. These methods are the *Method of Tenacity,* the *Method of Authority* and the *Method of Intuition.* The meaning of the first two methods is evident in their names. Only the Method of Intuition requires a description. By the intuitive, Morris Cohen and his pupil Ernest Nagel mean, not the empirical intuition of immediately apprehended fact, but the theoretical intuition of supposedly self-evident postulates or axioms. Of the latter they write as follows:

Unfortunately, it is difficult to find a proposition for which at some time or other "self-evidence" has not been claimed. Propositions regarded as indubitable by many, for example, that the earth is flat, have been shown to be false. It is well known that "self-evidence" is often a function of current fashions and of early training. The fact, therefore, that we feel absolutely certain, or that a given proposition has not before been questioned, is no guarantee against its being proved false. Our intuitions must, then, be tested.

The positive part of Cohen and Nagel's thesis is to be found in the method of science or reflective inquiry. It "differs radically [from the other methods] by encouraging and developing the utmost possible doubt, so that what is left after such doubt is always supported by the best available evidence." Also, as Charles Peirce had emphasized previously, unlike the other methods it makes provision "for correcting its own results."

What is the nature of scientific method as conceived by Morris Cohen and Ernest Nagel? An answer to this question should throw light on our initial query concerning the method to be used in initiating any investigation.

Their position shows in the quotation from T.*H. Huxley which they place at the head of their chapter on scientific method. "Those," Huxley writes, "who refuse to go beyond fact rarely get as far as fact. . . . Almost every great step has been made by the 'anticipation of nature,' that is, by the invention of hypotheses which, though verifiable, often had very little foundation to start with." Clearly, Huxley's quoted "anticipation of nature" refers to Francis Bacon. It will be recalled that for Bacon "anticipation of nature" should be rejected.

Morris Cohen and Ernest Nagel, like Huxley, oppose Bacon's thesis. "It is," they write, "an utterly superficial view . . . that the truth is to be found by 'studying the facts.' It is superficial because no inquiry can ever get under way until and unless *some difficulty is felt* in a practical or theoretical situation.

"We cannot take a single step forward in any inquiry unless we begin with a *suggested* explanation or solution of the difficulty which originated it. Such tentative explanations are suggested to us by something in the subject matter and by our previous knowledge. When they are formulated as propositions, they are called *hypotheses*.

"The function of a hypothesis is to *direct* our search for the order among facts. The suggestions formulated in the hypothesis *may* be solutions to the problem. *Whether* they are, is the task of the inquiry."

The answer of Cohen and Nagel to our query concerning the method to be used in initiating inquiry is now clear. Starting with the problem which initiates inquiry, coupled with skepticism with respect to traditional beliefs, one pursues hypotheses, testing them by the method of trial and error. Thus whereas in initiating inquiry Bacon placed the emphasis upon collecting data, and Descartes upon rationalistic logical deduction from what is indubitable, Cohen and Nagel urge us *immediately* to propose hypotheses and check them by determining whether predictions made upon the basis of them are confirmed.

(d) John Dewey

"Inquiry," writes John Dewey in his *Logic: The Theory of Inquiry,* *"is the controlled or directed transformation of an indeterminate situation into one that is so determinate in its constituent distinctions and relations as to convert the elements of the original situation into a unified whole."* This "indeterminate situation" has a setting which is both within nature and within culture. With respect to nature, it is "obvious without argument that when men inquire they employ their eyes and ears, their hands and their brains. These organs, sensory, motor or central, are biological. Hence, although biological operations and structures are not sufficient conditions of inquiry, they are necessary conditions." But the "environment in which human beings live, act and inquire is not simply physical. It is cultural as well."

Antecedent to inquiry there is, according to John Dewey, an "indeterminate situation." In fact, "it is of the very nature of the indeterminate situation which evokes inquiry to be *questionable;* or, in terms of actuality instead of potentiality, to be uncertain, unsettled, disturbed."

Nor are these characteristics present in merely a subjective sense. "It is the *situation* that has these traits. *We* are doubtful because the situation is inherently doubtful."

Although this indeterminate situation is antecedent to inquiry and a precondition for it, more is required before inquiry begins. This "more" John Dewey calls the "problematic situation." "The indeterminate situation," he continues, "becomes problematic in the very process of being subjected to inquiry."

This is a very important point. It means that for Dewey inquiry begins neither with the collecting of facts nor with either the projection of hypotheses or an act of thoroughgoing doubting followed by logical deductions from the remainder that is indubitable, but with the problematic situation.

Next in the pattern of inquiry, following the problematic situation, which in turn follows the indeterminate situation, comes "The Determination of a Problem-Solution." This involves getting the problem stated. For John Dewey this is a "progressive" matter. "If we assume, prematurely, that the problem involved is definite and clear, subsequent inquiry proceeds on the wrong track. Hence the question arises: How is the formation of a genuine problem so controlled that further inquiries will ' move toward a solution?

"The first step in answering this question is to recognize that no situation which is *completely* indeterminate can possibly be converted into a problem having definite constituents. The first step then is to search out the *constituents* of a given situation which, as constituents, are settled. . . . Since they are settled or determinate in *existence*, the first step in institution of a problem is to settle them in *observation*. . . . They constitute the terms of the problem, because they are conditions that must be reckoned with or taken account of in any relevant solution that is proposed.

"A *possible* relevant solution is then suggested by the relative factual conditions which are secured by observation. The possible solution presents itself, therefore, as an *idea*, just as the terms of the problem (which are facts) are instituted by observation."

This third stage of the pattern of inquiry as described by John Dewey is followed by two later stages, the one termed "Reasoning," in which the logical consequences of the suggested ideas or hypotheses are developed, the other termed "The Operational Character of Facts-Meanings." The latter has to do with the manner in which both facts given by observation and ideas suggested by hypothesis function operationally to resolve the problematic situation with which inquiry begins.

The latter stages are not relevant for our present purposes, since the question which we have been attempting to answer is concerned with the methods to be pursued in initiating inquiry rather than with those that bring it to final completion. To our persisting question Dewey's answer is clear: Since inquiry begins with a problematic situation, one must first observe the determinate facts in this problematic situation and allow these facts, together with the indeterminate uncertainties of the situation, to suggest hypotheses respecting the possible resolution of its problematic character, these hypotheses in turn to be pursued to their deductive consequences and thereby checked operationally.

Clearly, the authorities disagree about the procedure to be followed in initiating inquiry. To be sure, there is one prescription which they all hold, roughly, in common. Each maintains that at the beginning one should clear one's mind of traditional beliefs. With Bacon this takes the form of specifying the errors or Idols characterizing the usual erroneous traditional beliefs. With Descartes it takes the form of doubting all that can be doubted. Doubting is also prescribed at the initiation of inquiry by Morris Cohen and Ernest Nagel and John Dewey. With Morris Cohen and Ernest Nagel the form of the doubt is more Baconian and empirical in character, since they, like Bacon, designate empirically, certain traditional forms of belief which are to be doubted. John Dewey's doubting is perhaps more Cartesian than empirical and Baconian in its form, since it takes on the positive effort to be skeptical. But this emphasis upon doubting and clearing one's mind of traditional beliefs at least tentatively is a purely negative procedure.

When it comes to the positive prescription at the beginning of inquiry, our authorities are clearly in disagreement. Bacon tells us to put all hypotheses out of our mind and collect facts. This for him is even the best way to rid oneself of the Idols. Descartes tells us to reason rationalistically and deductively from the few clear and distinct factors remaining after doubting has been carried to its extreme limit. Morris Cohen and Ernest Nagel reject the prescription of both Bacon and Descartes. One should instantly put up hypotheses. In fact, one must, since nothing else is possible, according to them. Descartes' advice to use rationalistic deductive methods rather than Bacon's inductive empiricism is equally misguided, according to Morris Cohen and Ernest Nagel. Deduction, to be sure, is necessary, but it runs not from the indubitable data to one's theoretical conclusions, but in the converse direction, from the theory back to the facts. The initial step from the data to the hypothesis involves a psychological leap of the imagination which cannot be bridged by formal logic alone. Thus the proposal of the hypothesis must come first. The formal logic comes afterward, enabling one to deduce consequences from the hypothesis which permit one to put the hypothesis to an operational test. John Dewey is like Morris Cohen and Ernest Nagel, rather than either Bacon or Descartes, in emphasizing the role of hypothesis. But what distinguishes his position with respect to the initiation of inquiry from all the others is a primary and greater emphasis upon the problematic situation. With Bacon and Descartes this problematic situation is hardly noticed. With Morris Cohen and Ernest Nagel it is recognized but brushed aside rather quickly; the real initial emphasis is upon the use of hypotheses.

What can one conclude about the respective merits of these conflicting prescriptions concerning the initiation of inquiry? Must one arbitrarily choose between these different authorities? Or is there something in the nature of any inquiry at its initial stage which designates one of these authorities rather than the other to be right?

We can begin the attempt to answer these questions by asking why all agree on the negative procedure of being skeptical with respect to traditional beliefs. Why should this rule be followed? May not the traditional beliefs be correct? Why should one reject them thus *a priori* without any chance of a hearing?

The answer is clear. One must reject them because there is a problem. There would be no problem were the traditional beliefs adequate. It is precisely because there is a problem and because inquiry does not arise or become inescapable unless there is a problem. And the presence of a problem means that traditional answers are inadequate or at the very least that their adequacy is in question. To take them for granted when their very adequacy is at issue would be to beg the question.

This does not mean that the traditional belief may not turn out to be the scientifically correct one. But if this correctness has once been questioned, and this is what constitutes the problem which starts the inquiry, then the only way in which the traditional belief can save itself is by first losing itself. One must go back behind the traditional belief which is the answer to some problem to the problem for which it is the answer. This is the justification for the negative rule that at the initiation of inquiry one must question every traditional belief.

The point is that inquiry does not start unless there is a problem. And the presence of a problem means that the traditional beliefs are in question.

But the recognition that the initiation of inquiry is by its very nature tied up with a genuine problem provides the criterion not merely for the negative procedure upon which Bacon, Descartes, Cohen and Ernest Nagel and John Dewey agree, but also for the correctness of John Dewey's positive procedure at the initiation of inquiry as compared with the prescriptions of his rivals.

The positive thing to do, after one has doubted the traditional beliefs, is to concentrate attention on the character of the problem, or, to use John Dewey's words, on the problematic situation. One must begin not with the facts nor with Descartes' deductive reasoning nor with a hypothesis but with the problem and the problematic situation, because at the beginning of inquiry this is all that one has.

Inquiry starts only when something is unsatisfactory, when traditional beliefs are inadequate or in question, when the facts necessary to resolve one's uncertainties are not known, when the likely relevant hypotheses are not even imagined. What one has at the beginning of inquiry is merely the problem.

John Dewey has the correct answer to our question concerning the positive method to be used in initiating inquiry. His prescription is correct because it affirms a tautology, the tautology, namely, that one must begin inquiry with what one has at the beginning, namely, the problem. It is the problem and its characteristics as revealed by analysis which guides one first to the relevant facts and then, once the relevant facts are known, to the relevant hypotheses.

To follow Bacon's prescription is to gather facts before one knows what facts, among the infinite number in the universe, to gather. To proceed instantly to hypotheses is to put up wild and probably traditional irrelevant guesses before one knows the character of the problem for which any relevant hypotheses must be the adequate answer.

But even John Dewey, for all his emphasis upon the primacy of the problematic situation in the initiation of any inquiry, never reaped the full fruits of this important insight. For he, too, soon after the problem is faced, suggests, like Morris Cohen and Ernest Nagel, that one should propose hypotheses. But what hypotheses?

It is only an analysis of the problem confronting one which can answer this question. And the analysis of the problem which initiates inquiry is quite a different methodological procedure from the act of the imagination which proposes a hypothesis to solve the problem, after it has been fully analyzed and the relevant facts with respect to it have been thereby located and then determined. The analysis of the problem, therefore, requires special attention.

Francis Bacon. *Novum Organum*. Aphorisms Concerning the Interpretation of Nature and the Kingdom of Man.

René Descartes. *Discourse on Method.*
Metaphysical Meditations.

Charles Peirce. *The Collected Papers of*. Edited by Charles Hartshorne and Paul Weiss. Harvard University Press, Cambridge, 1931.

Morris R. Cohen. *Reason and Nature*. An Essay on the Meaning of Scientific Method. Harcourt, Brace and Company, New York, 1931.

Morris R. Cohen and Ernest Nagel. *An Introduction to Logic and Scientific Method*. Harcourt, Brace and Company, New York, 1934.

John Dewey. *How We Think*. D. C. Heath and Company, New York, 1910. *Logic: The Theory of Inquiry,* Henry Holt and Company, New York, 1938.

CHAPTER II

THE ANALYSIS OF THE PROBLEM

The problems which confront men are of many different kinds. Hence, before examining the technique for the analysis of any problem which initiates inquiry it is necessary to classify the major kinds of problems.

Failure to do this has resulted in the hasty and erroneously drawn conclusion that there is but one scientific method. Since inquiry begins not with a method known *a priori,* but with a specific problem, it is the problem which determines the method. Furthermore, in different portions of their experience, men are confronted with different types of problems raising different kinds of questions. Since it is the kind of question being raised by a given problem which determines the type of method appropriate for the answering of the question, it follows that there will be as many different scientific methods as there are fundamentally different kinds of problems.

This is clearly recognized in the exact sciences. Certain problems occur in mathematical physics or in pure mathematics which raise merely questions of logical consistency. For such questions no one supposes the empirical methods of observation and experiment to be either necessary or appropriate. The methods of formal logic are sufficient.

Again, there are problems where the consistency of a given theory is not in question, and one is confronted solely with the problem of its empirical truth. Clearly, such a question is not to be answered by the methods of formal logic alone, although they may be required in part. One must obviously also resort to empirical methods.

19

But besides problems of logical consistency and problems of the empirical truth of theory, i.e., problems of fact, there are also problems which, for lack of a better name, may be called problems of value. In the social sciences and in the humanities, where ideological issues are everywhere present, especially in the contemporary world, these problems are paramount. The characteristic of a problem of value, such as the issue between democracy and communism, is that, in part at least, it raises a question concerning what ought to be, rather than what is, the case. Clearly, a scientific method appropriate for answering a question concerning what ought to be the case must be different from the method which answers a question concerning what is the case.

It is popular today to deny this thesis, affirming that problems of fact and problems of value are quite identical, the content only differing, and hence to be solved by one and the same scientific method. But what this thesis presupposes is that the method defines the problem, rather than that the problem determines the method. But the thesis that the method defines the scientific character of the problem is a false thesis, for inquiry does not start with a method; it starts with a problem. Thus it is the problem that designates the method, not the method which designates the problem.

An examination in social science of problems of value and problems of fact makes the difference between them evident. Problems of fact in society involve the construction of hypothetically designated, indirectly verified scientific theories, after the manner of those in the natural sciences. It is the characteristic of the method appropriate for verifying such theories that they designate any theory to be false if one fact is out of accord with any deduced consequence of the theory. Thus theories in social science which are answers to problems of fact must necessarily designate a form of social organization which corresponds exactly to what is in fact the case in a specific society or culture to which the theory purports to refer.

Normative social theories, which are the only relevant answers to problems of value in the social sciences and the humanities, differ radically from this. No normative theory, neither Anglo-American democracy nor Russian communism, neither the Christian ideal nor the Mohammedan ideal for life, could ever hope, nor does it ever pretend, to be completely in accord with what is in fact the case in any specific empirical society. Yet no one takes it as proof of the inadequacy of democracy that there is no actual society anywhere in which the democratic ideal is perfectly realized. One does not take it as an argument against the Christian ideal for life that there are no perfect Christians. Yet, if normative social theories were handled by the same methods as those used for factual social theories, this is precisely what we should conclude when we find our normative social theories to be out of accord with specific facts in any actual society.

But the whole point of a normative social theory is that it is introduced to change the *de facto* situation at least in part, rather than to conform to it. It defines the ideal society at which we are aiming. It does not purport to designate, after the manner of a theory in natural science, the *de facto* state of affairs which we actually have. It is, in short, an answer to a quite different problem and question than the type of problem or question we are trying to answer when we ask for a factual social theory.

Thus in the social sciences and the humanities two kinds of problems must be distinguished, problems which require factual social theories for their adequate answer and problems which require normative social theories. It is because our recent social science and our recent moral philosophy, whether pragmatic, empirical or idealistic, have failed to distinguish these two types of problems, that our traditional social scientists and moral philosophers have so little to say with respect to a concrete and effective resolution of the inescapable and pressing ideological problems of the contemporary world.

The analysis of normative problems and the attendant determination of the method for solving them must concern us later.   First, we must examine a concrete example of the analysis of a problem of fact in the natural sciences.   None is more illuminating than Galilei's analysis of a problem left by the Aristotelean physics.   Galilei's analysis not only solved this problem but also, in doing so, provided the fundamental concepts of modern science.

The inquiry which led Galilei to the discovery of the basic and novel concepts of modern physics began with an inescapable sense of a problem left by the Aristotelean physics. The problem appeared in the motion of a projectile, such as a shell shot from a cannon.   More and more it became evident to Galilei and his contemporaries that the projectile does not move the way it should were Aristotle's physics true. This was Galilei's problem.   Something was wrong with the Aristotelean theory of the motion of a projectile.

It may help us to discover the rules governing the analysis of a problem of fact if we begin by asking what Galilei would have done had he followed the advice of our previously mentioned authorities.   Were Bacon right, Galilei would have thrown and shot off all kinds of projectiles, carefully observing and describing what happened, gathering more and more detailed empirical information until this information added up to a generalization which was the answer.   It is likely that had Galilei done this, he or his successors would still be observing, with the problem unsolved.   Had Galilei followed Descartes, he would have doubted everything.   This would have left him with certain minimum data from which he could have deduced the solution of his problem and the principles of modern mechanics.   This also would have been equally fruitless.   According to Morris Cohen and Ernest Nagel, and also with John Dewey, after thorough sensitivity to the problematic situation, he should have allowed his imagination to suggest hypotheses.   But it is not quite clear what hypotheses could possibly have occurred to his imagination except the traditional ones.

Galilei fortunately followed no such advice.   Instead, he analyzed his problem.   This analysis took on the form of tracing the problem back to its roots.   This was accomplished by stating clearly what the problem was and then noting the traditional assumptions which generated it.

Once this was done, it became evident that his problem centered not in the projectile but in the Aristotelean definition of force, a definition which applied not merely to projectiles but to any motion whatever.   This made it clear to him that it was hardly useful to pay any more attention to projectiles, or to become more sensitive to them.   For the difficulty concerning the projectile arose because according to Aristotelean physics force is that which exhibits itself as the motion or velocity of the object upon which it acts. In other words, force is that which produces velocity.   From this it followed that when a force ceases to act upon a body, the body should cease to move.

In millions upon millions of empirical instances this definition of force is apparently confirmed.   When one pushes the table, the table moves, and when one ceases to exert the force, the table ceases to move.   Yet in the projectile and its motion, this consequence of the Aristotelean definition of force is not confirmed.   The force has ceased to act the instant the explosion takes place.   Yet the projectile continues to move over great distances of space and over a considerable interval of time, following the cessation of the explosion.   Thus analysis of the theoretical source of the problem which presented itself in the motion of the projectile located the difficulty in the basic concept of force as it relates itself to any motion whatever.

Consequently, Galilei's problem, under analysis, took on

a much more fundamental and general form. The difficulty centered not solely in the motion of the projectile, but in the Aristotelean definition of force in general. Clearly, a new conception of force was required. This alone was sufficient to indicate that the real solution to the problem raised by the projectile would have consequences reaching far beyond the projectile and its motion, consequences which would alter the most basic concepts of the entire Aristotelean physics.

Galilei's analysis of his problem thus transformed it into that of finding a new and correct definition of force in terms of the motion of any object whatever. This permitted him to choose the simplest case of a force acting on a moving object which he could find, namely, a body falling freely under the force of gravitation. This is a much simpler case of a moving body than that of the projectile in which there is a freely falling vertical motion compounded with a horizontal motion perpendicular thereto.

It is important to note that up to this point no hypotheses have been put forward. Galilei has merely analyzed his problem of the projectile to trace it back to its source in the Aristotelean definition of force for any motion whatever. He has then chosen the simplest possible observable motion in which he can study the relation between motion and force in order to get a correct definition of the latter concept.

Having now cornered his problem in the motion of a ball which he can let drop from his hand to the floor, he proceeds again, not to form hypotheses, but to observe the factors involved in this directly observable phenomenon. In short, his method takes on a somewhat Baconian character. He notes that the ball falling from his hand to the floor exhibits three factors upon which the fall, as governed by the gravitational force, might depend, namely, (1) the weight of the ball, (2) the distance through which the ball falls, and (3) the time through which it falls.

It is these three observed factors which suggested to Galilei three hypotheses. Thus it is to be noted that he did not, after the manner of John Dewey, become sensitive to his initial problem and then allow his imagination to throw up whatever hypotheses chanced to come into it. But instead, he allowed an analysis of his initial problem to guide him to its roots in a more general and basic problem and then the latter more general and basic problem to guide him to the simplest possible phenomenon in which the factors in his basic problem might exhibit themselves. It was these factors which, when observed, prescribed his three hypotheses: (1) That force is simply proportional to the weight of the body upon which the force acts. (2) That force is simply proportional to the distance through which the body moves when the force acts. And (3) that force is simply proportional to the time through which the force acts.

His analysis having thus guided him to these three *relevant* hypotheses, his next task is to determine which one, or whether any one of them, is correct. This he does by the methods prescribed for hypotheses by Morris Cohen and Ernest Nagel and John Dewey. That is, he deduces from each hypothesis what follows if it is true and then attempts to put this deduced consequence to an empirical test.

If force is proportional to the weight of the body upon which it acts, it follows that bodies of different weights dropped at the same instant and acted upon by the same gravitational force, should arrive at the ground at different times. The famous Tower of Pisa experiment, which apparently was apocryphal as an historical fact, would have easily led to the rejection of this hypothesis had it been performed. Thus Galilei was left with his two other hypotheses.

Galilei believed that he demonstrated mathematically that the hypothesis that force is proportional to the distance through which the body moves leads to a contradiction. Ernst Mach has shown that Galilei's proof was invalid. Nonetheless, the hypothesis can be shown to be false. Thus

Galilei did not err in rejecting it.   This left him with the hypothesis that velocity is simply proportional to the time.

His problem then became that of putting this hypothesis to an empirical test.   He began first by deducing from it the consequence that the distance covered must be simply proportional to the square of the time.   This means that if a body covers one unit of distance in one unit of time, it must cover four units of distance in two units of time, nine units of distance in three units of time, and sixteen units of distance in four units of time, etc.   It was the need for putting this consequence of his third hypothesis to an experimental test which guided Galilei to his famous experiment in which a ball is allowed to roll down the side of an inclined plane.

The purpose of the inclined plane was to slow up the fall of the ball, so that it would be possible to measure the distances covered in different units of time and thereby determine whether the relation between distance and time is the one prescribed by the hypothesis.   The confirmation of this hypothesis in this experiment is well known.

The result was a new definition: Force is that which produces, not motion or velocity as Aristotle supposed, but change of velocity or acceleration.   This new definition of force is the foundation of modern mechanics.   According to this definition of force it follows that when a force ceases to act on a body the body will not cease to move; it will merely cease to change its velocity.

Once this new definition of force is discovered, the difficulty with respect to the motion of the projectile vanishes. During the very brief interval of time through which the powder in the cannon is exploding, it follows from this definition of force that the velocity of the projectile will be continuously changing.   In other words, the projectile will undergo a continuous acceleration from the zero velocity when the explosion begins, to the finite velocity which it reaches when the explosion ends.   Then, immediately following the explosion, when the force ceases to act, the body will cease further to change its velocity.   In other words, it will move with the constant velocity it attained when the force ceased to act.   Thus the fact that the projectile goes on moving when the force has ceased to act is accounted for.   Galilei's initial problem is solved.

But the consequences with respect to the projectile are even more explicit.   Were the force of the explosion the only force acting upon the projectile, it follows from the Galilean definition of force that the projectile will go on moving forever with a constant velocity in the direction in which it is projected.   It happens, however, that in addition to the force of the explosion there is also the force of gravitation acting in a direction perpendicular to the projected motion resulting from the explosion.   This gravitational force never ceases.   Its effect, according to Galilei's new definition of force, will be to accelerate the projectile uniformly toward the earth.   Thus the actual motion of the projectile must be a compound of a uniform velocity horizontal to the earth's surface and a continuously accelerated motion perpendicular thereto.   It can be shown by formal reasoning that the product of these two motions is a path which is a parabola.   This is precisely the path which the projectile follows.

Moreover, the implications of Galilei's solution of his initial problem reach far beyond the projectile.   The earliest portion of Galilei's analysis forewarned one of this result. For the analysis showed that the difficulty with respect to the motion of projectiles centered in the Aristotelean definition of force applied to any motion whatever.   This entailed that any force and any motion must be conceived in an entirely new way.   Consequently, Galilei's new definition of force entails a rejection of the whole of the Aristotelean physics.   Since there is not a major concept in Aristotle's metaphysics which does not appear in his physics, this change has the additional consequence of requiring the rejection of the Aristotelean philosophy and its attendant medieval Thomistic theology. The modern world, once it was forced by Galilei's analysis and experiment to replace Aristotelean physics and its attendant philosophy with the physics of Galilei, was required thereby to rear its philosophy also on attendantly new foundations. This was done first by Descartes in France and later by Locke in England.

Furthermore, when Newton proceeded to look at celestial as well as terrestrial motions from the standpoint of the requirements of Galilei's new definition of force, the modern science of mechanics, as we find it developed in Newton's *Principia,* was founded, and Kepler's previously verified three laws of planetary motion came out as logical consequences. Thereby the previously separated sciences of astronomy and mechanics were shown to be one science rather than two.

Such are the consequences of initiating inquiry by analyzing the problem which one has at the beginning of inquiry and by allowing the analysis of this problem to guide one step by step to its solution. It appears that this step by step procedure can be divided into the following explicit stages: First, the discovery by analysis of the basic theoretical root of the problem; second, the selection of the simplest phenomenon exhibiting the factors involved in the difficulty; third, the inductive observation of these relevant factors; fourth, the projection of relevant hypotheses suggested by these relevant facts; fifth, the deduction of logical consequences from each hypothesis, thereby permitting it to be put to an experimental test; sixth, the clarification of one's initial problem in the light of the verified hypothesis; and seventh, the generalization of one's solution by means of a pursuit of the logical implications of the new concepts and theory with respect to other subject matter and applications.

This unqualified and relentless generalization of a given

verified scientific theory might seem upon first thought to be exceedingly dangerous and unwarranted, since it assumes the application of the theory to a wide range of facts extending far beyond the restricted experimental evidence which is the sole empirical confirmation of the theory. But instead of this being a dangerous procedure, it is the most safe one. Nothing will exhibit the weakness of a given theory more quickly than a relentless generalization of it for all possible evidence. Common sense also has recognized the soundness of this procedure in its adage: Give a man enough rope and sooner or later he will hang himself.

If one restricts a theory solely to the evidence for which it is confirmed, then obviously the theory will seem to be true without qualification. But to extend it to all relevant evidence is to find as quickly as possible the point if any at which the theory is inadequate. When this new evidence appears, indicating the particular facts with respect to which the theory does not permit of unqualified generalization, a new theoretical problem arises, and a later Galilei must come forth to carry through its analysis. Thus the solution of one problem and the subsequent generation of new ones goes on endlessly, lifting science from problem to problem and adequate theory to more adequate theory with greater and greater generality.

In the handling of any specific problem certain stages are to be noted. The first stage is concerned with the analysis of this problem. This analysis leads one to the relevant facts to be observed, and these relevant facts in turn suggest the relevant hypotheses. Thus inquiry, as it proceeds, exhibits at least three major stages: (1) the analysis of the problem which initiates inquiry, (2) the Baconian inductive observation of the relevant facts to which the analysis of the problem leads one, and (3) the designation of relevant hypotheses suggested by the relevant facts.

It appears, therefore, that the Baconian inductive method

belongs to the second stage of inquiry and that the method of hypothesis belongs to the third stage. This conclusion is very important, for it means even with respect to problems of fact that there are different scientific methods for different stages of inquiry, and that the method which is scientific for one stage may be quite unscientific at a different stage.

The analysis given above of the final stage of Galilei's procedure indicates also that the relevant hypotheses proposed in the third stage of inquiry, when pursued to their logical consequences, designate the theoretically defined experiments or operations necessary to test them empirically. This fact has implications which have not been appreciated. It suggests that the concept or theory determines and defines the operation perhaps even more than the operation defines the concept. It is to be recalled in the case of Galilei that the hypothesis or theory, to the effect that force alters velocity simply proportional to the time came first; the operation, i.e., the inclined plane experiment, came afterward. Moreover, it was the theory which prescribed how the experiment had to be constructed and conducted. This consideration suggests that the operational theory of the concept needs a much more careful analysis than it has previously received. This analysis will be given in Chapter VII.

Our immediate concern, however, is with the first stage of any inquiry: The analysis of the problem. It remains to specify the rule governing this analysis.

The first stage of inquiry is concerned with the analysis of the problem which initiates inquiry. This analysis guides one by way of the basic theoretical roots of the problem to the relevant facts which must be determined by Baconian inductive methods before any further effective progress can be made. Consequently, *the rule governing the first stage of inquiry* may be stated as follows: *The problematic situation must be reduced to the relevant factual situation.* By the problematic situation is meant the situation which generates the problem that initiates inquiry. By the factual situation is meant the situation which contains the relevant facts to which the anlysis of the problem leads one.

This rule has been arrived at by examining the procedure used by Galilei in the first stage of his inquiry into a specific problem of fact in the natural sciences. The rule applies also to the analysis of problems of value in moral philosophy and the normative portions of the social sciences. Merely the steps from the initial problem to the designation of the relevant facts necessary to resolve it, and the attendant scientific methods, are greater in number and different in the case of a problem of value.

It remains to demonstrate the application of this rule to problems of value, by considering an analysis of a specific problem of value where this rule was applied. Such an application occurs in the writer's *The Meeting of East and West: An Inquiry Concerning World Understanding.*

The latter inquiry is concerned with the most pressing problem of value of our day — the problem, namely, of resolving the normative ideological conflicts which threaten the peace of the world. The first chapter, recording the first stage of inquiry, indicates how an analysis of this normative problem guides one to the specific factual information which must be determined before further effective discussion of the problem can occur, precisely in the manner in which Galilei's analysis of his problem concerning the projectile guided him to the observation of the motion of a freely falling ball. Chapters II to XI of *The Meeting of East and West,* representing the second stage of inquiry, then record the determination of these relevant facts by methods which are as inductive and Baconian as the subject matter will permit. This corresponds to Galilei's observation of the three factors — weight, distance and time — present in the freely falling ball.

Chapter XII, the third stage of inquiry, in *The Meeting of*

East and West, because of the more precise, purely factual information which the Baconian second stage of the inquiry provided, then succeeds in cornering the initial problem of value in a specific and empirically answerable question of fact, exactly in the manner in which Galilei in the later stages of his inquiry cornered his initial problem concerning the projectile in the inclined plane experiment. The important thing to note about the analysis of the problem of value in *The Meeting of East and West* is that as the analysis guided one to the relevant factual information necessary to clearly understand the problem, the initial question, which appeared first as a question of value to which scientific methods did not seem to apply, became transformed over, as the statement of the basic difficulty became more evident and precise, into a specific question of fact which scientific methods and scientific evidence could and did answer.

It appears, therefore, that the difference between problems of fact and problems of value is not that the former are answerable by scientific methods, whereas the latter are not. The difference instead is that the analysis of the problem and the attendant reduction of its problematic situation to a factual situation, which constitutes the major task of the first stage of any inquiry, is a much lengthier process and requires additional scientific methods, as the sequel will show, in the case of a problem of value than in the case of a problem of fact.

Nor should this surprise one. The reduction of problems of value to problems of fact must be possible if any normative statements are cognitive and true, rather than merely persuasive and hortatory. For to say that a statement is true is to answer a question of fact.

Scientists and philosophers alike have failed to realize this in a manner convincing to all because of a faulty or incomplete conception of scientific methods. The crux of the matter centers in the initiation of inquiry — the analysis of the problem.

This first stage of scientific inquiry, even when previously noted as in the case of John Dewey, has been brushed over too lightly. People have rushed on, either to the Baconian empirical method of the second stage of inquiry, saying that the identification of the word "good" with empirically given pleasures, preferences or interests will solve all problems of value, or to the method of hypothesis of the third stage of inquiry, affirming, as have John Dewey and the pragmatists, that trying out normative hypothesis, after the manner in which natural scientists try out the hypotheses of physics, will put all normative questions on a scientific basis. That both of these contentions are false is demonstrated by the fact that neither group of proponents has solved a single specific problem of value in our world.

Nor is the reason difficult to discover. Both groups assume that there is but one scientific method. Neither group realizes fully that not merely different types of problem, but even different stages of inquiry into the same type of problem, call for different scientific methods. In short, both groups have an *a priori*, rather than a scientific, conception of scientific method. Having this *a priori* conception of scientific method, they supposedly know what to do and what specific scientific method to use without going through the difficult labor of analyzing the problem. Consequently, no specific problem of value in modern times has been analyzed and solved to acquaint people with the sequence of diverse scientific methods necessary for the investigation of problems of value in a scientific manner. This specific sequence for the scientific solution of problems of value must concern us in the sequel, after we have obtained a clear conception of the simpler sequence of scientific methods required in the later stages of inquiry for the solution of problems of fact.

Nothing is more important, therefore, than to realize that the initiation of scientific inquiry constitutes a stage of scientific procedure by itself, with a specific scientific method appropriate to itself and different from the scientific methods appropriate to the later stages of inquiry. The task of the first stage of inquiry is the analysis of the problem. This is the case because all that one has at the beginning of inquiry is the problem which initiates it, and one must begin with what one has at the beginning. The scientific method of the first stage of inquiry is the method of analysis — analysis applied to the problem.

It is the aim of this analysis of the problem to guide one to the relevant facts necessary to clearly understand it. Hence, the rule governing the method of analysis used in the first state of inquiry is that *the problematic situation must be reduced to the relevant factual situation.* In other words, the initial question, which, as it stands, cannot be answered — otherwise there would be no problem — whether it be a question of value or a question of fact, must, by means of the analysis, be translated over into a more specific question which can be answered by means of the determination of certain facts to which the analysis of the problem guides one.

It is to be noted that it is the analysis of the problem which provides the criterion for selecting out of the infinite number of facts in the world the few that are relevant. When this method of analysis has guided one to these relevant facts, and not until then, one is ready for the second stage of inquiry.

Galileo Galilei. *Two New Sciences.* The Macmillan Company, New York, 1914.

Ernst Mach. *The Science of Mechanics,* Chapter II. Open Court Publishing Co., Chicago, 1919.

F. S. C. Northrop. *The Meeting of East and West.* The Macmillan Company, New York, 1946.

CHAPTER III

THE NATURAL HISTORY STAGE OF INQUIRY

Since the first stage of inquiry ends when the analysis of the problem has designated the facts which must be known in order to resolve the problem, the task of the second stage and the scientific method appropriate to it are thereby determined. Its task is to inspect the relevant facts designated by the analysis in the first stage of inquiry. The scientific method appropriate for this is the inductive method of Bacon.

As a rule, it involves not one method but three; namely, the method of observation, the method of description, and the method of classification. These methods and the rules governing them are well known.

The second stage of inquiry comes to an end when the facts designated by the analysis of the problem in the first stage are immediately apprehended by observation, expressed in terms of concepts with carefully controlled denotative meanings by description, and systematized by classification. The important thing to note is that the second stage of inquiry begins with immediately apprehended fact and ends with described fact.

Fact in these two senses must not be confused. Only fact in the former sense is fact independent of all concepts and theory. Described fact is fact brought under concepts and to this extent under theory. Furthermore, described fact is not a mere aggregate of atomic data. One inspects relations as well as sense data. Consequently, described fact takes on the form of propositions. Propositions are expressions of which it is significant to say that they are true or false. The importance of propositions is that they possess formal properties and thereby provide the type of material to which the formal methods of formal logic and mathematical calculation can be applied.

It cannot be too strongly emphasized that if one wants pure fact, apart from all theory, then one must keep completely silent, never reporting, either verbally or in writing, one's observations to one's colleagues. For the moment one reports or describes what one has observed, one has described fact rather than merely observed, or immediately apprehended, fact. In short, one has observed fact brought under concepts and propositionized. And to have concepts and propositions is to have theory.

In this second stage of inquiry, however, with its inductive, predominantly empirical, Baconian methods, the concepts and the theory which one achieves are different from the concepts and theory of the next stage of inquiry, where the method of hypothesis enters and deductively formulated scientific theory, with its concepts of a quite unique type, occurs. For since the methods of the second stage are inductive, involving merely observation, description and classification, the concepts are necessarily largely descriptive and excessively qualitative in character. In other words, they are concepts the complete meaning of which is given by something which can be immediately apprehended. Such concepts we shall call concepts by intuition, where intuition means, not a speculative hunch, but the immediate apprehension of pure empiricism, which occurs in direct inspection or pure observation. Descriptive, natural history biology with its classification of genera and species constructed in terms of directly observable characteristics is an example of a science in the second stage of inquiry.

It is necessary to have a name for this second stage of scientific inquiry. It is appropriate and in accord with traditional usage to call it the natural history stage. As has been indicated, the methods appropriate to it are the Baconian inductive methods of observation, description and classification. It is to be noted that in this type of science formal logic is not a necessity. It may be used, as it was by Aristotle, to insure that there is no inconsistency in the ordering of genera and species in one's scientific classification. But it is not required.

With respect to Aristotle, it should be noted that his science was so excessively qualitative and lacking in predictive power, not, as so many have supposed, because he was a speculative arm-chair thinker, but because he was such a pure empiricist, and so exclusively inductive in his procedure, using only the methods of observation, description and classification. Predictive power and a quantitative, non-qualitative science come only to a science which passes beyond Baconian empiricism to deductively formulated theory. This, Aristotelean science did not do, for scientific reasons relevant in Aristotle's time, but no longer relevant in our day. In fact, Aristotelean physics was the second stage in the physical inquiry of Western science, for which the deductively formulated physics of Galilei and Newton is the third stage.

Nor is the natural history type of science of the second stage of inquiry with its inductive Baconian method to be deprecated because it is not as effective in its predictive power as the deductively formulated type of science of the third stage. Instead, it is a necessary prerequisite for the third stage. Otherwise, the inductively given relevant data for which the hypothesis of the third stage must account, if it is to be effective, are not known.

In fact, if one proceeds immediately to the deductively formulated type of scientific theory which is appropriate to the third stage of inquiry, before one has passed through the natural history type of science with its inductive Baconian method appropriate to the second stage, the result inevitably is immature, half-baked, dogmatic and for the most part worthless theory.   As the expertly trained psychologist, neurologist and psychiatrist Warren McCulloch has said, this has been the fatal weakness of much of modern psychological theory. It moved too quickly to deductively formulated theory, without having gone through the lengthy, laborious inductive Baconian description of different observable personality traits and types, after the manner of the natural history biologists who are only now, at the end of the modern world, near the completion of the natural history description of their subject matter. Professor McCulloch also points out that one of the great contributions of recent psychiatry, especially that of the German descriptive psychiatry headed by Kretschmer, is that it has brought modern psychology back from its premature deductively formulated theories to the inductive natural history data in all its diversity and complexity, for which any adequate deductively formulated psychological theory must account.

Again we see the importance in science of emphasizing the different stages of scientific inquiry. We note also the importance of not supposing there is but one scientific method for all subject matters or for all the stages of inquiry of a single subject matter. Scientific methods, like space and time, are relative. A scientific method is relative to the stage of inquiry with which one is concerned as well as to the type of problem. The scientific method appropriate for the second stage of inquiry is different from the scientific method appropriate for its third stage. Moreover, the method of a later stage, to be effective, presupposes the method of the earlier stage.

These considerations indicate also that the traditional battles between logicians concerning the correctness of Bacon's, Descartes', Morris Cohen and Ernest Nagel's or John Dewey's theory of scientific method were concerned with a pseudo-problem. There was an issue between these combatants only upon the assumption that there is but one scientific method.   When it is noted that a scientific method is relative to the stage of inquiry with which one is concerned, and that different stages entail different methods, then the issue between the combatants vanishes.   Each is correct for a certain stage of inquiry.   Also, none gave a full account of the explicit methods appropriate for the respective stages of inquiry to which they are relevant.

Nothing is more important therefore for a clarification of scientific method, empirical logic and philosophy than a clear recognition of the different stages of inquiry.   Once this is appreciated the natural history type of scientific knowledge gains the importance which is its due.   In no empirical inquiry will anything ever take the place of looking and seeing.

But conversely, it is equally important not to assign to looking and seeing more than they will give one.   In other words, theoretically inferred knowledge must not be confused with immediately apprehended knowledge.

Yet this is continuously occurring.   Few people realize how little of what we believe is given by observation alone. Pure fact is much less than most people, including even many scientists, suppose it to be.

To confuse *pure fact* with *pure fact plus inferred knowledge* is a serious error.   For when it occurs inferred theoretically designated factors which are always subject to change with further information are given the indubitable status in knowledge which only pure fact enjoys.   If this very prevalent error is to be avoided, it is necessary for one to determine with extreme care the precise extent and character of pure fact.

The Nature of Pure Fact

Pure fact may be defined as that which is known by immediate apprehension alone.   It is that portion of our knowledge which remains when everything depending upon inference from the immediately apprehended is rejected.

Strictly speaking, as has been previously noted, we can say nothing about pure fact, since the moment we put in words what it is, we have *described fact* rather than merely *observed fact*. Nevertheless, we can use words to denote it, providing we realize that these words are concepts by intuition which require us to find in the immediacy of our undescribed experience, what the words mean.

But to recognize this is to learn a great deal about the character of pure fact. Words point it out; by themselves they do not convey it. This means that pure fact must be immediately experienced to be known. At least its elementary constituents cannot be conveyed by symbols to anyone who has not experienced them. But to say this is to affirm that pure fact is ineffable in character. For the ineffable is that which cannot be said, but can only be shown, and even then only to one who immediately experiences it.

Furthermore, since ineffability is the defining property of the mystical, it follows that the purely factual, purely empirical, positivistic component in human knowledge is the mystical factor in knowledge. The pure empiricists are the mystics of the world, as the Orientals, who have tended to restrict knowledge to the immediately experienced, clearly illustrate.

This somewhat surprising conclusion may be arrived at in another way, by beginning with the beliefs of common sense. The ordinary man supposes that the belief in tables and chairs existing as public, material, external objects independently of his sense impressions of them is guaranteed solely by observation or immediate apprehension, as pure fact. In other words, he believes that tables and chairs do not disappear when he shuts his eyes and that the heavenly bodies continue through the sky in their courses even when the astronomers are asleep. Yet such objects cannot be justified by observation or immediate apprehension alone. All that observation alone can give one is what one sees when one is looking; it, by itself alone, can tell us nothing about what exists when one is not looking. One cannot observe what exists when one is not observing. Thus the belief that tables and chairs and planets go on existing when no one is observing them is a belief which immediate apprehension or observation alone cannot justify.

But even the belief that there is a material table with constant, right-angle corners existing as an external object, independent of our sense impressions of it, is not given by sense awareness alone, even when one is immediately apprehending these sense impressions. For all that immediate apprehension or mere observation gives is what one's senses convey to one. And clearly, all that the senses convey are colors and sounds and odors, pains and pleasures. These are not external material objects. They are ineffable, aesthetic qualities, the kind of thing which the impressionistic artist rather than the physicist gives one. Thus again we come to the same conclusion. Pure fact is a continuum of ineffable aesthetic qualities, not an external material object.

Consequently, if one prefers to be thoroughly hard-boiled with respect to one's beliefs, rejecting all inference and theory as belonging to soft-minded speculative philosophers sitting in arm chairs, and if one forthwith proposes to restrict oneself to facts only, then it is not with the belief in external material objects or the other persons of common sense, or with the electrons, protons, electromagnetic waves and other unobservable scientific objects of the physicist that one can have anything to do. For all these common-sense and scientific objects are theoretically inferred objects; they are not purely empirically given, immediately apprehended facts. Instead, it is to impressionistic art with nothing but its sense impressions that one must restrict oneself. In short, were the supposedly hard-minded empiricist really to understand what he would be left with were he to reject all theory and restrict himself to pure fact, and were he then really to practice what he so glibly preaches, he would turn out to be, not the hard-boiled fellow he prides himself on being, but a very sensitive aesthetic dilettante, savoring flavors and fragrances and sensuous images in their ineffable immediacy and letting all solid natural objects go.

That this is the consequence of restricting oneself to knowledge given by Bacon's inductive, purely empirical method is demonstrated by the consequences of Bacon's method as these consequences worked themselves out in British empirical thought following Bacon.   Locke, who succeeded Bacon, saw that inductive empiricism gives one only what the senses convey.   Locke thought, however, that the senses conveyed two different kinds of qualities, (1) secondary qualities, which do not belong to the object of knowledge, and (2) primary qualities, which do give knowledge of the external object independently of our sense impressions of it.

Berkeley, however, had no difficulty in showing that empiricism puts all qualities in the same status.   All that we can say about them is that we immediately sense them.   We apprehend the qualities as qualities, or their particular relations as particular relations, and nothing more.   Certain qualities do not come with a tag on them saying "I am the sign of an external object beyond me which I qualify."   Nor do other qualities come with a tag on them reading "I am purely subjective in origin."   All that empiricism gives us are the qualities as qualities and their sensed particular transitory relations, nothing more.

Moreover, the qualities given empirically are different for different persons.   Thus the belief in a common public world is not given empirically.   Consequently, if the hard-boiled empiricist believes that difference of opinions is the curse of speculative philosophers and that objectivity and public agreement are the hallmark of genuine scientific knowledge, then he belongs with the speculative philosophers, not with the objective scientists, since his empiricism does not give objectivity.   In short, as Albert Einstein and most other expert scientists who have examined with care the methodological foundations of scientific knowledge clearly recognize, the belief in an objective public world with scientific objects in it the same for all observers, is a theoretically inferred, not a purely empirically given knowledge. It is, in other words, the type of knowledge to which the supposedly hard-boiled fellow who would restrict himself to nothing but pure facts, is not entitled.

What the astronomer sees as pure fact is the beauty of the sunset. This is an aesthetic continuum ablaze with ineffable, indescribable colors of subtle shades, differentiated by a two-dimensional circular yellow patch of color. This differentiated continuum alone is the immediately apprehended fact. The scientific object, the star called the sun, which is a three-dimensional spherical mass composed of molecules with a mean free path between them defining an exceedingly high interior temperature, is a theoretically inferred object. In short, the astronomer's sun is not an empirically immediate pure fact, but a highly complicated theoretical inference from pure fact. Furthermore, the existence of this astronomical ball of matter is only indirectly verified, through its deductive consequences checked against immediately inspected data such as those in the beauty of the sunset; the existence of the scientific object which is the sun is not directly observed as pure fact.

Furthermore, if the pure empiricist believes that speculative philosophers confuse illusions with factual knowledge, then he has left his own empiricism, for the distinction between the illusory and the veridical in knowledge is a theoretically designated, not an empirically given distinction. Empirically, we immediately apprehend what we immediately apprehend, the image of the snake on the bedpost with the same vividness and purely factual immediacy as the image of the snake in the zoo. Nor does the former image come with a tag on it saying "I am illusory," or the latter image come with a tag reading "I am the image of a real public, external animal." Both images are equally factual, the one as real, so far as pure empiricism can tell, as the other.

The pure empiricist must be careful also not to believe in his own existence as a persisting entity existing when he is not immediately apprehending himself. That the empiricist goes on existing when he is asleep he cannot know purely empirically by immediate apprehension alone, since when he is asleep he is not observing himself.

Thus, just as Berkeley, following Bacon's empiricism, showed that empiricism does not give one the belief in an external material object independent of the sense impressions, so Hume, in the same Baconian tradition, showed that the belief in a continuously existing self, independent of the intermittent inspected qualities is equally unjustified by pure empiricism.

This becomes clear once it is noted that all that one knows as pure fact is what one's senses convey, and the senses convey neither material common-sense and scientific objects nor persisting selves, but intermittent aesthetic qualities different from person to person and hence not giving either substance, causality in the sense of mathematical physics, or a public world. Again, it must be emphasized, if what one wants is pure fact, then it is neither to the beliefs of common sense nor to physics that one should go, but to impressionistic art, which presents only the sense impressions and omits the external material object.

It is not irrelevant, in this connection to note that the Orientals of the Far East, who brand all knowledge as illusory except that given as pure fact, or, to use their words, by intuition, arrived long ago at the same conclusion. This shows for example in the method which the Buddhists call the dialectic of negation. The principle upon which their dialectic of negation rests is the pure empiricist's thesis that nothing but what we immediately apprehend is genuine knowledge.

Their dialectic of negation forced them, therefore, to negate, i.e., reject, the common-sense man's belief in the reality of a persisting determinate substantial self underlying the empirically given sensuous qualities.   This happens in the realistic Hinayanistic School of Buddhism and corresponds exactly to the conclusion of David Hume following the latter's acceptance of Bacon's pure empiricism in the Modern West.   Next, the Buddhist dialectic of negation forced the rejection of the common-sense man's belief in the reality of external material objects; nothing exists but what the senses convey and these are sensuous qualities, not three-dimensional material objects. This happens in the Nihilistic Hinayanistic School of Buddhism and corresponds to Berkeley's similar demonstration of the consequences of Bacon's empiricism in the Modern West.

It is to be noted also that the beliefs of any theistic religion must be rejected by anyone who would restrict himself to pure fact.   For theism affirms that the determinate personality is immortal and that there is a determinate being in reality as a whole which is also immortal.   Both the Far-Eastern, non-theistic religions and the Western theistic religions, notwithstanding their disagreement on other basic points, agree on this: that all *immediately apprehended* determinate things are transitory and mortal.

No proposition appears more often in Far Eastern religions than the statement: All determinate things are transitory. Similarly, Christ made the same statement restricted to empirically given immediacy, when he said, "My kingdom is not of this world."   The point of this remark is that he knew, with the Oriental, that all immediately apprehended (i.e., this-worldly) determinate things are transitory, and hence that since the theistic religion which he represents affirms determinate things both in man and God to be immortal, there must be a reality other than purely empirically experienced, immediately apprehended reality.   Hence, the statement "My kingdom is not of this world," meaning thereby not some unverifiable world far off in the heavens, but the inferred, theoretically known, as opposed to the purely fact-ual, empirically known, component in things here and now.

St. Paul was recognizing the same fact that theism is not given by factual immediacy alone when he said, "The things which are seen are temporal; but the things which are not seen [the theoretically designated, scientifically known in-variants, as opposed to the purely factually given, transitory sense data] are eternal."

To become clear about the nature and extent of pure fact is to realize therefore that it is a very much smaller portion of our common-sense, scientific or theistic religious knowledge, and of a quite different character, than most people suppose. It is much less than what most people suppose, since it gives one neither common-sense or scientific objects nor theistic religious objects. No belief in any of these objects is justified by immediate apprehension alone.

Pure fact has a quite different character from what most people suppose, since it is customary to believe that tables, chairs, one's own self, and other public, and even theistic, religious objects are given as pure fact. When one notes, however, that one has as pure fact only the data which the senses convey and that these are aesthetic qualities, not ma-terial or scientific objects or theistic religious objects, then it becomes clear that pure fact is primarily aesthetic in charac-ter and aesthetic in the sense of the ineffable. The sunset in all its indescribable qualitative immediacy which is the pure fact cannot be described by either the propositions of the natural history scientist or the equations of the theoretical physicist with his deductively formulated theory. In short, the sunset in the sense of the pure fact which is immediately apprehended cannot be said; it can only be shown. And the instrument for showing pure fact is not science but impres-sionistic art.

This is the reason why modern impressionistic art (as op-

posed to the doctrinally defined classical art) and especially
the purely intuitive and purely empirical art of Georgia
O'Keeffe, which gives pure fact by itself without the inferred
external object, is so important. It keeps our sense of pure
fact unmixed with theory, ever fresh, vibrant and immediate.
It stands as a continuous reminder of how little of what we
believe is given as pure fact. Yet conversely, it tells us, as the
common-sense man with his inferred external three-dimensional objects and the scientists and theistic theologians with
their inferred, theoretically known objects are ever tending
to forget, that this little which is pure fact is in its own right
tremendously important, emotionally and spiritually satisfying and supremely beautiful, yet free and evident everywhere to anyone, richman or poorman alike, if he will for but
a moment stop thinking, inferring, and worrying to restrict
himself to merely looking and feeling.

No one has ever described this supreme capacity of intuitive
art to convey fact in its pristine purity better than Benedetto
Croce, when, in the Appendix to his Aesthetics, he identifies
art with pure intuition, meaning thereby not a speculative
hunch but the immediately apprehended, or pure fact.
There he writes: "Art therefore is *intuition,* in so far as it
is a mode of knowledge, not abstract, but concrete, and in so
far as it uses the real, without changing or falsifying it. In
so far as it apprehends it immediately, before it is modified
and made clear by the concept, it must be called *pure intuition.*

"The strength of art lies in being thus simple, nude, and
poor. Its strength (as often happens in life) arises from its
very weakness. Hence its fascination. If ... we think of
man, in the first moment that he becomes aware of theoretical
life, with mind still clear of every abstraction and of every
reflexion, in that first purely intuitive instant he must be a
poet. He contemplates the world with ingenuous and ad-
miring eyes; he sinks and loses himself altogether in that

contemplation. By creating the first representations and by thus inaugurating the life of knowledge, art continually renews within our spirit the aspects of things, which thought has submitted to reflexion, and the intellect to abstraction. Thus art perpetually makes us poets again. . . . Art is the root of all our theoretic life. To be the root, not the flower or the fruit, is the function of art."

To all these considerations with respect to the identity between the subject matter of impressionistic art and that of natural science in its second, *purely empirical,* stage of inquiry one important addition by way of summary must be made. As the Orientals in their relentless empiricism have realized, we immediately apprehended not merely the specific determinate aesthetic qualities which the senses convey, but also the all-embracing continuum of which they are the differentiations. This continuum must not be confused with the theoretically inferred public space-time of mathematical physics, from which the public space and time of common-sense usage are derived. It is important, therefore to have different terms for these two different continua.

Since the immediately apprehended is so inescapably aesthetic in its nature, it seems appropriate to call the immediately apprehended continuum *the aesthetic continuum.* The mathematically defined continuum, since it is inferred theoretically from the aesthetic continuum, is appropriately called *the theoretic continuum.* Since the aesthetic continuum is differentiated by the specific sense qualities which the specific senses convey empirically, the totality of pure fact may be unambiguously denoted by the words *the differentiated aesthetic continuum.*

Note what has happened. We began with a problem of fact of natural science in its second stage of inquiry. In this stage the more purely empirical inductive methods of Bacon are necessary and appropriate, since the task at this stage is not to construct hypotheses, but to observe the relevant facts to which the analysis of the problem in the first stage of inquiry has guided one. Only if these relevant facts are first observed and thereby known can be relevant hypotheses be even imagined. Observation, therefore, becomes very important.

But in order to understand observation and pure empiricism in natural science, it is necessary to become clear concerning precisely what pure empiricism, or mere observation, can give one. Thus the present inquiry concerning the extent and nature of pure fact arose.

Note that our concern with this topic initially was to throw light upon the empirical methods of natural science in their use to solve problems of fact. But consider the results of our examination of the nature of pure fact in natural science. We find that although the scientist in the second stage of inquiry is inescapably and primarily concerned with it, it is also the kind of thing which impressionistic art conveys, and is perhaps the most competent to convey. Now art is usually classified among the humanities, and what it conveys is usually classified as one of the human values. Thus we discover that problems of fact in the natural sciences and the purely inductive method of empiricism appropriate thereto at the second stage of inquiry are essentially connected with the method of impressionistic art and with problems of value in the humanities. The logic of the one is, at this particular point, identical with the logic of the other.

This identity in aim and subject matter between impressionistic art and the more purely inductive stage in scientific inquiry in the natural sciences holds, however, only for that type of natural history science which carries through its inductive empiricism consistently, restricting itself to pure fact. In actual practice, however, this restriction to pure fact rarely occurs.

Classical Art and Natural History Science

To be sure, sciences in the natural history stage of their development do not introduce the more obviously unobservable, subtle scientific objects such as electrons or electromagnetic waves. But they do go beyond pure fact, nonetheless, in that they introduce the inferred, external, public objects of common sense, and refer the purely empirically given sense qualities or impressions to these three-dimensional common-sense objects. This happens, for example, when the natural history biologist describes a robin as a bird with a red breast. By a "bird" he means not the mere sequence of impressions or sense qualities to which the impressionist and the pure empiricist must restrict himself, but the three-dimensional external, public, common-sense object. And by "red" he means not the number for a specific wavelength in electromagnetic theory (what we shall later call a concept by postulation), but the immediately sensed, ineffable color, a concept by intuition.

But this distinction between (1) restricting oneself to pure fact and (2) referring the sense qualities or impressions comprising pure fact to inferred common-sense objects, which lies at the basis of the difference between a thorough-going Baconian empiricism and the Baconian natural history stage of inquiry as it is actually practiced in the natural sciences, is also the distinction at the basis of the difference between the modern impressionistic art and the pre-modernistic classical art of the West.

The impressionistic painter focuses on the immediately apprehended sensuous data, the impressions, i.e., the pure fact. Consequently he either eliminates the inferred common-sense object entirely as in the case of certain paintings by Georgia O'Keeffe or he pushes it into a secondary position in the background, often dropping its theoretically conceived third dimension, after the manner of certain of her other paintings and those of Paul Gill, Prendergast, and most of the French Impressionists.

The classical Western painter, on the other hand, focuses on the inferred three-dimensional common-sense object — the Madonna and Child or the vase of flowers — as conceived by common sense. Consequently, the purely empirically given sense qualities are referred to and made subservient to the conveying of this three-dimensional external object as thus conceived. Hence, pure fact in all its sensed fuzziness is not presented after the manner of the earlier impressionists. Instead, the scientific laws of geometrical optics as they define the laws of perspective are appealed to. Note the additional essential connection between art and science which is now evidencing itself. As prescribed by the scientific laws of perspective relating the two-dimensional image as sensed to the three-dimensional external object as conceived by common sense, an image is foreshortened here and another image is enlarged there, and the edges of the different colors are made to conform precisely with the edges of the inferred external common-sense object. All this is done to the end that a canvas of two-dimensional colored shapes is made to convey to the thought of the beholder the inferred external common-sense object standing out in three-dimensions in the round.

The foregoing analyses enable us to provide an operational criterion of whether a painting or a given portion of a painting is impressionistic, or classical Western, art. If no common-sense objects can be found in the painting to which to refer the colored shapes, or if the edges where different colors on the canvas join do not conform to the edges of external objects, or if the third dimension is not shown but has to be added by a conscious act of the beholder, then the art is impressionistic. If, on the other hand, the edges where the different colors join do conform to the edges of common-sense objects and if the third dimension seems to be shown without any additional act of interpretation or postulation on the part of the beholder, then the art is of the classical form.

Impressionism, therefore, may be defined as art which uses pure fact, i.e., immediately sensed qualities or impressions of the aesthetic continuum, to convey this qualitatively differentiated aesthetic continuum for its own sake. It is to be noted that classical Oriental art, especially Chinese landscape painting, is nearer Western impressionism than it is to the classical art of the West. Its main difference from Western impressionism is that whereas the latter tends to concentrate on the differentiations as immediately sensed in the aesthetic continuum, the aim of much Oriental art is primarily to convey the all-embracing immediately apprehended aesthetic continuum apart from its differentiations. All such art which uses the immediately experienced, purely empirically given aesthetic continuum and its differentiated qualities to convey that continuum or those qualities for their own sake will be called art in its first function.

Art of the classical Western type, conversely, may be defined as art which uses these immediately apprehended materials to convey, not themselves for their own sake, but objects theoretically inferred from them, such as the three-dimensional objects of common sense, the more subtle objects of deductively formulated science or the theological objects of the Western theistic religions. Such art may be termed art in its second function.

A distinguishing property of such art is that it achieves its end by relating the colors on the two-dimensional canvas to the inferred three-dimensional object by means of the scientific laws of geometrical optics as applied to perspective. Again the human values of classical Western art are found to be rooted in the theories of Western science. The thesis of modern moral philosophy that human values are autonomous, having nothing to do with science and unknowable by the methods of science, is plainly false.

In the case of classical Western religious art a second symbolic reference is present. First, after the manner of classical Western naturalistic or humanistic art, the two-dimensional colors, when ordered according to the laws of geometrical optics, are made to convey to the beholder the three-dimensional bodies of the Madonna and Child. This is the first symbolic reference. Then, by means of a halo placed around the head of the child and by means of bright colors running from the upper right hand corner of the picture to the child's face and by reflection to the Madonna's face, these three-dimensional objects are made to convey the unseen God the Father who is completely outside the painting. This is the second symbolic reference. Thus God the Father in classical Western religious painting is two degrees removed from the pure facts, i.e. from the aesthetic qualities of the impressionists. This is a further confirmation of our previous demonstration that the objects of theistic religious belief are not given as pure fact.

These theistic objects of classical Western religious painting can be known literally only by scientific inquiry which has passed to the third stage, where the deductively formulated theory of natural science arises, and even then only when in addition the technique, termed by Socrates dialectic, by means of which theistic religious objects are identified with and thereby defined in terms of the timelessly invariant relational factors in such indirectly verified, deductively formulated scientific theory of natural science, is made methodologically explicit and clear. Either a purely natural history type of inquiry or a philosophy of intuition, as the purely inituitive philosophy of the Far East clearly shows, is quite incapable of scientifically, or in any other way, justifying the doctrines of a theistic religion. The theoretically known and theoretically inferred type of knowledge, necessary for a theistic religion, and without which such a religion degenerates into a vacuous verbalism, must concern us in the sequel, when we have mastered (1) the methods required for deductively formulated theory and its verification and (2) the additional methods of the philosophy of science for passing from such scientific theory to theistic theology. Our present concern is with knowledge of the natural history type, appropriate to the second stage of inquiry, where the inference is merely from pure fact to common-sense objects.

We have noted that the reference of the sensed qualities comprising pure fact to the inferred external common-sense objects is precisely what distinguishes the classical Western art from the modern impressionism. Thus the method of natural history science, when it similarly refers the red color to the breast of the three-dimensional robin, is identical in its object and method with classical Western art. There are many evidences of this identity within contemporary art and science.

One of the most recent examples is the large mural depicting the age of the dinosaurs, in the Great Hall of the Peabody Museum of Natural History in Yale University. This painting is exact as science of the natural history type, and equally professional and superb as a work of art of the classical Western type. Scientist and classical artist alike acclaim it. Truly in this fresco human values and scientific knowledge are one.

This identity of human values and scientific materials receives another verification in the work of two people also connected with Yale University. One of these persons, the late Emerson Tuttle, was by profession a painter and etcher, with an official position in the Yale School of Fine Arts. The other person, Stanley Ball, is by profession a biological scientist, with an official position in the Department of Zoology and as Curator of Zoology in the Peabody Museum of Natural History.

Both of these people have painted birds. The birds painted by Emerson Tuttle, the artist, are as accurate objects for scientific purposes as the birds painted by Stanley Ball, the scientist. Conversely, Stanley Ball's paintings of birds for scientific purposes have been shown also in exhibitions of paintings, where the interest was primarily that of the artist. Thus one and the same subject-matter, painted in the one case by a professional artist primarily for artistic purposes, and in the other case by a professional scientist primarily for scientific purposes, is in each instance both art and science. Both in method — namely, the use of aesthetic qualities to qualify and represent the inferred common-sense object — and in subject-matter this art of the classical type and this science of the natural history type are identical. Artist and scientist, as judged by the fruits of their professional labors, are one; it was only an artificial abstraction having its roots in the artificialities of university departmentalization which tagged the one as a humanistic artist and the other as a natural history scientist.

Facts such as these permit of but one interpretation: The modern theory of value which would completely separate human values from scientific methods and materials is in considerable part at the very least a false doctrine. In the second stage of inquiry in any natural science — the so-called natural history stage — where the aim is to get the directly observable facts, or these empirical data together with merely the inference to the common-sense objects which the directly inspected sense qualities seem to qualify, it is not merely true, as attested by the above-mentioned examples, but it is inevitable, that both the subject-matter and the method for the most effective presentation of this subject-matter, should be identical for the scientist and for the artist of the classical Western type.

The inevitability of this identity of subject-matter and method between the artist with his values for fuller human living and the scientist with his inductive materials for more complete and accurate human knowledge, arises from the fact that art by its very nature is always working with immediately experienced materials, the painter with his immediately sensed colors, the epicure with his flavors, the musician with his sounds; and these are precisely the kind of thing which the natural history scientist has given him by his inductive, purely empirical Baconian methods. Furthermore, both the Western artist of the classical pre-impressionistic type and the scientist of the natural history type make inferences from the aesthetic qualities which are the pure fact to the external common-sense objects. Hence, since art, rather than a mathematical formula, is the most effective way to convey the sensuous qualities, the method and subject-matter of classical art and natural history science not only *do* in fact, but they also *must*, become identical.

It appears that a clear realization of the limited extent and the qualitative nature of pure fact is very important. One finds that many things such as three-dimensional external public objects and the other people of common-sense beliefs are not given by pure fact alone, but entail, in addition, inferences beyond pure fact. It is to be emphasized that this dependence of our common-sense, scientific, and Western theistic religious beliefs upon inferences beyond pure fact, rather than upon pure fact alone, by no means makes such beliefs untrustworthy, providing the scientific methods of the third stage of inquiry for the verification of such beliefs are used.

The inclusion of other persons as well as external material objects among those factors which are not given by immediate apprehension alone is not irrelevant. Unless this is realized the procedure in law courts of mercilessly cross-examining witnesses will appear, as it does to most laymen, as a professional quibbling rather than the necessary method for the furthering of justice which it is. The point is that every statement by a witness to the effect that he saw Jones do so-and-so is an inference from the purely empirical deliverances of his senses; and it must be established that the specific sense impressions the witness had are compatible only with the inference that the source of those sense impressions was Jones and no one else.   Again and again each one of us thinks he is observing a friend coming toward him down the street, only to find on closer inspection that he has made the wrong inference from his visual images.   Such errors of inference would be impossible, were our knowledge of other persons given as pure fact alone.   Hence, the cross examination in the law court to insure that the inference made is correct.

This difference between pure fact and common-sense objects is important therefore in understanding the limitations of pure empiricism in natural science, philosophy and law and in clarifying the nature of the natural history stage of scientific inquiry.   It also clarifies the difference between modern impressionism and classical Western art, while at the same time establishing identities between art and science.

But, as has become evident, there are other kinds of knowledge than that which appears in the natural history type of science and in impressionistic or classical naturalistic art. This brings us to the third stage of inquiry in the natural sciences, with its method of hypothesis, its deductively formulated theory and its concepts by postulation. The art appropriate to the third stage of inquiry will be treated in Chapter IX.

Aristotle.   *Historia Animalium.*
        Analytica Posteriora.

Francis Bacon.   *Novum Organum.*

John Locke.   *Essay Concerning Human Understanding.*   1690.

Bishop Berkeley.   *A New Theory of Vision.*   1709.
        A Treatise Concerning the Principles of Human Knowledge.
        1710.
        Three Dialogues between Hylas and Philonous.   1713.

David Hume.   *A Treatise on Human Nature.*   1739.

John Stuart Mill.   *A System of Logic.*   1843.

W. Stanley Jevons. *Elementary Lessons in Logic,* Chapters III-V, XII, XXVIII, XIX and XXXII. London, 1870.

William James. *The Meaning of Truth.* Longmans, Green, New York, 1909.
A Pluralistic Universe. Longmans, Green, New York, 1909.
Essays in Radical Empiricism. Longmans, Green, New York, 1912.

Henri Bergson. *Time and Free Will: An Essay on the Immediate Data of Consciousness.* Paris, 1899; London, 1910.

George Santayana. *The Sense of Beauty.* Scribner's, New York, 1896.

Benedetto Croce. *Pure Intuition and the Lyrical Character of Art.* Third International Congress of Philosophy, 1908.
Aesthetics. Macmillan and Company, London, 1909.

David Prall. *Aesthetic Judgment.* Crowell, New York, 1929.
Aesthetic Analysis. Crowell, New York, 1936.

Karin Stephen. *The Misuse of Mind.* Kegan Paul, London, 1922.

F. S. C. Northrop. "The Complementary Emphases of Eastern Intuitive and Western Scientific Philosophy." Chapter VIII in *Philosophy: East and West,* Edited by Charles A. Moore. Princeton University Press, 1944.
The Meeting of East and West. Macmillan Company, New York, 1946.

CHAPTER IV

THE STAGE OF
DEDUCTIVELY FORMULATED THEORY

Having in the second stage of inquiry determined, described and classified the facts which must be known in order to resolve the problem analyzed in the first stage, one is, in the third stage of inquiry, able for the first time to proceed to fruitful and relevant hypotheses. This involves the introduction of a new type of knowledge and of attendantly different scientific concepts and scientific methods.

The problem which initiates inquiry may not be resolved even when all the relevant facts to which its analysis directs one are determined. This was the case, it will be recalled, with Galilei's particular problem. The analysis guided him to the simple observable phenomenon present in a freely falling object. The mere observation of this phenomenon was not enough to solve his problem. It was necessary in addition to use the observed factors to suggest hypotheses — hypotheses, furthermore, which by themselves were not directly verifiable.

It may be necessary also to regard the observable data as entirely too gross, complex and crude to provide the entities or relations necessary to resolve the problem with which inquiry begins. When this happens, unobservable scientific objects, such as electrons or electromagnetic propagations with incredibly high velocities, must be introduced. The key to whether the introduction of such unobservable entities and relations is justified is whether it is necessary to resolve the problem with which one is concerned. Again, the cru-

59

cial, basic importance of the first stage of inquiry reveals itself.

But if such unobservable entities are to be introduced, concepts quite different from those used in the second stage of inquiry are required. For it will be recalled that the concepts by intuition of the second stage are defined as concepts the complete meaning of which is to be found in factors which can be immediately apprehended. Obviously, therefore, unobservable scientific objects require for their designation concepts of a different type. We shall call such concepts, *concepts by postulation,* since they derive their meaning from and refer to entities and relations which are known to exist by means of postulation rather than by immediate apprehension.

The full definition of a concept by postulation requires the designation of the methods by which knowledge of the existence of such unobservable factors can be scientifically determined. These methods must now concern us.

Since entities and relations of this type are not directly observable, they must be proposed by the method of hypothesis. This does not mean that their status is merely subjective. What is proposed is proposed as objective, as belonging to the character of the subject-matter of scientific knowledge, not to the character of the scientist as positor. But the mere positing does not guarantee the existence of what is posited. How is this guarantee to be provided?

The methods are well known. They involve the construction of a deductively formulated system. The basic assumptions or postulates of this system designate unambiguously what is proposed to exist. To this proposal or hypothesis, formal logic is then applied to deduce theorems or consequences. Among these consequences one seeks for certain theorems which define experiments that can be performed, such as Galilei's famous inclined plane experiment. The experiment designated by the theorem or theorems of the

theory is then performed.   If in all instances the experiment
gives the result called for by the theorems, then the hypothesis
is said to be confirmed and the entities and relations designated by it are said to exist.   If the experimental result is
negative, the hypothesis or postulate set is known to be false
and some alternative hypothesis suggested by the data of the
second stage of the inquiry, is put in its place and subjected
to the same procedure.

It is to be noted that in this third stage of inquiry, which
permits the introduction of unobservable entities and relations in order to solve one's problem, and which is called the
stage of deductively formulated theory, the use of formal
logic is a necessity.   For it is only by recourse to formal logic
that one can deduce consequences from one's hypothesis concerning unobservable entities and relations and thereby put
this hypothesis to an empirical and experimental test.   Thus
those who affirm that science does not need formal logic are
more or less correct if they are referring to the second stage of
scientific inquiry, where one *may* progress without it; but
they are quite incorrect if science or any inquiry has reached
the much more mature stage of deductively formulated
theory, which every science in the Western world tries to
attain.

The deductively formulated theory of the third stage of
inquiry cannot be experimentally tested without recourse
to the formal logical methods of the theoretical scientist, as
well as to the more purely factual and experimental methods
of the experimentalist.   Physics recognizes this by having
two types of specialists: one type, such as Newton, Maxwell,
Gibbs and Albert Einstein who concentrate largely on the
theoretical, deductive side, called theoretical physicists; the
other type, such as Michelson and Morley, called experimental physicists, more empirical and operational in their
expertness and emphasis.   Yet even the latter are not pure
empiricists, for it is the theorems of the theoretical physicists

which designate when an apparatus is correctly constructed, when an operation with that apparatus is properly controlled and performed, and when a given experiment is relevant to answer the theoretical problem with which one is concerned.

We are now in a position to provide a definition of the concepts by postulation which enter at this third stage of inquiry. *A concept by postulation is one the meaning of which in whole or part is designated by the postulates of some specific deductively formulated theory in which it occurs.* It is only by means of such concepts that unobservable entities and relations are introduced into scientific theory, and thereby, as the sequel will show, into Western philosophical, or theistic religious, doctrine.

It is to be noted that one cannot find the meaning of concepts by postulation by observing anything. The source of their meaning is quite other than that of the meaning of concepts by intuition which belong to the natural history stage of any inquiry.

Moreover, when one deductively formulated theory in science is replaced by another deductively formulated theory in the same science, even though the same words may be used in the two theories, all these words undergo a complete sea-change with respect to their meanings. For example, the word "electron" in the deductively formulated electromagnetic theory of Lorentz has quite a different meaning and designates quite a different scientific object from what is designated by the same word in the deductively formulated theory of quantum mechanics. The reason for this is that the word "electron" is a concept by postulation, not a concept by intuition. And a concept by postulation is one the meaning of which is designated only in the postulates of some specific deductively formulated theory. Hence, when one changes the postulates of a given science, even though the same words may be used, each word undergoes a change in its meaning. The different possible kinds of concepts by postulation will concern us in the next chapter.

Concepts by postulation play a basic rôle not merely in the most mature of the Western sciences, but also in almost every system of Western philosophy. An examination of the major Western philosophers shows that they were first-rate scientists before they became philosophers. Moreover, the science in which they were expert was always mature science which had reached the third stage of inquiry where deductively formulated theory, requiring concepts by postulation, is introduced. This is true of Democritus, Plato, Aristotle, Albertus Magnus, Descartes, Leibnitz, Kant and Alfred North Whitehead, to include a contemporary and mention but a few.

Failure by historians of Western philosophy to distinguish the concepts by intuition of Oriental philosophy and of the natural history stage of Western scientific knowledge, from the concepts by postulation of the stage of deductively formulated theory in Western science and its attendant deductively formulated Western philosophy has resulted in incalculable error. Since a concept by intuition, such as "red" in the sense of the empirically sensed color, gets its meaning directly from immediately apprehended fact, a concept by intuition does not depend for its meaning upon the scientific or philosophical theory, into which it enters as a term. Thus a concept by intuition keeps its meaning constant whether it is used by one scientist or philosopher or by another.

This is not true, however, of a concept by postulation. Such a concept has no meaning apart from a specific deductively formulated theory. This follows from its definition, as previously stated: A concept by postulation is one the meaning of which in whole or part is proposed for it by the postulates of some specific deductively formulated theory. It follows, therefore, that when such a word is used in two different sets of postulates of two different deductively formulated theories, it has two quite radically different meanings; it ceases, in other words, to remain the same identical concept. A much less misleading procedure might be to have two quite different words for the scientific object "electron" as designated by the postulates of Lorentz's electromagnetic theory and the quite different scientific object "electron" as designated by the postulates of quantum theory.

The same thing is true of apparently similar words in the systems of different Western philosophers. Almost all these systems are, or can be understood properly only when put in the form of deductively formulated systems. Hence, the concepts in most of them are concepts by postulation, not concepts by intuition. Moreover, most of these Western philosophical systems had their basic concepts specified for them by the deductively formulated scientific theories of their time. This is why they seemed to their formulators to be, not mere speculative possibilities, but scientifically required and hence true. Since the concepts of deductively formulated scientific theories are concepts by postulation, the concepts of their attendant deductively formulated philosophical theories are concepts by postulation also. Hence, the next chapter will pay attention to the different possible kinds of concepts by postulation as they exhibit and illustrate themselves in comparative philosophy as well as in Western natural science and in common-sense knowledge.

Historians, even historians of philosophy, fall into serious continuous error because of the failure to distinguish the concepts by postulation which are basic in the mature forms of Western science and the diverse Western philosophical systems, from the concepts by intuition which are also present. The error is that if these two types of concepts are not distinguished, the Baconian method, which the historians tend to follow, leads them to suppose that every concept they come upon in their source materials is a concept by intuition. Consequently, whenever they find the same word or expression, such as "mind" or "the law of nature" or "reason," used by two or more philosophers, those using the prevalent philological and historical methods falsely assume that the words have the same meaning, quite overlooking the fact that whereas this is true for concepts by intuition, it is not true for concepts by postulation.

Not realizing that this error is occurring in what they are doing when they are apparently objectively quoting the words of two different philosophers and philosophical systems, such historians and historians of philosophy have no difficulty in proving to their own satisfaction and to the delusion of their innocent readers, that all the doctrines of radically modern thinkers like Descartes, Spinoza or Locke are in Hooker, Saint Thomas Aquinas, the Stoics or Aristotle. There will be no cure for such spurious conclusions from the studies of our supposedly most expert and scholarly historians and historians of philosophy until the humanists as well as the theoretical scientists are trained in the deductively formulated type of scientific method appropriate to the third stage of inquiry, upon which the major scientific, philosophical and theistic theological doctrines, and their attendant cultural institutions, of the Western world rest for their justification. Only such training in the character of deductively formulated theory with its concepts by postulation and in the scientific methods, quite different from those of Bacon with their concepts by intuition, will permit our civilization to throw off the tragic misrepresentations perpetrated upon it by our present pseudo-scholarly historians and historians of philosophy.

The textual fact that Locke speaks of a "law of reason" or a "law of nature" as did St. Thomas Aquinas or Aristotle proves nothing whatever concerning the derivation of Locke's conceptions from St. Thomas or the identities of the meanings of the same words as used by the two men. The reason is that these words or expressions are concepts by postulation, not concepts by intuition.   Hence, they have no meaning apart from the postulates of the philosophical systems of Locke and St. Thomas.   Since the postulates of Locke's philosophy are radically different, so different as to be the contradictory of the postulates of St. Thomas' system, the use of the very same words by the two men is proof of a basic difference, not of an identity, of meaning between the two men and their two philosophical systems.

Nothing is more important than to realize that the major theories and their verified laws of Western physical science and practically all of the systems of Western philosophy are the product of a type of investigation into the problems of mankind which has reached the third stage of inquiry, where unobservable entities and relations and the attendant concepts by postulation with their greater generality and predictive power are introduced.   Once this is realized one will also recognize that no such concept carries its meaning over intact from philosopher to philosopher or from philosophical theory to philosophical theory; each word is relative to the postulates of the system of the scientist or philosopher who uses it.

This means, for example, that the word "electron" as used by Lorentz is a scientific object of which it is meaningful to say that it has both a sharp position and a sharp momentum at one and the same time, because the postulates of Lorentz's deductively formulated electromagnetic theory assigned such properties to the electron.   Unfortunately, deductions from Lorentz's postulates failed to be confirmed before the phenomena of black-body radiation.   When postulates for electromagnetic theory, those of quantum mechanics, were substituted for those of Lorentz, which did fit the experimental facts, these postulates assigned properties to a scientific object designated by the term "electron" of a character such that by postulation it is impossible for this object to have both a sharp position and a definite velocity at one and the same time. Consequently, the scientific object designated by the word "electron" in Lorentz's electromagnetic theory is a quite different entity from the one designated by that same word in quantum mechanics. Also, the indirect method for verifying the existence of such unobservable scientific objects, by deducing logical consequences from the postulation of these entities and putting these logical consequences to an empirical experimental test confirms the fact that even though the electron as postulated by Lorentz conforms more nearly to common sense, it nonetheless does not exist, whereas the electron of quantum mechanics, which shocks common sense because of its lack of a sharp position and of a sharp momentum at one and the same time, nonetheless does exist.

Put concretely, in terms of philosophy, the recognition that most of the concepts of Western philosophical systems are concepts by postulation has the following operational consequence. It requires that whenever one reads a word such as "reason," "mind," "idea," or an expression such as "the law of reason" or "natural law" in the treatise of any Western philosopher, one will not expect to find its meaning in any immediately apprehendable fact or in any image which it chances to conjure up in one's imagination, or in the writings of some previous philosopher. Instead, one will ask oneself the question: What must this word mean upon the basis of the postulates of this particular philosopher's philosophy?

Failure to realize that this technique is necessary in the reading of theoretical physics or Western philosophy has resulted in many lay students of theoretical physics concluding that they cannot understand the subject and in many students of philosophy concluding that the subject is a jumble of vague words. If one treats the concepts of Western philosophy, which almost invariably are concepts by postulation, as if they were empirically given concepts by intuition, vague rubbish is precisely and inevitably what one will get.

Nor does the error here lie wholly with the reader or the

student.   Many teachers of philosophy, because of their training only in the historical and philological methods, almost
entirely Baconian in character, which fit one to use only concepts by intuition, and because of their complete lack of
training in the analysis of deductively formulated theory and
in the attendant scholarly use of concepts by postulation, attempt to convey concepts by postulation in philosophy by
means of intuitive empirical illustrations as if the latter concepts were concepts by intuition.   Thereby, in spite of apparent textual, historical and philological accuracy of a
verbal kind, they fall into the same vague verbalism which
overwhelms their helpless students.

What must be realized is that almost all the institutions of
Western civilization depend for the vital faith of men in
them, upon beliefs which can be justified and preserved only
by the methods appropriate to the third stage of scientific
inquiry.   Consequently, these scientific methods which require one to learn the art of thinking deductively and with
postulational precision in the conveyance of meaning, have a
greater relevance for the humanities and for problems of
value than do even the more inductive scientific methods of
the second stage of inquiry.

It is no exaggeration to say that the lukewarmness, the
honest skepticism and the widespread demoralization of
people generally with respect to the traditional human values
of Western civilization center in the failure of our educators
and preachers to provide their students and parishioners with
the postulationally determined ideas and modes of thinking,
necessary to justify and sustain the deductively formulated
scientific and attendant philosophic doctrines in terms of
which the classical human values of the West are defined.
Consequently, when the basic concepts by postulation are
taught or preached without their precise technical meanings
and thereby degenerate into a vague, mushy intuitive ver-

balism, as has happened in most contemporary education outside the physical sciences and in much contemporary Protestant preaching, the human values of Western civilization evaporate also. Men lose faith in them because men do not know with precision what they are.

Concepts by postulation have one other unique property. Failure to recognize its presence has also misled many historians and social scientists.

This unique property can best be appreciated if we first note the quite different property possessed by concepts by intuition. Since any one of the latter concepts refers to a particular factor within the totality of immediately apprehended fact, the meaning of any concept by intuition always refers to an item abstracted from a wider context. Consequently, unless we are to confuse an abstracted part of immediately apprehended fact with its totality, we must always keep in mind the empirical context, social and historical, of any concept by intuition.

Concepts by postulation, on the other hand, possess only those meanings which the postulates of the specific deductive theory in which they occur, confer upon them. Thus the meaning of a concept by postulation has nothing whatever to do with the previous historical contextual circumstances which led the scientist to postulate it. With respect to the meaning of such concepts, the emotional and family life of the positor is irrelevant; as are also previous historical social events or the so-called class conflict. A concept by postulation means merely what the postulates of the deductive theory in which it occurs designate it to mean.

Furthermore, such concepts or ideas are not caused by denotatively apprehended, previous historical or social events or economic conditions. Instead of being the effects of the latter factors, the primitive concepts by postulation in a deductively formulated theory are, precisely because they are primitive and elementary, the causal factors which determine the empirically given phenomena for which they were introduced to account.

The implications of this property of concepts by postulation with respect to the rôle in history of ideologies constructed in terms of such concepts, now become obvious. The frequent statements by historians and social scientists to the effect that most or even all ideas are rationalizations after the fact, and consequently the mere effect of the scientifically vague social trends in which all too many historians like to indulge, are to a certain extent justified, if the ideas in question are natural history descriptive concepts by intuition, since the latter concepts are abstracted from a wider empirical historical context and do not realize their full concrete meaning apart from this context; but such statements are quite erroneous if the ideas are concepts by postulation, as is the case with practically all the normative ideological theories of the West.

This unique property of concepts by postulation is the key also to the most baffling paradox of moral philosophy and normative social theory in the West — the paradox, namely, of how a normative theory can be verified in terms of a scientific appeal to something which *is* (as must be the case if it is significant to say that any specific normative theory is true or false), and at the same time avoid what we shall later term the "culturalistic fallacy" of identifying the "ought" of a normative theory for society with the "is" of a factual social theory. What a normative theory must do for the culture or epoch in which it holds sway, is provide a rigid, constant standard or measure of the good society, standing in the midst of and holding through all the contextually changing and, from its standpoint, legal or illegal acts of actual society.   It is this constancy of meaning of concepts by postulation, this independence from the past or present flux of events, which enables the moral and normative social theory of Western civilization to serve thus as a moral and social measuring rod, keeping its length constant after the manner of its physical counterpart in the Bureau of Standards.

It is this constancy of meaning provided by moral or social theory formulated in terms of concepts by postulation which permits such theory to be normative, that is, to prescribe an ideal good and a legally acceptable type of human behaviour and social organization with respect to which actual society may be judged. Herewith, however, arises a difficulty. By its very constancy and at least partial independence of what happens in actual society and by its very nature as normative, such theory differs from what is, in fact, the case. Were this not true, preachers, judges, law courts, legislatures and policemen would not be necessary in order to make the conduct and practices in actual society conform nearer and nearer to the conception of the good which the normative theory prescribes. Put very concretely, this means that a normative theory, by its very nature as normative, differs in part at least from what is in fact the case in actual society.

But it is generally recognized also that a normative theory applies to everybody, that it holds for the murderer as well as for his judge. This entails that the normative theory must be not merely normative but also true in a sense which holds for everybody; otherwise we have no right to punish anyone for not conforming to it.

But to be true a theory must conform to what is the case. Thus the paradox of moral authority arises. Normative theory which we apply to the other fellow must be both normative and true. To be normative, as we have noted above, it must not conform, at least in part, to what is the case. Yet to be true, a theory must conform to what is the case. Clearly, a single theory cannot both conform and not conform to what is the case, at one and the same time. Thus the social requirement that a single theory be both normative and true seems to be self-contradictory.

This contradiction exhibiting itself in the paradox of moral authority must concern us in detail in the later chapters of this book, when we examine the scientific methods for formulating and verifying normative moral and social theory. Certain basic points may be noted now, however. It is clear that the aforementioned contradiction is inescapable if a given normative theory refers its normative prescriptions and its cognitive verification as true, to the same subject matter. Certainly a theory cannot at one and the same time for one and the same subject matter, both conform completely to that subject matter, as it must if it is to be verified as true, and in part at least not conform to that subject matter, as it must if it is to function as normative, condemning certain *de facto* practices as bad or illegal.

Once this is recognized, it becomes evident that the contradiction can be escaped and the paradox of moral authority can be resolved only if normative theory applies its normative prescriptive reference to one subject matter and its cognitive appeal for verification as true to a different subject matter. There is no contradiction whatever in a single theory differing from what is the case in one subject matter and conforming completely to what is the case in another subject matter.

Nor is there any difficulty in recognizing what the two different subject matters must be. It is clear from history and from all cultures that normative theories apply their normative prescriptions to human conduct and to human social institutions and especially to the portion of each for which man himself is responsible. Thus the subject matter to which a normative theory applies its normative prescriptive reference is clearly the humanities including humanly created and controlled personal behaviour and social institutions. It is equally clear also that the subject matter with respect to which man gets theory which can be verified as true in a sense which holds for everybody, is nature. Thus the subject matter to which normative theory must apply for its cognitive verifiability is nature.

One other consideration supports the latter conclusion. It has been demonstrated in a previous paragraph that the paradox of moral authority can be resolved only if normative theory applies its normative prescriptive references to one subject matter and its cognitive verifiable reference to a different subject matter. There are at bottom but two possible subject matters; namely, culture and nature. Since the normative prescriptive reference of normative theory is clearly to culture, it follows that its cognitive reference must be to nature.

In *The Meeting of East and West* the writer has shown this prescriptive reference to culture and cognitive reference to nature to be true of the diverse normative theories of the major cultures of the world. When any one of these normative ideologies is made explicit with respect to its basic assumptions, it is found to be the case not merely that these assumptions function as the ground for prescribing the norms in the culture in question but also that they assert certain propositions about the character of man and nature and thus are of a character such that by means of the methods of natural science they can be verified as true or false. It is this two-fold reference, on the one hand normatively and prescriptively to voluntarily controlled human behaviour and man-made social institutions, and on the other hand cognitively to nature, which makes it possible without contradiction to have theory of which it can be said that it is both normative and true in a sense which holds for everybody.

It is to be emphasized, however, especially with respect to Western civilization, that such normative theory is made possible in the precise form which it has taken on only because of the constancy of meaning of concepts by postulation and the more deductive methods of natural science in its third stage of inquiry.

It appears, therefore, that the essential connection between the methods and subject matter of natural science and human values is more basic and thorough-going than even the analyses of the previous chapters have indicated. Consequently, it is imperative from the standpoint of the humanities and the social sciences as well as the natural sciences, that we now examine the scientific methods of the third stage of inquiry in detail.

It is best not to treat them in the abstract apart from specific scientific or humanistic materials. Consequently, the subsequent chapters will exhibit these methods as they operate with respect to problems of fact in different natural sciences and with respect to problems of value in the social sciences, in art in its second function and in the humanities, including philosophy and religion both Oriental and Western.

It happens in the third stage of inquiry that there are two different possible kinds of deductively formulated theory having different methods of verification. One occurs in the economic science of the Austrian and recent British school; the other in the physical sciences, especially modern mathematical physics.

These different kinds of deductively formulated theory in the third stage of inquiry arise because of the different types of concepts by postulation which they use and the different attendant methods which are required for relating the particular type of concept by postulation in a given kind of deductively formulated theory to the immediately observable data denoted by concepts by intuition and given by the more purely inductive Baconian methods of the second stage of inquiry.

It becomes necessary, therefore, to determine and distinguish the different possible kinds of concepts by postulation and to compare them with the different possible kinds of concepts by intuition. This must be our next concern.

As a rule, any single specific scientific theory illustrates but one of the possible kinds of concepts by postulation. Thus a concrete scientific theory is of very little use to illustrate the different possible kinds of scientific concepts by postulation and by intuition. It happens, however, that all these different kinds of concepts are illustrated in different philosophical systems. Thus comparative philosophy, which must treat of the different possible philosophical systems, provides the ideal subject matter for an illustration of the different possible kinds of scientific and philosophical concepts. Conversely, a designation and systematic classification of the different kinds of concepts by postulation and concepts by intuition are necessary prerequisites for a trustworthy method in comparative philosophy.

Aristotle. "De Interpretatione," "Analytica Priora," "Topica," Vol. I of *The Works of Aristotle,* translated into English. Oxford, 1928.

Euclid. *The Elements,* English Edition by T. L. Heath. Cambridge University Press, 1908.

Newton. *Principia,* Cajori Edition. University of California Press, 1934.

W. Stanley Jevons. *Elementary Lessons in Logic,* Chapters VIII-X, XIV-XIX, XXX, XXXI. London, 1870.

David Hilbert. *The Foundations of Geometry,* English Edition by E. J. Townsend. Open Court Publishing Company, Chicago, 1902.

Alfred North Whitehead and Bertrand Russell. *Principia Mathematica.* Cambridge University Press, 1925.

Louis Rougier. *La Structure des Théories Déductives.* Alcan, Paris, 1921.

Cassius J. Keyser. *Mathematical Philosophy.* Dutton and Company, New York, 1922.

H. M. Sheffer. *Notational Relativity.* Proc. Sixth Int. Cong. of Philosophy, 1926.

Paul Weiss. *The Nature of Systems.* Open Court Publishing Company, Chicago.

R. D. Carmichael. *The Logic of Discovery.* Open Court Publishing Company, 1930.

Ralph M. Eaton. *General Logic.* Charles Scribner's Sons, New York, 1931.

Morris R. Cohen and Ernest Nagel. *An Introduction to Logic and Scientific Method.* Harcourt, Brace and Company, New York, 1934.

J. H. Woodger. *The Axiomatic Method in Biology.* Cambridge University Press, 1937.

Clark Hull. *The Principles of Behaviour.* Appleton-Century Co., New York, 1943.

Underhill Moore and Charles C. Callahan. *Law and Learning Theory: A Study in Legal Control.* Yale Law Journal Company, Inc., New Haven, 1943.

CHAPTER V

THE POSSIBLE CONCEPTS BY INTUITION AND CONCEPTS BY POSTULATION AS A BASIC TERMINOLOGY FOR COMPARATIVE PHILOSOPHY

To determine the relation between diverse things it is necessary to express each in terms of a common denominator. One would not attempt to relate three-fifths to four-sevenths in mathematics without first reducing these two fractions to thirty-fifths. This is equally true of different philosophical theories, and especially so of systems which contrast as sharply as those of the East and the West. Before there can be a trustworthy comparative analysis of Oriental and Occidental philosophical doctrines there must be an unambiguous, commensurable terminology in which to express them. When such a terminology is provided, certain very interesting and important relationships appear.

This common denominator for international understanding is not given by the linguist's expert translation of the Sanskrit, Chinese or Japanese texts into the English language. This is necessary, but it is not sufficient. No one would suppose that the most competent translation of Albert Einstein's original paper on the Special Theory of Relativity from the German into English would provide a sufficient basis for comparing the theory of relativity with Newton's mechanics. A knowledge of physics would also be necessary. Similarly, the trustworthy student of comparative philosophy must be more than a mere linguist or possess more than trustworthy translations by linguists; in addition he must have a professional mastery of the problems, methods and theories of philosophy.

Additional difficulties remain. They arise from the nature of (a) the symbolism and (b) the subject matter of philosophy.

At first sight the symbolism of philosophy seems easy to understand. Words of ordinary discourse are used. A little reading of philosophical treatises soon discloses, however, that these words are not used with their common-sense meanings. Ordinary words are given technical meanings. What is even more puzzling, the technical philosophical meaning which a common-sense term has in one philosophical system is usually different from what it has in another system.

The reason for this confusing condition may be appreciated if one considers the two alternatives open to anyone who desires to convey a precise technical meaning for which the conventional language is too ambiguous. One may choose a term with no previous meaning and assign the technical meaning to this otherwise meaningless mark. In short, one may resort to a novel technical terminology. Or one may select some well-known word with the common-sense meaning which is the nearest to the precise technical meaning that one desires to convey, and then either add a restricting definition or depend upon the diverse contexts in which the word is used to direct the reader's attention eventually to the exact meaning intended. Generally speaking, science takes the former alternative, philosophy the latter.

Each choice has its advantages and limitations. A technical terminology reduces to a minimum the chance of ambiguity, but automatically restricts the comprehension of the language to the expert with a professional technical training in the subject. Philosophy, partly because of the relevance of its problems for the layman as well as the expert, chooses ordinary discourse, thereby reaching a wider audience, but at the same time it has to depend upon lengthy contexts to convey its technical meaning. This is one reason why philosophical treatises tend to be longer than scientific ones. A language which uses contexts to convey meanings cannot be terse.

The difficulties for comparative philosophy which such a contextual symbolism presents now become evident.

One cannot compare whole treatises. If the inquiry is ever to get beyond the usual most banal generalities one must come down to chapters and paragraphs and sentences. One must take up specific doctrines and designate them by specific words. But to do this is to pull the sentences and words from their contexts, thereby losing their technical and philosophically important meaning.

The utter inadequacy of the expert linguist's translation of diverse philosophical systems into a common language also becomes evident. All that such translations can do is to give the dictionary renderings of the individual terms, but these provide only the common-sense, not the technical philosophical meanings. Nor is the difficulty overcome if the expert translator is also an expert philosopher. As we have noted, the same common-sense word in the context of one philosophical theory has one technical meaning, in the context of a different philosophical theory a different meaning. This is especially true, as we shall see later, if one of the theories is from the East and the other from the West.

The point is that the terms of ordinary discourse are quite adequate when developed at length systematically in various contexts, to convey the technical doctrine of a single philosopher or philosophical theory, but they are utterly inadequate to serve as the common denominator into which one translates diverse philosophical systems for the purpose of comparison. This is true of different Western as well as of Eastern systems. When philosophy becomes comparative, the character of its symbolism necessitates the introduction of a technical terminology.

The subject matter of philosophy enforces the same conclusion. The total object of human inquiry embraces the
entire range of experience. This is entirely too complex and
extensive for any one discipline to investigate and comprehend. The task has to be broken up into its different portions, assigned to different specialists. Roughly speaking the
special sciences treat restricted local factors in experience,
such as living organisms or heavenly bodies, whereas philosophy has as its province the equally evident extensive factors
of experience which are common to these more local details.

Because of its localized subject matter, any special science
attains precise determinate concreteness and intensive accuracy with respect to details, but only at the cost of leaving
numerous equally important factors out of account, with the
attendant risk of a loss of one's sense of proportion. Philosophy, on the other hand, because of its attention upon the
more general extensive, but none the less factual, items in
experience is able to keep technical details in their actual
places, thereby preserving a sense of proportion, but only if
it includes the data of the special sciences and of common
sense in its own final extensive and systematic doctrine.

But to do this is to place the facts of common sense and
technical science in a wider context. The difference between
one philosophical theory and another is that this context is
defined in different ways. Consequently, the philosophically
important thing about any common-sense term as it enters
into any philosophical theory is not its bare dictionary meaning, but the particular contextual meaning usually unique to
the philosophical system in question. Philosophical mate-
rialists, idealists, dualists and neutral monists all admit the
existence of what common sense denotes by the term "mind,"
yet there is all the difference in the world in the ways in
which they analyze and conceive of this datum.

Hence, to learn from the expert linguist that the English
literal equivalent of a certain Chinese or Sanskrit word is

"mind" does not tell one very much that is significant for comparative philosophy. Such a translation provides us with the denotative associations of the common-sense symbol, but not with its technical philosophical, contextual connotative meaning. That which is directly apprehended is roughly the same in any philosophical system, but how it is analyzed and correlated with other factors, whether immediately given or postulated, is different; it is precisely these differences which concern us in comparative philosophy. Consequently, to reduce the diverse doctrines of Eastern and Western philosophy to the supposedly common denominator of the language of common sense is to be left with little more than denotative or dictionary meanings, and to lose the diverse technical contextual meanings unique to each system which are the important factors in any philosophical inquiry.

It is often said that Eastern philosophy is more "religious" or more "idealistic" than Western philosophy. Such statements, as we shall see, are very misleading and for the most part worthless, since they assume that the words "religious" and "ideal" have the same philosophical analysis and technical meanings in the East as in the West. For example, as the distinguished and scholarly Buddhist, Junjiro Takakusu, has indicated, the Buddhist religion is atheistic and skeptical with respect to precisely those traits which the West regards as essential for belief in religion. Similarly, in ethics, many doctrines, such as the emphasis on the individual, which the West tends to regard as "good," the East tends to treat as "evil." Conversely, in the case of immediately apprehended factors, different philosophical systems in the East and the West often use different common-sense terms to denote precisely the same thing. Thus the same word in different philosophical systems often designates quite different and even opposite technical philosophical meanings, and different common-sense terms in different systems often denote the same meaning. Consequently, until we have a technical terminology for the commensurable expression of the precise philosophical meanings of diverse philosophical systems, attempts at comparative philosophy are likely to be more misleading than clarifying.

A theory of any kind, whether scientific or philosophic, is a body of propositions, and a body of propositions is a set of concepts. Concepts fall into different types according to the different sources of their meaning. Consequently, the designation of the different possible major types of concepts should provide a technical terminology with the generality sufficient to include within itself as a special case any possible scientific or philosophical theory.

A concept is a term to which a meaning has been assigned. There are two major ways in which this assignment can be made. The otherwise meaningless term may be associated denotatively with some datum or set of data which is given immediately, or it may have its meaning proposed for it theoretically by the postulates of the deductive theory in which it occurs. We shall call these two basic types concepts by intuition and concepts by postulation respectively.

It is hoped that the terms "intuition" and "postulation" will guide the reader to the precise meanings intended. Since our aim, however, is to provide a technical terminology, it is important that this be not left to chance; hence, the following definitions:

A concept by intuition is one which denotes, and the complete meaning of which is given by, something which is immediately apprehended.

"Blue" in the sense of the sensed color is a concept by intuition. It is to be emphasized that in our terminology "intuition" refers to the direct opposite of what is given as a hunch; it is used to denote what is directly apprehended purely inductively. Were we concerned only with the West it might be better to call this type of concept a "concept by induction" rather than a "concept by intuition." Since we are concerned with the Orient as well, the latter terminology has advantages. Even so, the reader must keep our restricted use of the concept as prescribed in the above definition continuously in mind.

A concept by postulation is one the meaning of which in whole or part is designated by the postulates of the deductive theory in which it occurs. Any concept which can be defined in terms of such concepts we shall also call a concept by postulation. "Blue" in the sense of the number of a wavelength in electromagnetic theory is a concept by postulation.

A deductive theory is a set of propositions which fall into two groups called postulates and theorems, such that the postulates formally imply the theorems by means of the logical relation of formal implication. Given the postulates, the theorems can be proved.

In considering any theory, proof must not be confused with truth. Proof is a relation between propositions, i.e., between those which are postulates and those which are theorems; whereas truth is a relation between propositions and immediately apprehended fact. The former is a purely formal relation which it is the business of pure mathematics and formal logic to define; the latter is an empirical relation which it is the task of empirical science and empirical logic to designate.

The relation of proof, defined by the formal logical relation of formal implication, is quite independent of the truth or falsity of the propositions it relates. The proofs of the theorems in Euclid's *Elements* hold irrespective of the empirical question of truth-value, concerning whether Euclidean geometry is that of the space of our actual universe. Newton's proof that the propositions in his *Principia* follow necessarily on logical grounds from the fundamental axioms of his mechanics is just as valid today as it was before the truth of this mechanics was brought into question by the Michelson-Morley experiment and Einstein's analysis. Hence, when the postulates of a deductive theory are defined as those propositions of the theory which are taken as unproved and used to prove the theorems, this must not be confused with the quite independent question of the truth or falsity of the postulates.

If what is meant by a postulate and a deductive theory is clear, one is prepared to understand a concept by postulation. Our definition tells us that such a concept is one the meaning of which in whole or part is designated by the postulates of the deductive theory in which it occurs.   In other words the meaning which such a concept has is that which it gains by virtue of the properties or relations assigned to it by the postulate or set of postulates within which it is a member term.   It means what the postulates prescribe it to mean.

When it is recalled that the proof of the theorems in a deductive theory can be carried through regardless of knowledge concerning the truth of either the theorems or the postulates, and when to this is added the fact that propositions can be proposed as postulates, in the construction of a deductive theory, irrespective of whether there is anything denotatively given in immediate apprehension which is identical with what the propositions propose, then it becomes evident that concepts which gain their meaning from such postulates may have meanings neither derived from, nor *directly* referable to, anything which is immediately apprehended.   Such is the technical meaning of a concept by postulation.

Concepts by postulation are especially important in the Western world.   No serious attempt at a precise designation of the major difference between Western and Eastern philosophical systems can neglect them.   This importance exhibits itself .in three places: (a) Science, (b) Philosophy, and (c) Common-sense Beliefs.   These merit consideration in turn.

In modern science the first use of concepts by postulation and the first clear distinction between them and concepts by intuition was made by the man who formulated modern physics deductively — Sir Isaac Newton. At the beginning of his *Principia*, Newton wrote,

"I. Absolute, true, and mathematical time, of itself, and from its own nature, flows equably without relation to anything external, and by another name is called duration: relative, apparent, and common time, is some sensible and external (whether accurate or unequable) measure of duration by the means of motion. . . .

"II. Absolute space, in its own nature, without relation to anything external, remains always similar and immovable. Relative space is some movable dimension or measure of the absolute spaces; which our senses determine by its position to bodies; . . ."

In the more precise language of our technical terminology, what Newton is saying in his distinction between "mathematical" and "sensed" space is that there are two different types of concepts for which the one term "space" is used. There is "space" in the sense of "mathematical space" which is a concept by postulation, and there is "space" in the sense of "sensed" or immediately apprehended space, which is a concept by intuition. These two concepts must not be confused, he notes, if "certain prejudices" are to be avoided. In the deductive theory of physics it is always space, time or motion in the sense of the proposed concept by postulation that is used. Put more concretely, this entails that if one wants to know what Newtonian physics means by a "physical object," one does not immediately apprehend the colored shapes of the table or chair of common sense; instead, one examines the postulates of Newton's *Principia*. Newton means by a physical object the kind of entity having the properties and behavior which his three laws of motion prescribe.

Between "physical object" in this postulationally prescribed meaning and "physical object" in the sense of a concept by intuition there is all the difference in the world. From "physical object" in the latter sense nothing whatever can be deduced. As Hume showed, the relation between one immediately apprehended factor and another is external and contingent.   Newton's *Principia* demonstrates, however, that from "physical object" in the sense of his concept by postulation, the meaning of which is given by the "Axioms" of his mechanics, all the dozens upon dozens of propositions making up the major portion of his treatise can be deduced as necessary consequences.   Among these deduced or proved propositions can be found Kepler's three laws of planetary motion and all the important empiricially verified laws of the entire science of dynamics.

Recently, Albert Einstein has replaced Newton's postulates for mechanics with a different set.   But in Albert Einstein's theory the same distinction exists between postulated time which flows "equably" and sensed time which flows non-uniformly.   Thus, contemporary as well as traditional modern physics distinguishes between concepts by intuition and concepts by postulation and formulates its theory in terms of the latter.

The presence of concepts by postulation shows more obviously perhaps in the case of the scientific concept of the electron, which was given precise meaning in the postulates of the generalized electromagnetic theory of Lorentz, several years before the existence of an entity possessing the properties designated by Lorentz's postulates was found experimentally by J. J. Thomson.   Clearly, in this case, the concept was given a meaning postulationally before any denotatively given source for its meaning was known.   Moreover, an electron is too small to be immediately apprehended.   Its diameter is such, relative to the wave-length of light, that observation of it is not merely practically, but also theoretically, impossible.

This makes us aware of a second significance of concepts by postulation.   It is by means of them that science is able to introduce unobservable entities and relations into its theory, and to predict the existence of scientific objects theoretically which are confirmed experimentally only later, and even then only indirectly.

Were there only concepts by intuition our scientific or philosophical theories could refer to nothing but the immediately apprehended. Our conception of the nature of things would be exhausted with the crude limits of our sense awareness and powers of immediate apprehension, and all Western scientific and philosophical knowledge would have the inexpressible ineffability which attaches to everything given with immediacy.

It is not an accident that the most distinguished Western philosophers from Democritus, Plato and Aristotle through Albertus Magnus, Descartes, Leibnitz and Kant to Russell and Whitehead were mathematicians, physicists or biologists before they were philosophers. The verified science of a culture cannot use concepts referring to factors other than what is immediately apprehended without the effect upon epistemology and metaphysics becoming evident and inescapable. In fact, metaphysics, when unambiguously defined, is the thesis that there are concepts by postulation as well as concepts by intuition; positivism, conversely, is the thesis that there are only concepts by intuition. Curiously enough, it is not to the science of the West, but to the philosophy and religion of the East, that one must go if one wants to observe what happens when positivism is taken seriously.

Concepts by postulation were first introduced into Western philosophy by Democritus because of the need for them in Greek physics and mathematics. Plato merely continued what Democritus had initiated, analyzing the unobservable atoms of the Democritean theory into the intuitively given continuum which provided their "matter" and the ideal mathematical ratio which determined their geometrical form. Democritus' and Plato's distinction between the "sense world" and the "real world" is an example of our distinction between what is given to immediate apprehension as denoted by concepts by intuition and what is proposed by deductive scientific and philosophical theory as designated by concepts by postulation.

Aristotle, on the other hand, because of the breakdown of the postulates of the Democritean and Platonic theories in Greek mathematics, due to their incapacity to validate the Eudoxian method of exhaustion, and because of his concern with biology, was forced to reject all postulated scientific objects such as the physical atoms of Democritus or the stereometrical atoms of Plato, and to admit into science and philosophy only concepts by intuition. To such concepts, the content of which is given empirically, Aristotle did, however, add a postulated immortality, due to their logical character. This led him to deny any "bifurcation" between the real as given to the senses in observation and the real as comprehended postulationally in deductive theory; the former, when grasped in its logical character, exhausts reality. In his attack upon the "bifurcation" of traditional and contemporary modern science, Alfred North Whitehead has returned recently to this Aristotelian thesis.

Contemporary students have tended to go astray in their interpretation of Plato and Aristotle because of the failure to distinguish between concepts by postulation and concepts by intuition, not noting that "idea" for Plato is a pure concept by postulation, whereas for Aristotle it is in part a concept by intuition. The distinction in Plato's philosophy between "sensibles," "mathematicals" and "ideas," to which Aristotle refers in the first book of the *Metaphysics* and which has been shown to possess specific scientific content in the mathematical and astronomical theories of Plato's day, also turns around our distinction between concepts by intuition and concepts by postulation. A "sensible" is a concept by intuition the meaning of which is given by immediate apprehension through sense awareness. "Mathematicals" and "ideas" (i.e., ratios), on the other hand, are concepts by postulation. The clarification of the distinction between "mathematicals" and "ideas" must await the further development, in the sequel, of our technical terminology for comparative philosophy, and in particular the classification of the different possible types of concepts by postulation.

When this is done, it will become evident also that a certain qualification must be placed upon the designation of the Aristotelian and Whiteheadian theories of science and philosophy as ones which use only concepts by intuition. This would be the case in the Aristotelian system were the "sensibles" taken only in their purely psychological character by the "passive intellect"; the moment, however, that one takes them in their logical character as a "positive form," as one does in the transition from the "passive" to the "active intellect," then a slight element by postulation has been introduced. The change is not that one rejects denotatively given concepts by intuition from one's scientific theory, replacing them by purely theoretically designated concepts by postulation as do Democritus, Plato and the modern physicists, but that, retaining and using only concepts by intuition, one postulates for their intuitively given meanings a logical status and resultant immortal persistence beyond the brief spans during which they are actually sensed. In other words, one accepts only concepts by intuition and treats them, to use the language of Alfred North Whitehead, as "eternal objects." What is meant is something given only by immediate apprehension. To this immediately apprehended content which is transitory as sensed, there is added by postulation merely an immortal logical status and subsistence. It is precisely this slight element of postulation added to pure concepts by intuition which distinguishes obviously metaphysical theories like Aristotle's and Alfred North Whitehead's from positivism.

It cannot be too strongly emphasized that Whiteheadian "eternal objects" and Aristotelian "forms" are quite different from Plato's "ideas." An Aristotelian "idea," like a Whiteheadian "eternal object," is a Platonic "sensible" given an immortal persistence by postulation. A Platonic "idea," on the other hand, is not even in part a "sensible"; "ideas" and "sensibles" are totally different things. Plato agrees with the positivists and the philosophers of the East that "sensibles" are nominalistic and purely transitory. This is precisely why he says that the sense world is a world of becoming and not a world of being. It is only by giving up concepts by intuition (i.e., Platonic "sensibles") and formulating one's scientific and philosophical theory completely in terms of concepts by postulation (i.e., Platonic "ideas") that one can find the invariants obeying the principle of being which give "genuine knowledge" according to Plato.

Aristotle's and Alfred North Whitehead's formation of "ideas" by giving "sensibles" an eternal status is a necessary consequence of their rejection of "bifurcation." Having repudiated all scientific objects or factors whose conservation is guaranteed by postulation, no meaning can be provided for the laws of science which hold, even when the scientist is not observing, except by smuggling into the transitory data of sense awareness an immortal persistence which they do not possess.

Plato forms "ideas" by rejecting concepts by intuition entirely in the formulation of the deductive theory of his science and philosophy and by using only concepts by postulation. Moreover, these concepts by postulation are given such meanings by the postulates of the deductive theory in which they occur that they designate nothing either sensible or imaginable. In the Sixth Book of the *Republic,* when describing the passage of dialectic from the "mathematicals" in the hypotheses of the sciences to the "ideas," Plato asserts that one "makes no use of images" (510). It is not that one gives "sensibles" or "images" a logical immortal status; one does not use them at all. A Platonic "idea," with respect to its content as well as its immortality, is a quite different kind of concept.

But it is not merely Democritean and Platonic Greek philosophy and modern science which use concepts by postulation. This is true even of Western beliefs of common sense.

Berkeley and Hume have shown, as was demonstrated in Chapter III, that even our most ordinary beliefs, such as the supposition that there are public physical objects, or minds other than one's own, involve much more than mere observation or immediate apprehension can give. These beliefs, like the verified theories of modern science, are proposed by postulation and confirmed only indirectly by observation; they are not given completely, or guaranteed, by direct inspection alone. The errors in our perceptual judgments demonstrate this.

This presence of concepts by postulation in even the layman's ordinary beliefs is obscured by the fact that the postulates in question have been verified through their deductive consequences so many times in our daily experience that we have come to regard their trustworthiness as almost as secure as our belief in immediately apprehended factors such as colors and sounds. Also the inference has by child training been conditioned as a habit so that it happens automatically without a conscious effort.

When one passes from common-sense objects to the more deductively fertile and adequate postulated objects of science the amount of meaning introduced into Western theory by postulation increases, and what is meant diverges more and more from the meanings provided by concepts by intuition which restrict themselves completely to the immediately apprehended. This will be made clear in Chapter VIII.

We can postulate entities or structures which we can imagine but cannot sense, and we can postulate factors which we can neither sense nor imagine. A concept by postulation which designates the former we shall term a concept by imagination, one which designates the latter a concept by intellection.

Centaurs, the atoms of Democritus, the Platonic regular solids of Book XIII of Euclid, and the atomic models of Neils Bohr's and Rutherford's classical atomic physics are examples of concepts by postulation which are concepts by imagination. The many-dimensional structures of mathematical physics in those cases in which the dimensions are greater in number than three, are examples of concepts by postulation which are concepts by intellection. One cannot imagine more than three dimensions, yet by the use of concepts by postulation mathematical physicists have no difficulty in defining a space of any number of dimensions. The ratio ("idea") which defines the respect in which two similar geometrical figures ("mathematicals") in Platonic mathematics are identical, considered apart from the two sensed or imagined figures of different sizes in which the identical ratio is analogically represented, is another example. Thus, the Platonic distinction between "mathematicals" and "ideas" is, when unambiguously expressed in our technical terminology, the difference between a concept by postulation which is a concept by imagination and a concept by postulation which is a concept by intellection. The deductive theories of the physics of the nineteenth century which required imaginable physical models used concepts by imagination. The deductive theories of contemporary physics which can only be expressed mathematically dispense with concepts by imagination and use only concepts by intellection.

Concepts by imagination and concepts by intellection each fall likewise into two groups, which we shall term pluralistic and monistic. Monistic concepts designate a single all-embracing factor; pluralistic concepts designate many externally related factors.

The kinetic atomic theory of Democritus or the kinetic

theory of heat and gases of classical modern particle physics are examples of a pluralistic concept by imagination. The ether substance of a prerelativistic field physics is an instance of a monistic concept by imagination. The four primitive ratios of the four atomic triangles of the Platonic mathematics exemplify a pluralistic concept by intellection. Albert Einstein's tensor equation for gravitation, which designates the invariant metrical properties of four-dimensional space-time, illustrates a monistic concept by intellection.

In addition to concepts by imagination and concepts by intellection, there is a third major type of concept by postulation which our consideration of common-sense beliefs has indicated. Not merely atoms and tensor equations represent postulated factors, but ordinary external objects and other people's minds do also. Concepts designating those common-sense objects we shall term concepts by perception. Tables, chairs and the ordinary objects and persons of social discourse are examples. In designating such concepts as concepts by perception it is important to distinguish "perception" in this usage from immediate apprehension. As Berkeley and Hume have shown, and as we have previously indicated, "perceptual objects" are not immediately apprehended factors; they are postulates of common sense so thoroughly and frequently and unconsciously verified through their deductive consequences that only the critical realize them to be postulated rather than immediately apprehended.

Concepts by perception also fall into two groups, pluralistic and monistic. The many physical objects and people of ordinary discourse exemplify pluralistic concepts by perception. The single, publicly perceived space within which these pluralistic perceptual objects are located is an example of a monistic concept by perception.

Our consideration of the difference between Plato's "ideas," which are concepts by postulation that are concepts by intellection, and Aristotle's "ideas" or Whiteheadian "eternal objects," which are concepts by intuition for which an immortal logical status has been postulated, indicates the possibility of a fourth, borderline type of concept by postulation. We shall call this fourth type logical concepts by intuition. They are concepts whose content is given by immediate apprehension and whose immortal persistence is proposed by postulation.

There are also pluralistic and monistic logical concepts by intuition. "Hot," in the sense of the immediately apprehended sensation functioning as a "form by privation" in the physics of Aristotle and Whiteheadian "eternal objects" in their relation of disjunction to each other are examples of the pluralistic case. The "Unmoved Mover" of Aristotle's theology, in which the pluralistic forms are treated as a hierarchical unity is a monistic example.

The following classification of Concepts by Postulation results:

I Concepts by Intellection = Concepts by postulation designating factors which can be neither imagined nor sensed.
   (a) Monistic. e.g., The space-time continuum of Einstein's field physics.
   (b) Pluralistic. e.g., Plato's atomic ratios.

II Concepts by Imagination = Concepts by postulation designating factors which can be imagined but cannot be sensed.
   (a) Monistic. e.g., The ether concept of classical prerelativistic field physics.
   (b) Pluralistic. e.g., The atoms and molecules of classical particle physics.

III Concepts by Perception = Concepts by postulation designating factors which are in part sensed and in part imagined.
   (a) Monistic. e.g., The public space of daily life.
   (b) Pluralistic. e.g., Other persons, tables, chairs, and the spherical moon with its back side which we do not see as well as its presented side which we do see.

IV Logical Concepts by Intuition = Concepts designating fac-
    tors, the content of which is given through the senses or by
    mere abstraction from the totality of sense awareness, and
    whose logical universality and immortality are given by
    postulation.

>   (a) Monistic. e.g., The "Unmoved Mover" in Aristotle's
>   metaphysics.
>   (b) Pluralistic. e.g., Whitehead's "eternal objects," San-
>   tayana's "essences," or Aristotle's "ideas."

Since logical concepts by intuition are concepts by postulation merely so far as their immortality is concerned and are
concepts by intuition with respect to their content, they provide a natural transition from the one generic type of concept
to the other.

Since concepts by intuition gain their entire meaning from
the immediately apprehended, it is necessary to consider its
general character and the factors it contains in order to designate the possible types of such concepts.

We must start with the all-embracing immediacy from
which any theory, Eastern or Western, takes its inception.
This immediacy exhibits itself as a continuum or field which
is differentiated. It would seem that all people could agree
on this as a correct designation of what one immediately apprehends, however differently they might analyze it as inquiry
proceeds. It will be well to have a name for this all-embracing, initial, immediately apprehended fact with which any
attempt to arrive at a description of experience must begin.
We have called it the differentiated aesthetic continuum.
The word "continuum" is used to denote the fact that what
we immediately apprehend is an all-embracing field. The
word "differentiated" is chosen to indicate that within this
field there occur factors in one part different from those in
another. We immediately apprehend a field which is white
here and blue there. The adjective "aesthetic" is added to
insure that it is the qualitatively ineffable, emotionally

moving continuum of colors, sounds and feelings which the artist presents in its immediacy, not the logically defined continuum of mathematical physics which is a concept by postulation, that is indicated. Also only what Prall termed the "aesthetic surface" considered in and for itself is immediately apprehended; the common-sense external object which the aesthetic object sometimes symbolizes is a concept by postulation, not a concept by intuition. This initial, complex, denotatively given fact considered in its totality with nothing neglected is what we mean by the concept of the differentiated aesthetic continuum. It is not to be confused with the field concept of field physics or the public space of common-sense perceptual objects, both of which, as we have previously indicated, are monistic concepts by postulation.

Since the differentiated aesthetic continuum with all its aesthetic and emotive immediacy includes everything that is immediately apprehended, all other concepts by intuition derive from it by abstraction. By "abstraction" we mean, throughout this chapter, the consideration of certain immediately apprehended factors apart from their immediately apprehended context; we do not mean the "abstract" in the sense of the postulated. It has been noted already that the differentiated aesthetic continuum contains two abstractable factors. There is (a) the field or continuum apart from the differentiations within it or the definite properties which characterize it, and there are (b) the differentiations or definite properties apart from the continuum which runs through them and embraces them. The former, (a), we shall call the indefinite or undifferentiated aesthetic continuum, the latter, (b), since they are many in number, the differentiations.

We arrive, therefore, at three major possible concepts by intuition. They are:

    I   The Concept of the Differentiated Aesthetic Continuum,
   II   The Concept of the Indefinite or Undifferentiated Aesthetic Continuum,

III The Concepts of the Differentiations. These, for reasons indicated later, we shall also term Concepts by Inspection.

It follows from the designations given above that the following relations hold:

$$I = II \text{ with } III;$$
$$II = I \text{ without } III;$$
$$III = I \text{ without } II.$$

It is important to note that these relations do not define the meanings of these three concepts in the manner in which the postulates of a deductive theory prescribe the meaning of the concepts by postulation within the postulates. Concepts I, II, and III are concepts by intuition. Hence, the reader, to get their meaning, must find what they denote in immediate apprehension. Even then the full meaning can be gained only by contemplating what is apprehended.

The most difficult of these three concepts for the Westerner to appreciate is the second. This happens because of the influence of Berkeley and Hume. They insisted that all concepts are concepts by intuition but tended to regard the continuum as nothing but an aggregation of secondary and tertiary qualities. That this is false, an examination of what one immediately apprehends will indicate. We directly inspect not merely the white and the noise but also these in a field. The field is as immediately given as any specific quality, whether secondary or tertiary, within it. Moreover, most of the directly experienced field is vague and indefinite. Only at what William James termed its center is there specificity and definiteness. Thus it is evident that the indefinite, indeterminate, aesthetic continuum is as immediately apprehended as are the specific differentiations within it. Hence, the concept of the indefinite or undifferentiated continuum, gained by abstraction from the differentiated aesthetic continuum, is a concept by intuition, not a concept by postulation.

The concepts by intuition which are concepts of the differentiations fall into two groups. The differentiations which one immediately apprehends may be given (a) through the senses or (b) introspectively. The former we shall call concepts by sensation, the latter concepts by introspection. "Blue," in the sense of the immediately sensed color, is a concept by sensation. "Wants," which Chapter XIII will show to be the basic entities in the Austrian theory of economic science, and the images of phantasy are examples of concepts by introspection. We shall also call concepts by sensation or concepts by introspection, following C. I. Lewis, "concepts by inspection." Concepts by inspection are, in this technical terminology, identical with concepts of the differentiations. The latter terminology is better in reminding us that sense data and tertiary qualities have no existence apart from the aesthetic continuum or field within which they appear and from which they are abstracted. C. I. Lewis's terminology is better in providing a single concept for designating either concepts by sensation or concepts by introspection. We shall use whichever terminology is more suggestive at the time. No confusion will result provided the reader remembers that concepts of the differentiations and concepts by inspection denote, and hence mean, since they are concepts by intuition, precisely the same thing.

George P. Conger has called attention to an additional concept by intuition which is obtainable from the differentiated aesthetic continuum by abstraction. It is a specific inspected quality in the aesthetic continuum with all other differentiations, but not the continuum itself, neglected. Such a concept by intuition we shall term a field concept by inspection. A philosophy which takes this type of concept as basic and sufficient will be positivistic in that it admits only concepts by intuition but will differ from most modern Western positivism by holding a monistic rather than a pluralistic theory of the immediately apprehended. In this connection the philosophy of Bradley is suggestive, as is also Gestalt psychology.

We arrive at the following classification of the major possible concepts by intuition:

I The Concept of the Differentiated Aesthetic Continuum = The totality of the immediately apprehended with nothing abstracted away.

II The Concept of the Indeterminate or Undifferentiated Aesthetic Continuum = The immediately apprehended continuum apart from all differentiations.

III The Concepts of the Differentiations = Concepts by Inspection = Atomic Concepts by Inspection = The specific inspected qualities or differentiations considered apart from the continuum.

 (a) Concepts by Sensation = III given through the senses.

 (b) Concepts by Introspection = III given introspectively.

IV Field Concepts by Inspection = any instance of III considered as inseparable from II.

This completes the classification of the different possible types of concepts from which any scientific or philosophical theory may be constructed. Since it exhausts the major possible ways of providing terms with meanings, our technical terminology for comparative philosophy may be regarded as provided.

Different philosophical doctrines can now be compared by noting which of the possible types of concepts they admit. By means of this terminology, also, diverse philosophical theories can be defined. Positivism, for example, is the thesis that there are only concepts by intuition. Western positivism has tended to maintain, in addition, that all concepts by intuition are definable in terms of or reducible to atomic concepts by inspection. A metaphysical theory, on the other hand, is one which maintains that there are also concepts by postulation. As we have indicated, the general tendency of Western science and philosophy has been to require concepts by postulation.

Only at those transitional periods in the development of Western thought, like the present, when the traditional concepts by postulation are breaking down and before the new scientific ones which have replaced the old are made articulate philosophically does positivism and its attempt to restrict the whole of reality to the immediately apprehended appear in the West.

Concepts by intuition are especially and continuously important in the traditional Orient.   This happens because the Far Easterners have tended to be pure empiricists restricting reality to the immediately apprehended.   In fact, they identify the Divine with the timeless undifferentiated aesthetic continuum.   Consequently, Far Eastern religion is a positivistic, empirical and, hence, scientifically veridical religion.

This chapter was presented first at the East-West Philosopher's Conference at the University of Hawaii in 1939.   It is reprinted here with the kind permission of the Editor of the Princeton University Press from pp. 168-190 of Chapter VIII of *Philosophy — East and West*, Edited by Charles A. Moore. Princeton University Press, 1944.

Aristotle.   *Physica* BkI.7.190b25
    De Anima.

Newton.   *Principia,* Cajori Edition.   University of California Press, 1934.

William James.   *A Pluralistic Universe.*   Lectures VI, VII, VIII. Longmans, Green & Company, New York, 1909.

Alfred North Whitehead.   *The Concept of Nature.*   The University Press, Cambridge, England, 1920.

Arthur O. Lovejoy.   *The Revolt against Dualism.*   W. W. Norton & Company, New York, 1930.

S. Luria.   *Die Infinitesimals Theorie der Antiken Atomisten in "Quellen und Studien zur Geschichte der Mathematik."* Abteilung B, Band II, 106-185.   Springer, Berlin, 1930.

O. Toeplitz.   *Das Verhaltnis von Mathematik und Ideenlehre bei Plato.   Ibid.,* Band I, 3-33.

Erich Frank. *Plato und die Sogenannten Pythagoreer.* Niemeyer, Halle, 1923.

F. S. C. Northrop. "Mathematical Background and Content of Greek Philosophy," in *Philosophical Essays for Alfred North Whitehead.* Longmans, Green & Co., New York, 1936.
"The Complementary Emphasis of Oriental Intuitive and Western Scientific Philosophy," in *Philosophy — East and West. Loc. cit.*

CHAPTER VI

THE TWO KINDS OF
DEDUCTIVELY FORMULATED THEORY

One of the basic problems in the unification of scientific knowledge is that of clarifying the relation between those concepts which a given science uses in the early natural history stage of its development and those which enter into its final and more theoretical formulation as a verified deductive theory.

Consider the science of chemistry. By the concept of sulphur as used in the natural history approach to this subject, the chemist means, among other things, a yellowish something which, when heated in conjunction with certain other things, disappears as a visual datum and is superseded by what may best be described as a very disagreeable odor. By the concept of sulphur as used when chemistry begins to develop deductively formulated theory, the chemist may mean a certain concatenation of outer electrons around a nucleus, or a set of energy-levels defined as part of a system which behaves according to rules designated by the postulates of quantum mechanics.

Or consider the science of physics, and a particular branch thereof, optics, with its treatment of colors. By the concept "blue" in the natural history stage of the science, the physicist means the immediately sensed color; by the concept "blue" in the later deductive theory of optics, he means a specific number, termed a wave-length, which is part of a system of electromagnetic propagations defined by the postulates of Maxwell's, or some other, electromagnetic theory.

Countless examples could be given. But these are sufficient to enable us to clearly distinguish the two types of scientific concepts.

Those concepts used in the natural history stage if the development of a science gain their meaning purely empirically from factors which can be immediately apprehended. Consequently, if one is called upon to give the meaning of such a concept one must find something within the immediacy of experience.

In Chapters III and V, following Oriental usage, such concepts were termed concepts by intuition, where, it is to be emphasized, by intuition is meant neither a speculative hunch or wild guess which chances to come off, nor an axiom assumed to be self-evident, but the immediacy of the purely empirically apprehended, i.e., pure fact. The concept by intuition denoting the whole of immediately apprehended fact is most appropriately symbolized as *the differentiated aesthetic continuum*. We shall also term this totality of immediately apprehended fact *the aesthetic component* of things. Conversely, inferred fact designated by concepts by postulation is called *the theoretic component* of things.

In most natural history science, due to specialization, it is the differentiations within the differentiated aesthetic continuum which most concern the scientist. The concepts by intuition denoting these differentiations alone are termed *concepts by inspection.*

Concepts by intuition fall into two groups, according to whether what one immediately inspects is given through what later theoretical interpretation calls the outer senses or by inner introspection. The former are termed *concepts by sensation;* the latter, *concepts by introspection.* A color is an example of a concept by inspection which is a concept by sensation. An immediately felt pain or a want in the Austrian or recent classical Anglo-American theory of economic science (see Chapter XIII) is a concept by inspection which is a concept by introspection.

Those scientific concepts, on the other hand, which appear in the third stage of inquiry with its deductive formulation of a given scientific subject matter, gain their meaning, as has been made evident, from the postulates of the scientific theory in which they occur. They mean what is prescribed for them by the postulates or theorems into which they enter. Apart from these postulates and the deduced theorems they are meaningless marks. Thus, the meaning of these concepts, instead of being presented to the empirical scientist by what is immediately inspected or observed, is proposed by the theoretical scientist drawing upon the full play of his material imagination and upon the investigations by pure mathematicians into the formal possibilities. Afterwards, by definite scientific methods to be described shortly, the empirical scientist determines whether the entities and relations designated by the system of meanings thus prescribed by the theoretical scientist's postulates are verified as existing and as adequate for the natural history data of the science in question.

In calling such concepts concepts by postulation one caution must be kept in mind. By concepts by postulation is not meant merely those concepts of a deductively formulated scientific theory which appear in the postulates; the concepts in the theorems, since they are defined in terms of the primitive ideas of the postulates, are concepts by postulation also. In short, any concept in a deductively formulated scientific theory, whether it appears in the postulates or in the theorems of that theory, is a concept by postulation.

In distinguishing these two types of concepts, one additional point is to be noted. In the case of concepts by inspection one has the empirical immediately observable fact first to provide the meaning and then constructs a scientific concept by merely assigning a given mark uniquely to this empirically given meaning; whereas in the case of concepts by postulation one has first a meaning assigned systematically and consistently to a mark by the theoretical scientist exer-

cising the full play of his material or formal imagination, and
then one looks around afterward, if at all, for directly inspectable empirical facts by means of which to check the
existence or non-existence of the entities and relations designated by the system of postulationally constructed meanings.

In the construction of such deductively formulated theory,
the theoretical scientist has two modes of procedure open to
him. He may identify the undefined concepts by postulation, the primitive entities and relations, in his deductively
formulated theory with directly sensed entities and relations
or he may not do so.

If the former alternative is pursued, then the concepts by
postulation of his deductive theory are, what the previous
chapter termed, *logical concepts by intuition.* Referring to
directly observable entities and relations for their meaning,
they are *concepts by intuition,* and having a logical universality prescribed for them by the postulates, specifying that what
is sensed holds for *all* instances, they are *logical* concepts by
intuition. If the other alternative is pursued, then the concepts by postulation of the deductive theory are, what the
previous chapter termed, either *concepts by imagination* or
concepts by intellection.

Which alternative is pursued depends upon the problem
which initiates the inquiry in question. Again the inescapable importance of the first stage of inquiry reveals itself.

If the problem with which the inquiry is concerned can be
solved by means of observable entities and relations alone,
the first alternative is chosen. Then the scientist orders the
undefined or primitive concepts by postulation of his deductively formulated theory exactly as the natural history
concepts by inspection of his subject matter order themselves
in direct awareness. In this case, what the concepts by intuition of the second stage of inquiry mean and what the concepts by postulation of the third stage of inquiry mean is
identical; in other words, the relation between concepts by

intuition and concepts by postulation in this first possible type of deductively formulated theory is the relation of identity.　Such theory we shall call *abstractive deductively formulated theory*.

For abstractive deductively formulated theory, the philosophy of science of Alfred North Whitehead is valid.　The two following principles from his *Concept of Nature* hold: Nature is the terminus of sense awareness.　All scientific concepts are derived from the continuum of sense awareness by the method of extensive abstraction.　It is to be noted that the latter proposition is true only if all concepts by postulation are logical concepts by intuition.

The thesis that all scientific concepts and all deductively formulated theories are of this character, however, raises certain queries.　Why, for example, if this be true, is the indirect method of verification forced upon natural scientists as it unquestionably is, whereby deductively formulated scientific theories cannot be tested directly by testing the postulates, but, as John Dewey, Morris Cohen and Ernest Nagel, Albert Einstein and countless others have emphasized, can be tested only indirectly by deducing theorems from the postulates and checking the theorems?　If a deductively formulated theory, including all its entities and relations are mere abstractions from the continuum of sense awareness, then it should be possible to confirm theories in natural science categorically and directly, rather than hypothetically and indirectly, by empirically confirming the postulates.　We should then believe in the postulates because they are known empirically to be true and believe in the truth of our theorems on formal logical grounds because they are the logical consequences of our empirically confirmed postulates.　But the actual procedure of natural scientists is the reverse of this, as succeeding chapters will demonstrate.　The empirically verified propositions in the deductively formulated theory are the theorems, and the postulates are believed to be verified not directly by themselves alone, but only indirectly by way of the empirically verified theorems which are their logical consequence.

It is interesting in this connection to note, as Chapter XIII will show in detail, that the economic science of the Austrian and the Classical Anglo-American School is an abstractive deductively formulated scientific theory with the attendant basic concepts by postulation which are logical concepts by intuition. Furthermore, experts in this science affirm that they believe in the theory because the postulates are directly verified empirically and that they believe in the theorems, not because the latter are or always can be empirically verified, but because the theorems are the logical consequences of the empirically verified postulates.

This should not surprise one, even though it is completely counter to the epistemology of pragmatism which locates not merely all verification but even all meaning in the future consequences of one's hypothesis, i.e., the future verification of the theorems, and even though it is counter to the claims of most logicians who assert that there is but one scientific method, namely, the method by which postulates are verified not directly but only indirectly by way of their logical and pragmatic consequences. For, since the concepts by postulation of the economic science in question are identified with concepts by intuition, not only can the direct method of verification of the postulates of science occur, as the experts in the sciences affirm, but, as we noted in the previous paragraph, this must be the case for any theory constructed in terms of such concepts.

Again, the error becomes evident of assuming *a priori* that there is but one scientific method. Even in the case of the deductively formulated type of science of the third stage of inquiry, the scientific method for verification is different in the case of the economic science of the Austrian and classical current British Schools than it is in the case of modern

mathematical physics.   Both sciences are deductively formulated; yet, as Chapters VIII and XIII will establish in detail,
the method of verification in the two cases is different.   The
economist empirically verifies his postulates directly by directly inspecting what they affirm, and believes in the truth of
the theorems, even when they are not, or cannot be, directly
verified, because they are the necessary logical consequences
of his empirically verified postulates.   The mathematical
physicist, as Albert Einstein and others have emphasized, on
the other hand, does not verify his postulates directly, but
believes them to be tentatively true providing the theorems
logically deduced from them are directly verified.

Why, it may be most properly asked, do not the mathematical physicists use the same method of verification as the
aforementioned economists?   Certainly, other things being
equal, the economist's method of verification is preferable
for two reasons: First, the basic assumptions of a deductively
formulated science are the postulates, and it is certainly
preferable, if one cannot directly verify all propositions in a
science, to verify the basic propositions making up the postulates than the secondary and derived propositions making up
the theorems.   Second, the mathematical physicist's method
of verification, as the next chapter will illustrate, commits a
formal logical fallacy of the hypothetical syllogism, whereas
the economist's method of verification does not.

This can be shown in the following manner: Let A and B
represent respectively the postulates and theorems.   Then
the logic of the economist's method is as follows: A is the
case.   If A, then B.   Therefore, B is the case.   This is a
formally valid argument.   The logic of the mathematical
physicist's argument, on the other hand, is as follows: If A,
then B.   B is the case.   Therefore, A is the case.   Even the
most elementary text-book in logic will indicate that the
latter argument commits a formal logical fallacy, the fallacy

of the hypothetical syllogism, called the fallacy of affirming the consequent.

And common-sense considerations will support the logician's verdict. The mere fact that B follows logically from A, and that B is true, does not prove necessarily that A is true. For some other postulates not yet dreamed of or perhaps some other postulates already known might also logically imply B. Hence, the empirical confirmation of the theorems B does not formally guarantee the truth of the postulates A.

Why, then, does the physicist use a formally fallacious method for verifying his deductively formulated theory instead of the formally valid method of verification of the economist? The answer to this question centers in the previously noted fact that in the construction of any deductively formulated theory, the theoretical scientist has two modes of procedure open to him. He may identify the concepts by postulation in his deductively formulated theory with concepts by intuition. In this case he obtains *abstractive deductively formulated theory,* which because of the concepts out of which it is constructed, permits a direct empirical verification of its postulates. Or he may construct his theory in terms of concepts by postulation which are either *concepts by imagination* or *concepts by intellection.* Since the latter types of concept designate basic entities and relations differing from those immediately sensed, the postulates of such theory cannot be verified directly and can be tested only indirectly by way of their deductive consequences, the theorems. Such theory, exemplified in mathematical physics, we shall call *hypothetically inferred deductively formulated theory.* Which alternative the scientist chooses depends upon the problem which initiates the inquiry with which he is concerned.

If his problem and the natural history data are such that the problem can be solved by identifying the concepts by postulation with directly inspectable data denoted by concepts by intuition, as is the case in the Austrian theory of economic science, then it follows by the very nature of such concepts by postulation, their identification with concepts by intuition, that the postulates can be directly verified. Hence the logic of verification is and must be that exemplified in the deductively formulated economic science of the Austrian School.

If, on the other hand, the problem which initiates inquiry is such that it cannot be solved by an appeal solely to directly inspectable entities and relations, as turns out to be the case again and again in mathematical physics, the scientist has no recourse but to appeal to hypothetically designated, unobservable entities and relations. In this manner the scientific objects, such as electrons, electromagnetic propagations with exceedingly high velocities, and the four-dimensional space-time continuum with the mathematical properties designated by Albert Einstein's tensor equation for gravitation arise.

In certain instances the unobservable entities can be imagined, even though they are not sensed. In this case the concepts by postulation of the deductive theory are concepts by imagination. A model theory in physics, of the type so popular at the end of the 19th century, may be defined as a deductively formulated theory constructed in terms of concepts by postulation which are concepts by imagination.

In other cases, such as the aforementioned four-dimensional space-time continuum or the subject matter of physics as conceived in quantum mechanics, where both the wave and the particle model theories break down, the subject matter of science, as designated by its experimentally verified deductively formulated theory, cannot even be imagined, to say nothing about being sensed. In this case the concepts by postulation, in terms of which the deductively formulated theory is constructed, are concepts by intellection. The sciences which provide the primitive ideas necessary to construct such theory are pure mathematics and mathematical logic. It is because of the increasing role of concepts by postulation which are concepts by intellection in contemporary physical science that the investigations of the pure mathematicians and the mathematical logicians are becoming increasingly important.

We find, therefore, that there are two kinds of hypothetically inferred deductively formulated theory. Both are constructed out of concepts by postulation which are not logical concepts by intuition. The one kind, exemplified in model theories, uses concepts by postulation which are concepts by imagination; the other kind, more recently growing in importance, is constructed out of concepts by postulation which are concepts by intellection.

Strictly speaking, concepts by postulation which are concepts by perception, exemplified in the objects of common sense belief, belong in this group also. For we noted in Chapter II that they involve a hypothetical inference beyond what Bacon's purely inductive methods give one, just as do the scientific objects of the more deductively fertile theories of mathematical physics. Since it is customary, however, to include such common-sense objects in the natural history type of science of the second stage of scientific inquiry, we shall neglect their inclusion and consideration here, having previously treated them in Chapter III.

It is to be emphasized, however, that inference to scientific objects, such as electrons or the four-dimensional space-time continuum, is not different in kind from the inferences made by the common-sense man to tables and chairs, his persisting self and other minds. The process of inference is, to be sure, less self-conscious in the latter case, since the deductive consequences of the hypothesis that one is confronted by a chair are so many and so easily discoverable, that we check the hypothesis instantly, and have done so upon so many different occasions, that we hardly realize the presence of a hypothesis.

Also, from early childhood we have been conditioned in the face of a penalty of pain to instantly infer certain external objects from certain sense impressions. The child gets his hand slapped if he toys too long with the sensation of hotness and does not instantly infer the presence of a stove and respond in ways appropriate thereto. Thus the inferences to common-sense external objects are conditioned habits. This explains why such inferences occur automatically without the conscious effort of postulation entailed in inferences to scientific objects.

The same thing happens, however, even with respect to scientific objects in the case of the professional scientist. After many indirect experimental verifications of his theory concerning inferred scientific objects, he becomes so accustomed to conceiving of his empirically given data in terms of these directly unobservable, postulationally designated scientific entities and relations that, like the ordinary man with respect to common-sense objects, he almost forgets that he is not directly observing them.

All hypothetically inferred, deductively formulated theory has certain characteristics. Its concepts, since they refer to factors which are not directly inspectable, cannot be derived from the continuum of sense awareness by the method of extensive abstraction. This means that for such concepts and such deductively formulated theory, Alfred North Whitehead's philosophy of science becomes invalid. It is the postulates of the deductive theory which designate the basic entities and relations. No abstractive set such as those described in Chapters III and IV of Whitehead's *Concept of Nature* can designate or define them.

Nor can the concepts of hypothetically inferred, deductively formulated theory such as that of contemporary mathematical physics be defined in terms of the common-sense objects to which the logical positivists with Neurath moved in order to escape the methodological solipsism of Rudolf

Carnap's *Logische Aufbau der Welt* and in order to obtain publicly valid verification and objectivity.

The trouble with "physicalism," this second position of the logical positivisits of the Vienna Circle, is that the common-sense objects of physicalism lack the deductive fertility necessary to account for the richness of detail of the natural history data in the physical sciences. Were common-sense objects adequate, the physicists would never have moved on to the more subtle and less obvious scientific objects such as electrons. This means that instead of defining scientific objects in terms of common-sense objects, as physicalism suggests, the scientific procedure is quite the reverse. The common-sense objects, that is, the scales and clocks and Geiger counters have to be defined in terms of the more subtle and deductively fertile scientific objects. In other words, concepts by postulation which are either concepts by imagination or concepts by intellection are the basic scientific concepts, and concepts by perception are defined in terms of them.

Put more concretely, what this means is that an electron, for example, is neither a short-hand linguistic symbol for a wider set of purely empirical propositions about sense data as Rudolf Carnap's *Logische Aufbau der Welt* attempted to maintain, nor a short-hand linguistic expression for a longer set of statements about common-sense objects, as the "physicalism" of Neurath would attempt to maintain. Both of these earlier notions of the logical positivists arise from a failure to clearly distinguish concepts by intuition from concepts by postulation and an attendant failure to realize the character of the latter type of concept. A concept by postulation gets its meanings from the postulates of some specific, deductively formulated theory in which it occurs. This is what it means, and this is all that it means. No reduction to common-sense objects or to sense data is necessary or required. There are many signs that contemporary logical positivists have now come to this position.

In any event, the great merit of logical positivism and its main aim is satisfied, even when one leaves the scientific concepts and their meanings just as one finds them, as prescribed by the scientist in the postulates of some specific deductively formulated scientific theory.   The important desideratum at which the logical positivists were aiming, namely, operational verification, can nonetheless be obtained.   Thus theories of any kind whatever, even metaphysical and religious theories, as will be shown later, can be brought down to the earth of empirical fact and can be tested with respect to their truth or falsity.   This test is made by relating the propositions of one's deductive theory to empirically given, directly inspectable data.   This can be done in one of two ways, either by joining the postulates to directly observable data or by joining the theorems.

The former procedure in verification is possible only for an abstractive deductively formulated theory; that is, for a theory the basic concepts of which are concepts by postulation which are logical concepts by intuition. The latter procedure in verification is required for a hypothetically inferred deductively formulated theory; that is, for one the basic concepts of which are concepts by postulation which are either concepts by imagination or concepts by intellection. The reason for the indirect mode of verification by way of the theorems is clear. Since the problem in question can be solved only by regarding unobservable entities and relations as the basic factors in one's subject matter, and since the postulates are restricted to the designation of these basic unobservable factors, it follows necessarily that verification cannot occur by relating the postulates directly to immediately apprehendable factors; the only possible means of verification must be indirect by way of the theorems.

So far but one reason for this second mode of verification and the appeal to unobservable entities and relations upon which it rests has been indicated. This reason is that the character of one's problem is often such that it cannot be resolved by means of an appeal to directly observable data alone. There is, however, a second reason for introducing unobservable entities and relations and constructing a deductively formulated theory of the hypothetically inferred rather than the abstractive type. This reason has to do with prediction.

It is often said that the criterion of a scientific theory is its predictive power. Predictive power depends upon establishing connections between the present and the future. The more these connections between the present and the future can be shown to be necessary, the greater and the more unequivocal the predictive power.

David Hume, who was the first Western thinker perhaps to fully realize the exact character of purely empirically given knowledge, pointed out that such knowledge exhibits no necessary connections. This means that a science which restricts itself to directly observable entities and relations automatically loses predictive power. The science tends, even when deductively formulated, to be merely descriptive and to accomplish little more so far as prediction is concerned than to express the hope that the sensed relations holding between the entities of one's subject matter today will recur tomorrow. This is an excessively weak and deductively empty type of predictive power. Little can be deduced from a mere subjective psychological hope.

The strongest relation of necessary connection between any two factors, such as the present and future states of a system, is logical implication. This relation between the present and the future is a far more powerful relation with respect to prediction than the mere subjective psychological hope which is all that a science restricting itself to directly observable entities and relations can give one.

Thus it happens that even when scientists solve the problem initiating inquiry in terms of the observable entities and relations of the subject matter in question, they nonetheless often go on to unobservable entities and relations and the deductively formulated theory of the hypothetically designated, rather than the abstractive, type. The reason is that the appeal to such entities and their more timeless laws and relations often enables one, given a knowledge of the present state of their subject matter, to rigorously and logically deduce the future state. This is probably the major reason for the introduction of unobservable scientific entities and relations into scientific theory. Such entities and relations provide a scientific theory with a predictive power which even deductively formulated theories of the abstractive type do not enjoy.

In fact, it is this predictive power relating the present to the future by means of the logical relation of formal implication which defines what the mathematical physicist means by causality. This causality, which is a concept by postulation, is a quite different notion of causality from Hume's empirically given subjective hope, which is a concept by intuition.

The correctness of this analysis of causality and predictive power will be confirmed in the subsequent chapters, when we examine in more detail the hypothetically inferred type of deductively formulated theory of mathematical physics and the abstractive type of deductively formulated theory of the economic science of the Austrian School. The former is able, given the knowledge of the present state of its system, to logically deduce a future state. This is what is meant by saying that the science has not merely a theoretical statics but also a theoretical dynamics. The latter, abstractive type of deductive theory, illustrated in the economic science of the Austrian School, has a theoretical statics but no theoretical dynamics. Such is the consequence, as Hume indicated, of restricting the basic entities and relations of one's scientific theory to directly inspectable data.

While the introduction of unobservable entities and relations is a necessary condition for the rigorous, formal logical type of prediction and for the presence of a theoretical dynamics in any science, it is not a sufficient condition. It is possible to have unobservable entities and relations designated by one's postulates of a nature such that the prediction of a future state of a system cannot be deduced. The additional requirement is that the factors defining the state of the system at any time must obey conservation laws. In other words, the total quantitative volume of them must neither increase nor decrease with time.

The latter consideration makes it possible to put two of the most basic propositions of metaphysics upon an experimental basis. When the basic entities and relations of one's scientific theory obey conservation laws, this is equivalent to asserting what the Greek metaphysical philosophers termed the principle of being. The negate of this metaphysical principle is the principle of becoming. When the latter principle holds, the causal passage of nature entails the introduction of ultimate novelty with time. Then the mechanistic type of causality of a theoretical dynamics becomes impossible. Thus all these metaphysical questions are scientifically solvable by the postulational technique of the deductively formulated science of the third state of inquiry.

It remains to designate more in detail the major steps involved in the construction and verification of a deductively formulated theory of the hypothetically designated type. It happens, as subsequent chapters will show, that the steps involved are greater in number than has been previously supposed. This occurs because verification entails the relating of the unobservable factors designated by the concepts by postulation of the deductively formulated theory to the directly observable data denoted by concepts by intuition. This relation cannot be the relation of identity which occurs in an abstractive deductively formulated theory. It is instead the relation which we shall term *epistemic correlation*. It is this relation which makes operational definitions and the verification of the existence of unobservable objects possible in science and philosophy.

Aristotle. *De Anima.*

A. N. Whitehead. *The Concept of Nature,* Chapter IV. Cambridge University Press, 1920.

A. E. Taylor. "Concepts by Suggestion and Concepts by Abstraction," in *Platonism and Its Influence.* Marshall Jones Company, Boston, 1924.

Albert Einstein. *The World As I See It,* pp. 24-40. Covici Friede, New York, 1934.

W. Stanley Jevons. *The Theory of Political Economy.* Macmillan and Company, London, 1911.
Elementary Lessons in Logic, Chapter XIX. Macmillan and Company, London, 1870.

Lionel Robbins. *The Nature and Significance of Economic Science.* Macmillan and Company, London, 1935.

O. Neurath. "Physicalism," *Monist,* p. 41, 1931 .
"Soziologie im Physikalismus," *Erkenntnis* 2, 1931.
"Protokollsatze," *ibid.* 3, 1932.
"Radikaler Physikalismus und 'wirkliche Welt,' " *ibid.,* 4, 1934.

Rudolf Carnap. *Der Logische Aufbau der Welt.* Berlin, 1928.
Logische Syntax der Sprache. Springer, Wien, 1934.
"Testability and Meaning," *Philosophy of Science,* Vol. 3, pp. 419-471; and Vol. 4, pp. 1-40, 1936 and 1937.

Charles Morris. *Signs, Language and Behaviour.* Prentice-Hall. New York, 1946.

CHAPTER VII

EPISTEMIC CORRELATIONS AND OPERATIONAL DEFINITIONS

An epistemic correlation is a relation joining an unobserved component of anything designated by a concept by postulation to its directly inspected component denoted by a concept by intuition. Such relations are two-termed relations. This means, also, that an epistemic correlation joins the aesthetic component of a thing to its theoretic component.

These relations are termed "epistemic" to distinguish them from other correlations in scientific or philosophical knowledge. The adjective "epistemic" derives from the noun "epistemology," which refers to the science of knowledge. Thus an epistemic correlation joins a thing known in the one way to what is in some sense that same thing known in a different way. The usual correlations of scientific knowledge, on the other hand, always relate factors which are known in the same way.

Epistemic correlations are inescapable in any type of knowledge which introduces entities, relations or events which are not directly inspected. Consequently, they occur as much in common-sense knowledge as in that of modern science. When one concludes that the two-dimensional colored patch before one is the sign of the presence of a three-dimensional desk, one has epistemically correlated the two-dimensional colored patch which one directly inspects with one side of a theoretically postulated, three-dimensional, right-angled cornered, external material object which one terms a desk. Again, when the man in the street interprets the yellow circular disc in the blue sky as a sign of the presence of a three-dimensional spherical object termed the moon, an epistemic correlation has occurred. The two-dimensional, directly inspected, circular colored patch is conceived as correlated with one hemisphere of the three-dimensional, spherical, astronomical body. Similarly, if one closes one eye and inspects a fuzzy, angular, whitish shape which one interprets as the side of one's nose, again an epistemic correlation has occurred, in which the fuzzy, whitish, angular shape is assigned to one portion of the surface of a three-dimensional anatomical object.

In mathematical physics and the other natural sciences these epistemic correlations appear in a more subtle, but nonetheless real, form. The epistemic correlation which joins the immediately sensed color to the number for the length of an electromagnetic wave has been instanced. A slightly more spectacular example of an epistemic correlation is present in the famous Wilson cloud-chamber experiment. This experiment comes the nearest to giving direct experimental confirmation of the existence of the unobservable scientific object termed the electron. Actually, in this experiment one directly inspects merely a fuzzy aesthetic continuum differentiated by a curved line, any two different points of which are directly inspected flashes. Such a directly inspected flash denoted by a concept by intuition is epistemically correlated with an unobserved event termed an ionization, designated by a concept by postulation. The ionization is conceived according to the postulated theory as a collision of the negatively charged electron with a molecule of the gas. Neither the electron or molecule nor their collision is directly inspected. All that can possibly be inspected are what the senses convey to us, and these are ineffable, sensuous qualities, that is, aesthetic objects; they are not scientific objects.

Nonetheless, it is possible by means of these epistemic correlations to verify the existence of the unobservable scientific objects. One postulates the latter objects and sets up epistemic correlates ahead of time between them and the factors which one can directly inspect. If the directly inspected data are in accord with what the postulated or deduced theorems plus the epistemic correlations specify with respect to the continuum of immediately apprehended fact, then the unobservable scientific objects are said to exist.

In this connection it is important to note that the epistemic correlations themselves are not directly observed. All that one observes is the immediately apprehended end term in the relation of epistemic correlation. Neither the relation itself nor the unobserved, theoretically designated term at the other end of the relation is inspected.

The problem in inductive scientific procedure is to inspect the directly presented data and to find by trial and error the postulated entities and relations which are the epistemic correlates of the inspected data. The task of the deductive scientist, on the other hand, is to begin with the postulated entities and relations of his deductively formulated theory and to find directly inspected data with which certain of his postulated entities can be epistemically correlated, so that the existence of the latter entities can be put to an experimental test.

An instance of the inductive procedure from directly inspected data to postulated entities occurs when one attends a theatre. It often happens, early in a play, that one is unable to determine whether the directly inspected data which one notes backstage are merely two-dimensional images of bookends painted on a curtain or the correlates of the bookends of real three-dimensional books located on a shelf. Hence, one is confronted with the problem concerning whether the visual image which one inspects is to be epistemically correlated with merely a two-dimensional surface on a two-dimensional curtain or with one two-dimensional surface of

a three-dimensional book.   As the play develops one of the
characters goes backstage and pulls out the book.   The
images associated with the latter act are compatible only with
one of the two possible hypotheses concerning the epistemic
correlate of the original data.   Thus one interpretation is
eliminated, the hypothesis of real three-dimensional books is
confirmed and the correct epistemic correlation is established.

An example of the converse procedure of the deductive
scientist confronted with certain postulated factors and forced
to discover their empirically given epistemic correlates occurred with Albert Einstein in the case of his general theory
of relativity.   In this theory he was attempting to put the
laws of mechanics in such a form that they would be valid
and experimentally verified, regardless of where the scientist
stands in nature when he makes his measurements and other
observations.   Mathematical considerations indicated that
laws which possess this property must be of a tensor form.
Mathematics showed also that, assuming conditions of sym-
metry, the tensor equation for such a law of gravitation must
contain ten variables if, as is the case, nature has four dimensions — three for space and a fourth for time.   Albert
Einstein's problem, therefore, consisted in finding the empirically given epistemic correlates of these ten variables.   He
solved this problem when he noted that a physical field is
defined in a determinate manner when its potential distribution is empirically determined.   It followed immediately
that the operationally empirical epistemic correlates of the
postulationally and theoretically designated ten variables in
the required tensor equation are potentials and that an adequate law of the gravitational field must contain ten potentials rather than merely the one potential prescribed by
Newton's law.

It is by means of epistemic correlations that unobservable
entities and relations designated by concepts by postulation
take on an operational meaning and thereby become capable

of being put to an experimental test. Thus it is the relation of epistemic correlation which makes the operational meaning of a theoretical concept of science possible and which makes the operational definitions of scientific concepts important.

It must be emphasized, however, that in an inferred, deductively formulated theory operational meanings are derived meanings obtained by way of the epistemic correlations. The operational meanings are not the basic meanings of the concepts constituting the deductively formulated theory. The latter meanings are derived from the basic concepts of mathematics and mathematical logic and from the images of the imagination — even the most speculative metaphysical imagination. As Albert Einstein has emphasized, the basic concepts and principles of science are not given empirically but are instead "free inventions of the human intellect."

There is no limit whatever to the sources of meaning upon which one may draw for the construction of deductively formulated theory in science. The mind of the deductive scientist is absolutely free and open in this respect, getting meanings from any source whatever. The only prescription is that these meanings must be rigorously and precisely designated by being unambiguously prescribed in the postulates of the deductive theory, and that the theory must be verified by way of epistemic correlations with directly inspectable data before what its postulates designate may be said to exist.

For this reason the prevalent notion that metaphysical theories are unscientific theories is quite erroneous. Providing one specifies one's metaphysical postulates unambiguously and sets up epistemic correlations between the entities of one's metaphysical theory and directly inspected data, thereby permitting verification, every requirement for scientific procedure is met.

It is precisely because this has been the case with respect to all the major traditional metaphysical systems in the Western world that we are able to show that most, if not all, of them, however justified or even scientifically verified in their time, are now outmoded. They do not have the deductive fertility to give rise by way of epistemic correlations to all the empirical data.

The universe in which we live is very complicated. In order to obtain theories adequate to understand it, it is necessary to open the basic concepts of scientific theory to every possible source of meaning. Flights of the imagination, speculation — both physical and metaphysical — and mathematical investigations not merely of this empirical world but, as Leibnitz and Bertrand Russell following him have noted, of all possible worlds are not merely permitted but required.

Nor is there the least harm or danger in this. Providing one specifies one's meanings postulationally, and epistemically correlates the entities in one's deductive theory with directly inspectable data to permit theorems deducted from the postulates to be put to an experimental or empirical test, every canon of scientific method is satisfied.

It is difficult enough to understand one's world when every type of meaning from every source of insight whatever is at one's disposal. There is no justification, from an analysis of scientific method itself, nor is there any other reason, for supposing that it is necessary to reduce every concept in one's deductively formulated scientific theory to the type of meaning which only those who think merely with their hands can understand. In the case of most scientific theories only some of the theoretical concepts by postulation have operational meanings and denotatively given epistemic correlates.

Nonetheless, the operational theory of the concept is exceedingly important. Emphasis upon it insures that one obtains speculatively discovered theories which nonetheless can be verified with respect to their truth or falsity. Otherwise one's scientific and philosophical theories remain perpetually in the clouds.

Every scientific theory must have operational definitions for at least some of its concepts. These operationally defined meanings are joined to the theoretically designated meanings of the theory by means of epistemic correlations. Consequently, operational definitions are not the sole definitions of a deductively formulated scientific theory. Instead, they are merely correlates of quite different meanings existing throughout the entire deductively formulated theory which are designated by concepts by postulation. Failure to clearly distinguish purely empirically given meanings denoted by concepts by intuition from the theoretically proposed meanings designated by concepts by postulation has introduced an incalculable amount of confusion into the analysis of scientific method and scientific theory. It has also obscured certain difficulties in the traditional account of the operational theory of the concept. These difficulties must now concern us.

The present century has been marked by an increasing emphasis upon the importance of operational definitions in philosophy and science. In the former field this emphasis has been fostered by that branch of pragmatism known as instrumentalism, which is associated with the name of John Dewey. In physics, its major proponent has been P. W. Bridgman. In law, it was used by the late Justice Holmes, and more recently it has been applied in a much more precise and controlled form by Underhill Moore. As the century has moved on, it has become evident in the field of pragmatic philosophy, realistic pragmatic law, education and the other social sciences that this emphasis upon the practical, upon instrumentalism and upon operations has tended to solve very few problems and to introduce more and more rhetoric and less and less science into the subject matter. Underhill Moore, precisely because he has gone to deductively formulated theory and postulationally defined and controlled concepts, is a notable exception to this observation.

The difficulty centers in the fact that few words are more ambiguous than the word "operation." There is the denotatively given, immediately apprehended operation. There is also the theoretically conceived operation. When one uses the word "operation," which meaning does one have in mind? Because those who have formulated and defended the operational theory of the concept have shifted back and forth surreptitiously between these two meanings of the word "operation," their theory has gained much of its plausibility and resulted in much of the attendant rhetoric and obscurity.

An important point to note is that if one means by "operation" the denotatively given, immediately inspected experiment, then it is true that the operation would completely define the scientific concept. But if one means by an operation or an experiment in science the theoretically conceived operation or experiment, then it is the concept which is defining the operation and not the operation which is defining the concept.

In this connection one must ask oneself whether the purely denotatively, empirically given operation proves anything, scientifically. Suppose that a thoroughly intelligent man arrived on earth from Mars and found himself in a physics laboratory looking at the Wilson cloud-chamber experiment as it was performed. Let us assume also that he knows nothing about modern physical theory. He has, however, very good sense organs and a very good habit of concentration. Consequently, he understands the experiment fully and completely in its empirically given, denotatively presented meaning. What would this experiment prove to him with respect to the existence of electrons? The answer seems to be "Nothing." He would assert that it demonstrates merely that a fuzzy aesthetic continuum is present in which there is a curved line. Without the theoretically designated epistemic correlations and the postulationally prescribed concepts by postulation of the deductively formulated theory of electro-magnetics the experiment would be merely a natural history datum, not an operational verification of the existence of a negatively charged quantum of electricity termed an electron. It is only the theoretically conceived operation epistemically correlated with the empirically given operation which verifies the existence of the latter scientific object.

Another concrete illustration, this time found among the social sciences, will reinforce this conclusion. The story has to do with a certain educational institution. It is undoubt-edly, in considerable part, apocryphal, but whether it ever happened is irrelevant so far as its implications are concerned. According to the story, a group of social scientists, who be-lieved they could obtain the normative prescriptions neces-sary for the guidance of governmental action, by means of the collection of empirical data about actual social phenomena, had gathered their data, secured the answers to their question-naires and had poured the resulting evidence into a comput-ing machine.

The crank of this machine was turned and a conclusion came out at the other end of the apparatus. This conclusion was so remarkable, the story goes, that the social scientists felt themselves duty-bound to inform the governmental officials about it. Forthwith they telegraphed the results to Wash-ington. After the telegram had been sent, someone dis-covered, however, that the wires in the machine were crossed.

The pertinent question in this connection is What tells one that the wires in the machine were crossed? The ma-chine as actually used, gave a perfectly definite result. The operation, as actually performed, was a perfectly definite operation. Other people could have put in the same data, operated the machine in precisely the same way and received the same answer. Hence, in this precise operational sense, the experiment gave a result which was objectively the same for everybody. Furthermore, as an operation, it was a perfectly good operation. The switch was turned, the crank was revolved, the readings were correctly made.

Why, then, are we amused by the story? Furthermore, why, according to the story, did the empirical operators withdraw their report to Washington? They had gathered certain empirical information and performed an objectively repeatable operation upon it which would give the same result for all cases.

The answer to the foregoing queries seems to be that without theory there is no criterion to designate when the wires are crossed. Thus, again, we have the conclusion reinforced that a scientifically significant operation is one in which the theoretical concept defines the operation, rather than one in which the denotatively given operation defines the scientific concept.

The point of all this is not that operational definitions are misleading or unimportant. They are tremendously important. Without them no scientific theory can be put to an empirical test. The point instead is that in a scientific theory there are the two types of concept noted in Chapter V. We have called them concepts by intuition and concepts by postulation. An operation in the denotatively given sense of the term is a concept by intuition. An operation in the theoretically significant sense of the term is a concept by postulation. The latter concepts are not operationally defined; they are postulationally designated.

Furthermore, in a properly constructed, deductively formulated scientific theory every concept in the theory, as deductively formulated, must be a concept by postulation. Utter confusion and nonsense enter into scientific discourse when concepts by intuition are put in the same proposition with concepts by postulation. Then such expressions as "electrons are pink" arise. When concepts belonging to two different worlds of discourse are treated as if they belonged to the same world of discourse, nonsense is the result.

One of the major difficulties which confront any scientist when he first constructs a deductively formulated theory for the natural history data of a given fresh subject matter is to give postulational meanings for every one of the concepts in his deductive theory. This is fairly easy to do for certain of one's concepts. But sooner or later one surreptitiously smuggles words into the deductive theory which have only an intuitively or empirically given meaning and no postulationally prescribed meaning. When this happens the theory never works. And until one has carefully distinguished concepts by postulation from concepts by intuition and noted that one can never make up for the absence of concepts by postulation as correlates for all one's intuitively given data by substituting the attendant concepts by intuition — until one recognizes this, one's attempts at deductively formulated theories strike an impasse, the cause of which one does not understand.

Thus the truth is not that in a deductively formulated theory made up of postulates and theorems some of the concepts are operational in the denotative sense of the word only, and other concepts are concepts by postulation. Instead, every concept must be a concept by postulation, and wherever there are operationally defined meanings, purely empirical and denotative in character, the latter meanings are epistemic correlates of concepts by postulation in the deductively formulated theory.

This means that a deductively formulated scientific theory must be constructed quite independently of one's operational definitions. Every concept must be postulationally prescribed as to its meaning, with all other concepts in the theorems derived from the primitive ones in the postulates by the method of definition. The specification of epistemic correlations and the designation of the specific empirically given operations is an addition to the theory and to all its concepts by postulation, not a substitute for some of them. It is the independence of the concepts by postulation from the operational definitions of which they are the epistemic correlates which permits the theoretical scientist, by means of his concepts by postulation, to designate novel and previously undreamed of operations and experiments.

Again and again in the history of science deductively formulated theories such as Albert Einstein's theory of the finite universe have been constructed as answers to theoretical questions, and at the time of their construction no conceivable operation for testing them was at hand. With further theoretical investigation it often turns out to be possible to derive theorems which do permit the theory to be put to an experimental test. Were all concepts in a scientific theory solely operationally defined concepts, it would be difficult to understand how this could be the case. Then there could be no scientific theory without the operation for verifying it automatically being present.

The importance of operational definitions is that they make verification possible and enrich meaning. They do not, however, exhaust scientific meaning. Furthermore, unless the epistemic correlates of an empirically given, operational experiment are designated by concepts by postulation, the experiment in question is not scientifically understood.

One additional point is to be noted. It is customary for those who emphasize the operational definition of a concept to insist also upon objectivity. The question one must ask with respect to objectivity is whether it is an empirically or a theoretically designated item of scientific knowledge. Our analysis of the nature of pure fact in a previous chapter forces us to answer this question in favor of the latter alternative.

As Bishop Berkeley demonstrated, public external objects, independent of the observer, are not sensed; sensed qualities vary from person to person. And, as Newton emphasized in the Scholium at the beginning of his *Principia,* and as Albert Einstein reaffirms in his rejection of the sensed simultaneity of spatially separated events as a basic for public time, public space and time are not directly observed; instead they are theoretically and postulationally know factors. This is why Newton called sensed space and time "relative and apparent" and postulated, mathematically designated space and time "real," meaning thereby that which is objective and public. This is why Albert Einstein affirms, as the next chapter will show, that natural science requires the assumption of an external world, necessitated by the distinction between empirical factors which vary from observer to observer and theoretically known, postulationally designated factors which remain the same or invariant from observer to observer. It is also why he adds that this public external world is known by science, as by common sense, "only by speculative means."

All these considerations indicate that it is the theoretically designated concept, not the empirically given operation which designates objectivity in science. Empirically given operations become a criterion of objectivity in science only by way of the epistemic correlations which join them to the objective entities and relations designated by concepts by postulation. But conversely, verification of one postulated theory of the invariant or objective rather than another, depends upon concepts by intuition, epistemic correlations and operational definitions.

Henry Margenau. "Methodology of Modern Physics," *Philosophy of Science,* Vol. 2, pp. 48-72 and 164-187.

F. S. C. Northrop. "The Significance of Epistemic Correlations in Scientific Method." Paper read before, and Abstract printed for, the International Congress of Unified Science, Harvard University, Sept., 1939.
The Meeting of East and West, Chapter XII, Macmillan Company, New York, 1946.

John Dewey. *Essays in Experimental Logic,* University of Chicago Press, 1917.

P. W. Bridgman. *The Logic of Modern Physics.* Macmillan Company, New York, 1927.

Newton. *Principia,* Cajori Edition. University of California Press, Berkeley, 1934.

Albert Einstein. *The World As I See It,* Covici Friede, New York, 1934.

"The Foundation of the General Theory of Relativity" in *The Principles of Relativity* (By Albert Einstein and Others), Methuen, London, 1923.

Relativity: The Special and General Theory, 4th Edition. Methuen, London, 1921.

CHAPTER VIII

* THE METHOD AND THEORIES OF PHYSICAL SCIENCE IN THEIR BEARING UPON BIOLOGICAL ORGANIZATION

By the organization of a living creature we mean its relatedness both morphological and physiological. Not merely the distribution of material at any instant of growth, but the entire process of growth itself, together with the subsequent maturity and senility, is organized. The problem of growth may be regarded therefore as a special case of the more general and fundamental problem of organization.

This approach has certain advantages. It permits us to bring to bear upon our understanding of the particular phenomenon of growth, all that we have learned from many sources concerning the factors and principles involved in the underlying problem of organization. Also, it prevents us, in a way that we shall see to be important, from attributing to factors unearthed by a direct attack on the problem of growth, a greater significance than they deserve, due to the neglect of other equally important factors in organization, solely because the latter do not come within the purview of the experimental investigation under consideration. In addition, it enables us to discover the insufficiency of certain concepts and theories we are using, even when these conceptions have experimental evidence in their support, by enabling us to deduce from them consequences which reveal their empirical shortcomings as a complete solution of the problem. An example will appear in the sequel in our consideration of the thermo-dynamical theory of organization.

By establishing the insufficiency of traditional theories, the theoretical approach makes us aware of the need for a new hypothesis and often indicates the character which it must possess, thereby guiding one to new modes of experimental investigation and to the empirical discovery of new evidence.

These advantages are possible, however, only if we appreciate the rôle of theory, concepts, and deductive logic, as well as of inductive observation and experimentation in natural science, and master the scientific method for relating deductively formulated theory to inductively and experimentally controlled data in a trustworthy manner. This method has been developed over the centuries by the physical and mathematical sciences.

The history of science shows that any empirical science in its normal healthy development begins with a more purely inductive emphasis, in which the empirical data of its subject matter are systematically gathered, and then comes to maturity with deductively formulated theory in which formal logic and mathematics play a most significant part. Geometry, for instance, began with the earth measurements of the ancient Egyptians and early Greeks and came to maturity in the deductively formulated *Elements* of Euclid. Physics took the whole of the Greek period and the entire Middle Ages to develop its early natural history phase, and passed to deductively formulated theory when Galilei discovered its new key primitive concepts and Newton, taking Euclid's geometry as his model, generalized Galilei's concepts and developed them systematically in the deductive theory for mechanics which constitutes his famous *Principia*. These two stages in the normal healthy development of an empirical science are (a) the natural history stage and (b) the stage of postulationally prescribed theory.

It appears that biology is at present struggling with the transition from the first of these stages to the second. It is nearing the completion of the systematic observation, descrip-

tion, and classification of living creatures, both in their naturally and experimentally observed manifestations, which
Aristotle inaugurated in his founding of the science. Many
signs are present that it is now passing to the stage of deductively formulated theory. Mendel's and especially Morgan's
work on heredity forms such a theory for a special branch of
the science. The formal, deductive character of Woodger's
work (1937) is self-evident. Rashevsky's application (1938)
of mathematics to specific physiological processes is a third
striking example.

There are, however, other evidences prevalent in the work
of practically every biological scientist. I refer to the use of
the entities, concepts and principles of chemistry and physics
in the elucidation and understanding of biological processes.
More and more biologists are leaving purely natural history
biological concepts for those of physics and chemistry in their
experimental approach to and scientific analysis of living
systems. This is now a commonplace.

The significance of this development of biology is not,
however, so fully appreciated. In passing thus from the
purely biological concepts of the early stage of development
of the science to the concepts of physics and chemistry, biologists are carrying their science from the natural history stage
to the stage of deductively formulated theory. Whereas the
concepts of the natural history stage refer to directly observable factors such as the shapes, colors, etc., of living creatures,
the concepts now being used signify protein molecules, hydrogen ion concentrations, etc., of physics and chemistry. These
are scientific objects or systems which are not directly apprehended. Instead, they are unobserved, postulated entities
known only by theory and consequently requiring a fundamentally different scientific method for their trustworthy
treatment than the method in which biologists are trained in
the natural history stage.

This point can be put more precisely by saying that in the

passage of a science from the natural history stage of its development to that of deductively formulated theory a fundamentally new type of scientific concept appears which entails, in turn, a radically different type of scientific method. This means that the kind of scientific training which is adequate for the natural history stage is necessary but quite insufficient when the science passes to deductively formulated theory.

The nature of the two stages of this development will make this clear. It will also throw light on the difference between the two types of scientific concepts for the two stages.

At the beginning of any empirical science, its obvious task is to determine the natural history materials of its subject matter. It must gather the data for which the deductively formulated theory of the next stage is to account. Consequently, the method of the science in its natural history stage is predominantly inductive. The emphasis is upon immediate apprehension and observation. The scientist's task is meticulously to observe, describe and classify.

Because of this a specific type of concept arises in the natural history stage. We have termed it a concept by inspection. *A concept by inspection is one the complete meaning of which is given by something immediately observable.* Thus when Linnaeus described flowers in terms of the color and shape of their petals, he was formulating a biological science in the natural history stage in terms of concepts by inspection. Scientific papers which present pictures of the structure of cancer, or of the shape of the salamander, resort to the same type of concept. "Blue" in the sense of the seen color is another example.

To be sure, even in this natural history stage with its preponderant emphasis on inductive science, one does not have "pure fact" apart from all concepts and theory. The popular fallacy that science is concerned only with facts and has nothing to do with concepts and theory rests upon the failure to draw a distinction between what may be termed observed fact and described fact. "Observed fact" may be defined as that which is immediately apprehended apart from all concepts and theory; "described fact" is observed fact brought under concepts and hence under theory. To have purely observed fact apart from all concepts a scientist could merely stare at his data and never report his observations in scientific meetings and in scientific journals.

Futhermore, every description throws individually observed data into classes with respect to some abstracted character. These classes fall within each other as species within genera. Since Aristotle, it has been realized, as Alfred North Whitehead in our own time has repeatedly emphasized, that there are many possible modes of abstraction from the same observed data, defining many possible principles of classification. Thus it becomes inevitable, even in the most emphatically inductive natural history type of science, that inescapable elements of theory are present. Charles Darwin, whose work and theory belong exclusively to the natural history stage in the development of biology, says, "How odd it is that anyone should not see that all observations must be for or against some view, if it is to be of any service." Even natural history science, using only concepts by inspection, involves concepts and theory.

It also finds formal logic useful. Its method of classification, including species within genera, has implicit in it the logical relation of class inclusion. From this relation the syllogistic deductive logic of Aristotle and the logic of classes of Boole can be developed. Thus even the natural history stage of any empirical science entails theory and deductive logic as well as directly apprehended fact and induction. This is fortunate; otherwise natural history theories, such as Darwin's theory of evolution, which assert more than is immediately observable, could never be put to an empirical test by appeal to their deductive consequences.

None the less, scientific theories in the natural history stage are inductive to a degree and in a sense which is not true of theories in the next stage of development of a science. This happens because the theories of the natural history stage are developed entirely in terms of concepts by inspection. What each concept in the theory means is given by something directly apprehended.

In the next stage of a science an entirely different type of concept is introduced. The reason for this, in physical science, has been stated clearly by Professor P. A. M. Dirac (1931), at the beginning of his famous paper on generalized quantum mechanics. He writes, "The steady progress of physics requires for its theoretical formulation a mathematics that gets continually more advanced. This is only natural and to be expected. What, however, was not expected by the scientific workers of the last century was the particular form that the line of advancement of the mathematics would take, namely, it was expected that the mathematics would get more and more complicated, but would rest on a permanent basis of axioms and definitions, while actually the modern physical developments have required a mathematics that continually shifts its foundations and gets more abstract." In short, it is not merely by accumulating more experimental knowledge in terms of old, theoretical concepts but by changing the basic theoretical concepts in terms of which both old and new experimental knowledge is expressed and understood that physics has advanced. Professor Dirac adds, "There are at present, fundamental problems in theoretical physics awaiting solution, e. g., the relativistic formulation of quantum mechanics and the nature of atomic nuclei (to be followed by more difficult ones such as the problem of life), the solution of which problems will presumably require a more drastic revision of our fundamental concepts than any that have gone before. Quite likely these changes will be so great that it will be beyond the power of human intelligence to get the necessary new ideas by direct attempts to formulate the experimental data in mathematical terms."

This last sentence explains why empirical science introduces a new type of concept in passing from the natural history stage to that of deductively formulated theory. The reason is that concepts by inspection referring to directly observable factors ("direct attempts to formulate the experimental data") turn out to be inadequate to account systematically for all the observable data. With the passage of time and the accumulation of evidence, the empirical scientist finds it impossible to account for his natural history subject-matter in terms of directly observable factors and their relations. Recourse, in the construction of adequate, empirical scientific theory, has to be made to unobservable, postulated entities and factors rather than to directly inspectable items. Thus a fundamentally new type of scientific concept appears. We have termed it a concept by postulation. "Electron" and "blue" in the sense of the number for the wave-length in electro-magnetics, are examples. *A concept by postulation is one the meaning of which is proposed for it by the postulates of the deductive theory in which it occurs.* The crucial factor to note in this definition is that one does not determine the meaning of a concept by postulation by inspecting something which is directly observable; instead, one must examine the postulates of the deductive theory in which the concept occurs.

Since we are concerned with the empirical science of biology, we shall analyze a deductive theory in terms of empirical propositions referring to an empirical subject matter. Were we expounding a deductive theory in pure mathematics, propositional functions rather than propositions would be introduced.

Any empirical scientific theory is a body of empirical propositions. An empirical proposition is an expression of which it is significant to predicate truth or falsity.

The propositions of any empirical scientific theory fall into two groups, termed "postulates" and "theorems." The propositions termed postulates are related to those termed theorems by the formal logical relation of formal implication. Given the postulates, the theorems can be derived by nothing but the rules of formal logic.   In short, the theorems can be deduced from the postulates; hence, the name "deductively formulated theory."   The postulates of a deductively formulated theory are those propositions which are assumed in the theory in question as logically unprovable and which are sufficient to enable one to prove, i.e., to logically deduce, the theorems.   The theorems of a deductively formulated theory are all the empirical propositions in the theory other than the postulates.   They have the additional essential property of being provable in terms of the postulates.   Thus, if one assumes the postulates, formal logic requires one to accept the theorems.   This is quite independent of the empirical, as opposed to the formal logical question, of the truth or falsity of the postulates.

A postulate or a theorem, i.e., any proposition, in any empirical scientific theory is a collection of concepts.   Just as the propositions of a theory fall into two groups, termed postules and theorems, so its concepts fall into two groups, termed "primitive" or "undefined concepts" and "defined concepts." The defined concepts are derivable from the primitive concepts by the method of definition.   Any scientific theory involves primitive or undefined concepts.   This follows necessarily because definition involves nothing more than the statement of certain concepts in terms of others.   The attempt to define all concepts in a theory, therefore, either sends one off in an infinite regress or leads one in a vicious circle.   In a carefully formulated deductive theory the postulates are stated solely in terms of primitive concepts, together with logical constants.   A logical constant differs from a primitive concept of an empirical scientific theory in that the primitive concepts hold only for the empirical science in question, whereas logical constants are concepts which are required for the expression and formulation of any deductive theory whatever.

The above analysis of a deductive theory makes it clear that the heart of any such theory is specified when the primitive concepts and the postulates are indicated. Given these, all other concepts in the theory can be obtained by the method of definition, and all other propositions by the method of formal implication.

The terming of the basic concepts of a deductive theory as primitive or undefined does not mean that these concepts are meaningless. It entails merely that their meaning is not given by definition. It is designated, instead, by postulation. The meaning of a primitive concept in a deductive theory is prescribed for it by the relations in which it is joined to other primitive concepts of the theory by the postulates. More precisely stated, a primitive concept gains its meaning syntactically, rather than by definition or denotation. This is what we meant when we said earlier in this chapter that the meaning of a concept by postulation is prescribed for it by the postulates of the deductive theory in which it occurs. Since one can prescribe for primitive concepts any possible relations to other primitive concepts which the imagination of the empirical scientist, creative philosopher, or the pure mathematician can conceive, quite independently of whether such conceivable entities are directly observable, it is possible, as Professor Dirac suggested, to construct scientific theories in terms of scientific elements and structure quite different from anything which the empirical scientist directly observes. In this manner and by this procedure, the scientific objects, such as electrons, hydrogen ions, wave lengths, protein molecules, etc., of physics and chemistry have arisen.

Empirical science is concerned not merely with conceivable, but also with empirically verified theory. Hence, the question immediately arises concerning how deductively formulated theories using concepts by postulation referring to unobservable entities can be empirically confirmed or repudiated.

One consideration with respect to concepts by postulation must be noted. Their definition informs us that a concept by postulation is one the meaning of which is given solely by the postulates of the deductive theory in which it occurs. It follows from this that the concepts in the theorems of such a deductive theory are concepts by postulation also. For we have noted that all concepts in the theorems are either the primitive concepts of the postulates or concepts which reduce to them by definition, these being the only concepts in any deductive theory. Hence, since the concepts in the postulates are concepts by postulation, the concepts in the theorems must be also.

This consideration lays the basis for a more precise understanding of our present question: How can scientific theory, constructed in terms of concepts by postulation referring to unobservable objects, be empirically confirmed or repudiated?

The usual answer proceeds as follows: Scientific theories which postulate unobservable scientific objects and structures, can none the less be verified by deducing from the postulates of such theories, theorems referring to factors which can be directly observed. Unfortunately this account of the scientific method will not do. If the theorems are to refer to directly observable factors, their concepts will by definition be concepts by inspection. But we have just shown that in a deductive theory whose postulates are composed of concepts by postulation, the concepts in its theorems must be concepts by postulation also. Consequently, the theorems can refer no more to observable factors than do the concepts of the postulates.

Also, since formal logic, which takes one from the postulates to the theorems, has the power to function only in the world of discourse of the primitive concepts and postulates with which it starts, no manipulation by formal logic can take one from postulates formulated in terms of concepts by postulation to theorems expressed in terms of concepts by inspection. It is one of the merits of formal logic that it never gives one in the conclusion more than is necessarily implicit in the premises. The theory, therefore, that one can verify scientific postulates referring to unobservable entities by deducing from them theorems denoting directly observable factors is untenable. It rests upon a failure to distinguish concepts by postulation from concepts by inspection, and a consequent muddling of two distinct worlds of discourse.

It appears, therefore, that another factor, previously overlooked, is involved in the empirical verification of deductive scientific theories formulated in terms of concepts by postulation. This factor must be a relation correlating the concepts by postulation in the theorems of the deductively formulated theory of the theoretical scientist with the directly inspectable data denoted by the concepts by inspection of the natural historian and experimental scientist. It follows, therefore, that the method for experimentally testing deductive theories using concepts by postulation, such as those of physics and chemistry, is much more complicated than has been usually supposed. It involves four major factors: (1) the specification of the primitive concepts and the postulates of the deductively formulated theory using only concepts by postulation; (2) the derivation of the defined concepts and deduced theorems of the theory by the logical methods of definition and formal implication, giving rise also only to concepts by postulation in the theorems; (3) the specification of relations, termed epistemic correlations, joining systematically and unambiguously the concepts by postulation of the deduced theorems to the concepts by inspection which denote the directly observable natural history materials; (4) the direct, controlled, empirical observation of the prescribed natural history data.

In 1940 in *Science,* Albert Einstein wrote as follows: "Science is the attempt to make the chaotic diversity of our sense-experience correspond to a logically uniform system of thought. In this system single experiences must be correlated with the theoretic structure in such a way that the resulting coordination is unique and convincing." The important thing to note in this description of science is the word "correlated." Albert Einstein is saying that the concepts by postulation of the "logically uniform system" of the theoretical physicist are not identified with the immediately apprehended "sense experience(s)" denoted by the concepts by inspection of the empirical scientist, but are, instead, related to sense experience by epistemic correlations. The correlation of "blue" in the sense of the seen color to "blue" in the sense of the wave in electro-magnetic propagations is an example of an epistemic correlation.

Epistemic correlations are not to be confused with the usual statistical correlations of science. The latter always relate items in the same world of discourse, i.e., either they relate one factor designated by a concept by postulation to other factors designated by a concept by postulation, or they relate an inspectable item denoted by a concept by inspection to other inspectable items denoted by the same type of concept. Epistemic correlations, on the other hand, always relate a postulated factor designated by a concept by postulation to an inspectable datum denoted by a concept by inspection. It is precisely because they join factors given by two different ways of knowing that we term them "epistemic."

An examination of the diagram and the fourfold process of verification which its exhibits indicates the logic which is involved. Let (A) represent the primitive concepts and

postulates of the deductive theory which designate the unobserved entities and structures of the scientific theory.
Let (B) designate the deduced theorems together with the

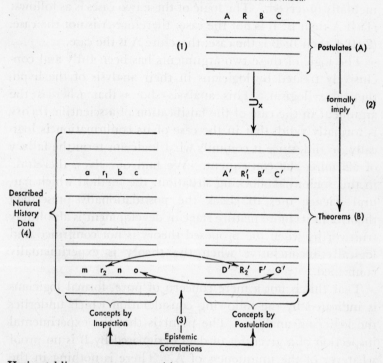

DIAGRAM OF INDIRECTLY VERIFIED DEDUCTIVELY FORMULATED THEORY

Horizontal lines represent propositions
Capital letters represent concepts by postulation
Small letters represent concepts by inspection
ARBC represent primitive or undefined concepts
A′ R′ B′ C′ D′ F′ G′ represent defined concepts
Rr represent relations
ABCabc, etc. represent entities
$\supset_x$ represents the relation of formal implication

epistemic correlation joining the concepts by postulation of
these theorems to their corresponding concepts by inspection
referring to directly inspectable items.   It is to be noted that
upon this basis a theory is shown to be false when the epi-

stemic, inspectable correlates of its deducted consequences differ from what is naturally or experimentally observed, and the theory is said to be confirmed when the inspected correlates of the deduced theorems are naturally or experimentally observed.   The logic of these two cases is as follows: (1) If A then B; B is not the case; therefore A is not the case. (2) If A then B; B is the case; therefore A is the case.

The logic of these two arguments has been fully and conclusively treated by logicians in their analysis of the hypothetical syllogism.   This analysis shows that whereas the argument in the case of the falsification of a scientific theory is formally valid, that in the case of its confirmation is logically invalid, since it commits what logicians term the fallacy of affirming the consequent.   We find ourselves, therefore, in this somewhat shocking situation: the method which natural science uses to check the postulationally prescribed theories in its more mature stage of development is absolutely trustworthy when the proposed theory is not confirmed and logically inconclusive when the theory is experimentally confirmed.

That this is not a mere concern of pure, formal logicians is indicated by the following consideration which underlies the logicians' analysis.   The point is that the experimental inspection of a given set of data designated by B is no proof whatever of the uniqueness of A.   There is nothing in the inspectable empirical data themselves which insures that some other quite different theory designated by a set of postulates, C, could not also give rise to the theorems B.   In short, it may be the case not merely that if A then B, B is the case; but also if C then B, B is the case.   Albert Einstein has indicated this uncertain status of even our experimentally confirmed scientific theories in the opening paragraph of a paper of his on the work of Clerk Maxwell.   There Albert Einstein writes (1934), "The belief in an external world independent of the perceiving subject is the basis of all natural science.

Since, however, sense perception only gives information of this external world or of 'physical reality' indirectly, we can only grasp the latter by speculative means. It follows from this that our notions of physical reality can never be final. We must always be ready to change these notions — that is to say, the axiomatic substructure of physics — in order to do justice to perceived facts in the most logically perfect way. Actually a glance at the development of physics shows that it has undergone far-reaching changes in the course of time."

Why, you may ask, in a chapter concerned with physics and biology, has it been necessary to labour these logical and methodological details in this manner? There is a very important reason. These considerations show that when a science passes to the third stage of its development, using concepts by postulation and deductively formulated theory, even its experimentally confirmed theories are never absolutely guaranteed by the factual data. As Albert Einstein has indicated in the last quotation, even our experimentally confirmed scientific theories always assert more than the bare factual data guarantee. This is what the presence of the fallacy of affirming the consequent in the accepted scientific method of mathematical physics indicates. Were the logic of the confirmation of deductive theory as logically impeccable as that of its non-confirmation, experimentally confirmed theories could never turn out to be false with the passage of time. As Albert Einstein puts it, "We can only grasp" the subject matter of physics "by speculative means," and "our notions of" this subject matter "can never be final." This entails that our scientific conclusions always involve a theoretical factor going beyond what the facts logically guarantee and thus makes it absolutely essential in scientific inquiry that we make these theoretical factors explicit and carry on theoretical investigations as well as the accumulation of empirical data. When a science passes to the later, more mature stage of its development, attention upon theory as well as upon data is absolutely essential for scientists if we are to avoid fooling ourselves and are to understand what we are doing.

There is a second reason for consideration of these logical and methodological details. A frank facing of the presence of the fallacy of affirming the consequent has caused physical scientists to supplement the method of verification of physical theories as indicated above, by an additional scientific procedure.

The key to this more complete method centers in the point previously noted with respect to the fallacy of affirming the consequent. The mere experimental confirmation of a deductive theory through its deductive consequences commits this fallacy because it fails to show that the postulates of the theory are unique in their capacity to give rise deductively to the confirmed theorems. This being the case, scientists concluded that one can avoid the danger implicit in accepting a theory upon the basis of an argument which commits a formal, logical fallacy, providing we can supplement the mere experimental confirmation of a given theory, with theoretical investigations going to show that this theory is, to some extent at least, unique in its capacity to give rise deductively to the confirmed consequences.

This raises the second question: What method is there, in addition to experimental confirmation, which will indicate the uniqueness of a given set of postulates? The answer to this question is fairly definite and universally accepted by competent scientists.

To achieve uniqueness approximately for a deductively formulated scientific theory it is necessary not merely to have experimental confirmation but also a theoretical investigation of every conceivable theoretical possibility. It is precisely for this reason that the most spectacular advances in modern physics and its most trustworthy theories have depended for their discovery not merely upon the data of the experimentalists but also upon the development and investigations of pure mathematics. For, as Bertrand Russell has said, pure mathematics is the science of all possible worlds and not merely of this higgledy-piggledy job-lot of a place. The point is that a scientific theory carries very much more certainty if one can say not merely that its deductively formulated theorems have been confirmed, but also that after one has investigated all the conceivable or imaginable theoretical possibilities, it is the only one of these possibilities known to date which is confirmed. In fact, this is the only precise way to define a crucial experiment. Such an experiment is not merely one which confirms a given scientific theory; it is, instead, one of a character such that while confirming one theory it repudiates others. Such an experiment is impossible to define without recourse to at least two theoretical possibilities.

This brings us to the final reason for all these technical logical and methodological considerations. The introduction of crucial experiments in order to mitigate the danger of the fallacy of affirming the consequent in the mere experimental confirmation of a scientific theory without the consideration of other theoretical possibilities, means that there can be no trustworthy science, even with experimental confirmation, in the mature stage of development of an empirical science unless as much attention is given by scientists to the consideration of theory and of rival theoretical possibilities and to deductive logic as is given to induction, factual data, and experimentation. The point is that the mere experimental confirmation of a scientific theory through its deductive consequences is not generally regarded by competent scientists as a sufficient criterion of the scientific validity of that theory. One must go further and show as far as is possible that the theory in question is the only one which is capable, through its deductive consequences, of taking care of the natural history data. This is what Albert Einstein meant when, in

the designation of science, which we first quoted, he wrote
that the "single experiences must be correlated with the
theoretic structure in such a way that the resulting coordination is *unique*...." Only by formulating rival theories,
learning to think deductively with respect to them by pressing them to their deductive consequences — in short, only by
emphasis upon theory and deductive logic as well as upon
facts and experimentation can the uniqueness of an experimentally confirmed scientific theory be established.

If these considerations are appreciated, we are now prepared to understand the scientific importance of the following investigation of the rival theories of biological organization. We are also equipped with the precise understanding
of the scientific method for carrying on such an investigation.

The results of our analysis of the method of the mathematical and physical sciences may now be summarized. Any
science in its normal development passes through two stages
— the first, the natural history stage, the second, that of
postulationally prescribed theory. To each of these two
stages there belongs a definite type of scientific concept. The
type of concept for the natural history stage we term a concept
by inspection; that for the postulationally prescribed stage,
a concept by postulation. A concept by inspection is one the
complete meaning of which is given by something immediately apprehended. A concept by postulation is one the
meaning of which is prescribed for it by the postulates of the
deductive theory in which it occurs.

Since it is possible to postulate entities and structures quite
different from any immediately observed, science is able to
introduce, by recourse to concepts by postulation, unobserved
entities and structures into its scientific theories. The
existence of such scientific objects is none the less verifiable.

The method for this verification is fourfold: The postulated system is prescribed by the postulates of the theory
which designates it. From these postulates, by formal logic,

theorems are deduced. Between the concepts by postulation in the deduced theorems and concepts by inspection denoting immediately apprehendable natural history data, epistemic correlations are set up. When the directly observable epistemic correlates of the deduced theorems of the postulationally prescribed theory are naturally or experimentally observed, the theory is confirmed. If they are not observed or the inspected data are contrary to what is called for, the theory is rejected. In the case of confirmation, a theoretical investigation of alternative hypotheses is pursued, with the purpose of showing as far as is possible not merely that a given theory is confirmed by the data, but also that it is the only theory which is so confirmed.

In the light of these considerations, our task in determining an adequate theory of biological organization is the following one: to find a postulated theory designating a system of related entities which will correlate uniquely with the directly apprehended biological organization exhibited in the natural history data. Let us now examine certain theories of biological organization from this standpoint.

The major natural history theory of biological organization is that formulated by Aristotle. In modern biology it carries the name of Vitalism. The essential point in this theory is that the concepts of biology are unique and irreducible, in part or whole, to those of any other science. From the standpoint of natural history this is the case. Observed, living creatures are different from observed, inorganic objects. Thus it is natural, in the natural history stage of development of biology, that the irreducibility of this science should be emphasized.

Also, living creatures as immediately observed do exhibit a persistence of form or organization through the influx or outgo of material. This makes it natural to conceive of the living organism as a combination of two main factors: its observed material and its observed form. When one observes also, in the developing embryo, a distribution and rearrangement of the material, so that a given form is produced, it is quite in accord with what one observes to say that the form as well as the matter is an irreducible, causal factor determining the final, mature system. Thus the Aristotelian foundation of science with its repudiation of any concepts in science or philosophy except those first given through the senses and with its doctrine of both material and formal causes becomes a natural theory for biologists to hold. The great merit of this theory is that it does provide a reasonable solution of the biological problem of organization. If there are irreducible formal factors as well as the material factors, we are then able to understand why there is a persistence of form through a flux of materials and why the matter in the developing embryo arranges itself so that a definite form is actualized.

None the less, this theory, plausible as it seems in the light of the natural history data, runs into certain difficulties. In the first place, all organisms die. Death means a breakdown of directly observed organization. This points toward the conclusion that the organization is not an ultimate, irreducible factor, but something that can come and go. Thus organization seems to point beyond itself to some other more ultimate factors as its own condition. Secondly, there is the modification of species and the origin of new species emphasized by Darwin. This discovery emphasizes the non-irreducibility of form for the species which death emphasizes for the individual. Finally, there has been a third and even more conclusive consideration. Biologists have found for their science what Dirac, in our previous quotation from him, emphasized for physics: a more consistent, adequate conception of the natural history data in biology has been attained by giving up the attempt to understand this data in terms of concepts deriving from directly inspectable items, and by having recourse to the postulated entities of physics and chemistry. Papers in biological journals give an eloquent demonstration of this point. In short, biologists have come to find that the concepts by postulation of physics and chemistry are more fertile in understanding their own subject matter than the concepts by inspection of an autonomous theory of natural history biology.

Before turning to the consideration of these physical and chemical theories of biological organization, one danger must be noted. In such a transition period in biology from the natural history stage with its concepts by inspection to the stage of postulationally prescribed theory, with its concepts by postulation, it cannot be too strongly emphasized that these two types of concepts belong to two fundamentally different worlds of discourse. Consequently, biological information coming in terms of one type of concept cannot be added together with biological information in terms of the other type of concept to produce anything more than nonsense.

Permit me to make this point more clear with a concrete example. As has been suggested, and as has been emphasized by all leading modern biologists since Claude Bernard, the fundamental problem of modern biology is that of organization. We know with reasonable certainty what the entities are that constitute a living organism. There is every reason to believe, in the light of the experimental evidence, that these entities are those of physics and chemistry. But when this is admitted, the major problem still remains concerning whether the persistent organization of a living system can reduce to physical and chemical principles also. It is reasonable to say that this problem has not yet been solved. In such a situation it is very easy to attempt to solve the problem by introducing the physical and chemical elements to take care of the constituents of a living organism and including the intuited biological organization from the natural history approach to biology to take care of the organization of these constitutents. In fact, this is precisely what Hans Driesch and J. S. Haldane have proposed. It must be emphasized, however, that such a thesis is not a scientific theory but non-sense, since it combines, as if in a single world of discourse, the intuited datum of organization which is a concept by inspection, with the entities of physics and chemistry, which are concepts by postulation. This constitutes a muddling of two distinct worlds of discourse.

In the situation in which we find ourselves there are but two alternatives. Either we develop a strictly natural history theory of biology, using only concepts by inspection, or else we have recourse to the entities of physics and chemistry which are joined, as Einstein has indicated, to what we imme-diately inspect in the natural history stage, by epistemic cor-relations, in which case we must also have concepts by postulation to take care of the organization of these entities. Since biologists have unequivocally decided to appeal to the entities of physics and chemistry, our task, therefore, is to find a postulated relational factor provided by physical and chemical theory which can be epistemically correlated with the immediately observed organization given in the natural history data.

There are three theories of this organic factor. We shall call them the chemical theory of life, the thermo-dynamical theory of life, and the electro-dynamic theory of life respec-tively.

It is to be emphasized that all three of these theories are implicit in the chemical factors which have already been experimentally demonstrated to be present in living organ-isms. Certainly chemical elements involve all the chemical relations which the theory of chemistry prescribes. Unfor-tunately, the concepts and theory of chemistry have not been formulated deductively with the precision and rigor of physi-cal science. It will be necessary, therefore, for us in con-sidering the chemical theory of life and its deductive consequences with respect to biological organization, to develop this theory somewhat step by step in terms of certain piecemeal experimental findings. In this connection, we shall draw very heavily on the work of Lavoisier.

But chemical elements in their interactions also obey the laws of energy. Consequently, if living organisms involve chemical constituents, the structure of these systems is subject to the laws and postulates of thermo-dynamics. Hence, we have at our service, in attempting to understand biological organization, not merely the laws and information of chemical theory and analysis, but also the deductive consequences of the science of thermo-dynamics.

In addition, chemical entities are known to be constituted of electrical components. Life depends for its very existence upon energy radiated to it upon the earth from the sun. This radiation is an electro-magnetic phenomenon. Consequently, living organisms depend for their very existence upon electro-magnetics. This means that not merely the postulates of chemistry and thermo-dynamics, but also those of electro-dynamics are available to provide a postulational structure which may or may not uniquely correlate epistemically with the observed organization of living creatures.

Chemistry postulates a collection of atoms, some ninety odd in number, each with unique properties. These atoms enter into combination according to certain proportions and pass out of combination. Thus the emphasis in chemistry is more on the constancy of the entities than on the constancy of the relatedness. This would lead us to expect that the chemical theory of life would be quite effective in accounting for the constituents of living organisms, but somewhat ambiguous in providing an adequate account of the persistence of biological organization. This expectation is not far from the case. Claude Bernard certainly had an appreciation of the tremendous rôle of chemical constituents and processes in living organisms, yet he was equally well aware that the problem of organization remained a problem under this theory. Nevertheless, there are certain findings arising from a chemical approach to biological processes which must be kept in mind and which are absolutely essential for an understanding of biological organization. No one has made them more evident than the founder of modern physiological chemistry, Lavoisier.

It was Lavoisier who demonstrated that a living system, when viewed chemically, cannot be conceived as the mere collection of chemical compounds within its visible bodily surface. His investigations of metabolism and respiration showed that the very existence and persistence of a living system depend upon the continuous chemical decomposition of the food materials taken into the organism's body. It is not by finding compounds which hold themselves fixedly together by their chemical bonds, after the manner of the inorganic stone, that the persistence of the living organism has been achieved, but by a continuous breaking down and reorganization and reassembling of chemical constituents. Moreover, this breaking down of carbohydrates which occurs in the animal body in metabolism is impossible without a continuous supply of oxygen. This oxygen has its basis not inside the organism but in the tension of the atmosphere of the earth's surface without. Furthermore, if the carbon dioxide released by the oxidation of the carbohydrates in metabolism were not removed from the organism into the surrounding environment, death would ensue, even though oxidation occurred. Thus the picture we must have of a living organism is not that of a set of local protein molecules with a certain constant structure, whether that structure be conceived of the chain or the pattern type. These molecules constitute but one of a tremendous number of chemical factors not merely within but without the bodily organism, all of which are in continuous flux and interaction. It is in a most complicated relationship between chemical materials external and internal to the body surface of the organism in which every term in the relationship is in continuous motion and chemical transformation that we must find the concept of the living organism when viewed from the standpoint of the investigations of bio-chemistry.

This is the organism as we find it in the light of chemical analysis. How does it compare with what we would expect upon the basis of the postulates of chemical theory? Curiously enough, the findings are in a way the direct opposite of what chemical theory alone would lead one to expect. According to the theory of atoms upon which chemistry is founded, the persistence should be in the entities, and not in the structure. Yet what we actually find is the reverse. The chemical constituents of the living organism are in continuous motion and flux, and it is the relatedness which persists, or at least changes itself slowly in comparison with the flux of the entities in and out of the relational structure. Rudolf Schoenheimer's investigations of the behavior of protein molecules in the living organism as exhibited with the technique of "tagged atoms" confirms this point in a spectacular way. These investigations show that the protein molecule must be continuously built up as constituents are passing out of it and replaced by others continuously. Not even the individual protein molecule persists because of the chemical bonds which hold its constituents together.

These considerations show that while the chemical theory of life is experimentally confirmed and even a uniquely confirmed theory of the constituents of biological organization, it provides, at least in the present stage of its application, very little basis for an understanding of the organization of living things. This does not mean that the theory is false; it means merely that it provides an account of part but not all the problem of organization.

Rudolf Schoenheimer's investigations have a second significance. His findings are precisely what one would expect if one conceived of a living organism from the standpoint of the thermo-dynamical theory of life.

The science of thermo-dynamics informs us that any system which is not in equilibrium in the technical thermo-dynamical sense of this term, will automatically break down, because of the operation of the second law of thermo-dynamics, unless energy is provided for that system from outside.   All competent students of living organisms from the standpoint of thermo-dynamics are in agreement upon the fact that living organisms are not in equilibrium in this thermo-dynamical sense.   In fact, when a living system passes to a state of maximum entropy, or in other words to a state of thermo-dynamical equilibrium, death takes place.   From this it follows that the organization of living systems can only persist if energy comes into them from outside.

This is but another way of saying that the physical-chemical structure of living organisms cannot persist by itself, but must be continuously maintained by energy supplied in the form of food or radiation from without.   This is precisely what Rudolf Schoenheimer's investigations indicate for even so small a structure as the protein molecule.   Left to itself, it would disintegrate.   Even to persist, it must have new parts continuously put into it.   For this work must be done.

It is because living organisms are not in thermo-dynamical equilibrium, and hence are continuously dependent for their maintenance upon energy from without, that animals depend upon plants directly or indirectly for their food and energy supply, and that plants in turn depend upon energy from the sun.   These thermo-dynamical considerations make it evident that if we are to attain a correct physical-chemical theory of the living organism, we must think about it not merely in terms of the relationship between atoms within the organism and those in the earth's atmosphere and on the earth's surface, but also in terms of the energy relationship and temperature difference between the earth and the sun.

Because of the evolution of living organisms from systems exhibiting relatively simple organization and differentiation to species which become more and more complicated and heterogeneous in their organization, certain students have concluded that the processes of biological growth and evolution are incompatible with the second law of thermo-dynamics. The reason for this merits our consideration and requires a more detailed analysis of the meaning of the first two laws of thermo-dynamics.

The fundamental concept of thermo-dynamics is energy. Energy may be defined roughly as the capacity to do work. The first law asserts that the total amount of energy in any isolated system remains constant.

This total amount of energy divides into two parts. One part is in a form available to do work on organized systems; the other part termed dissipated energy, is in a form unavailable to do work on organized systems. The second law of thermo-dynamics asserts that in an isolated system the amount of energy in this dissipated form unavailable for work on an organized system, continuously increases. The dissipated energy unavailable for work is termed entropy. Thus the second law takes on the form stated by Clausius: the entropy of the universe tends toward the maximum.

Since it takes more energy in a form available to do work to maintain a complicated and highly organized biological system than to organize and maintain a simpler system, and since biological evolution does proceed from a relatively homogeneous type of organism to a more and more heterogeneous species, it would seem, upon first sight, that biological systems go directly counter to the second law of thermo-dynamics, by proceeding from a state involving a lesser amount of energy in a form capable of doing work to a state involving a greater amount of such energy. Certain students of thermo-dynamics in its relation to biological evolution, notably Sir James Jeans, have reached this conclusion.

Later, F. G. Donnan (1934) pointed out, quite correctly that there is no contradiction between biological evolution towards systems requiring more and more energy in a form available for work and the second law of thermo-dynamics.

The second law does not assert that the entropy of a system can never decrease with time. It asserts merely that this can never be the case in an isolated system. The second law of thermo-dynamics is quite compatible with a decrease of entropy in the evolution of a given system, providing that energy in a form available for work is brought into that system from outside. This we know to be the case since animals depend directly or indirectly upon plants for their food and energy supply, and plants in turn derive energy from the sun.

This means, however, that we cannot expect to find the scientific basis of biological growth and organization solely within the chemical constituents of the animal's body. Growth and organization involve chemical factors within and without the animal's body on the earth's surface and in its atmosphere, and these in turn depend upon energy relations with our solar system. Were it not for the temperature difference between the sun and the earth, biological growth, organization, and evolution as we know it, would be impossible on thermo-dynamical grounds. Such considerations must make one exceedingly skeptical of all attempts to find the key to growth and biological organization in some local chemical factor, whether it be auxin or the structure of the protein molecule, important as these items are as one among a tremendous number of variables in the complicated, many-termed chemical and thermo-dynamical relationship which constitutes the living organism.

There is a sense, however, in which Sir James Jeans as well as F. G. Donnan may be correct, with respect to the relation between biological evolution and the second law of thermo-dynamics. The point is this: By an appeal to energy coming to the earth and into biological systems from the sun, one does quite properly reconcile biological evolution with the second law of thermo-dynamics after the manner indicated by F. G. Donnan. This presupposes, however, a certain assumption concerning what happens so far as the second law is concerned in the astronomical universe as a whole. To maintain the second law in the face of biological evolution, it is necessary to affirm for the astronomical universe as a whole, that the decrease in entropy taking place in the evolution of biological systems is more than equalled by a corresponding increase in entropy somewhere else in the universe, so that the sum total of entropy in biological evolution and the rest of the universe tends toward a maximum. This is a topic upon which there is no absolutely conclusive astronomical evidence and one with respect to which there are rival hypotheses. These hypotheses will vary, furthermore, depending upon whether one postulates, as traditional, modern science did, an astronomical universe with infinite extension, or as contemporary astro-physics is inclined to do, an astronomical universe which is finite.

The important point from thermo-dynamics in its bearing on biological growth and evolution, for our present purposes, however, is that it forces us to conceive of biological systems as a complicated, many-termed relation between chemical entities in continuous motion and flux, both internal and external to the organism's body and surface. Moreover, the relation between these many moving chemical entities is continuously dependent upon energy coming into the system from a solar source outside.

The latter fact is important for two reasons. First, it reminds us that biological organization is not a static, chemical bond between persistent chemical entities. In short, the persistence of the organization does not have its basis in the persistency of the entities which are the terms in its relatedness. Biological organization, instead, is a relation with certain formal properties, holding between entities continuously passing in and out of this relatedness. It is, to be precise, the form of the relation between the motion of its parts. Secondly, the thermo-dynamical dependence of biological growth and evolution upon energy from the sun establishes, in the most literal sense of the word, that biological organization has its origin in electro-magnetics as well as in chemistry and thermo-dynamics. This follows because the energy coming into the conglomeration of chemical materials from outside is brought to the earth and to plants upon its surface from the sun by electro-magnetic propagations. In fact, the synthesis of carbohydrates and the resultant storing of solar energy which takes place in plants by the mediation of chlorophyll is an electro- or photo-chemical process. This brings us to a third theory of physical science which must have significance for biology.

Our consideration of chemical theory and thermo-dynamical theory in relation to biology informs us that the postulates of chemistry are adequate to account for the constituents of organization and that the principles of thermo-dynamics are necessary and consistently able to account for the energy necessary to organize those constituents.

Although these two theories are necessary, they are by no means sufficient. The insufficiency of the chemical theory has been summarized by saying that it could account for the persistence of biological organization only if organization had its basis in the persistence in the organism of the individual entities which are the chemical terms of that organization. That this is not the case is shown by the fact that although the organization persists, the chemical atoms and molecules within this organization are in continuous motion and flux. The insufficiency of the thermo-dynamical theory as a complete account of biological organization centers in the fact that there is nothing in the theory to prescribe the particular relatedness into which the energy organizes the moving, chemical materials. This can be put in more technical language by saying that there is nothing in thermo-dynamics itself which prescribes at what point precisely in the tendency toward a state of maximum entropy the energy from outside the system compensates that tendency, to produce the steady state, or the state of mean compensated entropy, which is a living organism.

What seems to be called for in addition to the concepts by postulation of chemistry and of thermo-dynamics, is a postulational theory of physics which will prescribe an irreducible relatedness between moving physico-chemical entities. This is precisely what field physics provides. The electro-dynamic theory of life is merely the conception of living organisms from the standpoint of field physics.

The fundamental postulate of field physics has been stated clearly by Clerk Maxwell, the first scientist to formulate this theory mathematically and deductively. In his first famous paper on electro-magnetics, entitled *On Faraday's Lines of Force,* after indicating that Ampere's theory of electric currents assumes "attracting forces considered as due to the mutual action of particles," Maxwell adds that "we are proceeding upon a different principle, and searching for the explanation of the phenomenon, not in the currents alone, but also in the surrounding medium." In other words, instead of beginning with the particles related by forces acting instantaneously at a distance, and attempting to define the field and its organization by mere compounding, as does particle physics, Maxwell is forced in order to account for the existence of light and other electro-magnetic propagations in the universe, to begin with the field with its relatedness as in fact continuous and irreducible and to derive in part at least the location and motion of the charged particles in the electric current.

Furthermore, form as well as continuity is assumed for the field. Maxwell writes, "The distribution of the currents due to these field forces depends upon the form and arrangement of the conducting medium." In his final paper on electro-magnetics, containing his famous equations, he adds, "this medium must be so connected that the motion of one part depends upon the motion of the rest." One might think it were a biologist talking about the type of assumption requisite for an adequate theory of biological organization.

A few pages later, when Maxwell describes his specific procedure, he is even more explicit in his designation of the relatedness of the system as in part an original irreducible causal factor determining the mechanical motions of the parts. We begin, he says, with "the form of the relation between the motion of the parts," given in the laws of induction, and "the second result, which is deduced from this, is the mechanical action between conductors carrying currents." At last, we have a physical theory which if it applies to a living creature, begins to make sense of the fact that it is not merely a collection of chemicals requiring energy but also an individual which is organized.

The important point to note is that the introduction of the postulates of field physics has been found to be necessary to account even for phenomena in the inorganic world. Following the tremendous success of Newtonian mechanics with its postulation of mass particles related by forces acting instantaneously at a distance the attempt was made by Ampere and others to formulate electricity, magnetism and optics in such terms. With electricity and magnetism this attempt was successful, although Faraday had brought forth convincing experimental evidence suggesting that it might be more naturally conceived in terms of a field concept. Before the phenomenon of optics, requiring an undulatory theory of light, particle physics broke down completely. Consequently, when Maxwell developed Faraday's field concept mathematically and deductively, and was able to show that the undulatory theory of light followed from it necessarily, field physics triumphed not merely in optics but also in electricity and magnetism. Since Maxwell's time it has gone on to further triumphs. With Lorentz and Larmor it was generalized, so that it permitted the prediction of the negatively charged electron on theoretical grounds before this postulated scientific object was discovered experimentally by Sir J. J. Thomson. In this connection it must be realized that the electron is not, as so many people suppose, a concept of particle physics, but is instead defined in terms of the assumptions of field physics. With Albert Einstein, these assumptions, in his theory of relativity received an even more spectacular generalization and experimental confirmation.

As Albert Einstein has written, "For several decades most physicists clung to the conviction that a mechanical substructure could be found for Maxwell's theory. But the unsatisfactory results of their efforts led to gradual acceptance of the new field concepts as irreducible fundamentals" (1940). In short, what Maxwell termed "the form of the relation between the motion of the parts" has been accepted by physicists as irreducible.

If physicists have been driven to such assumptions to account for inorganic phenomena, is it not all the more reasonable to suppose that this postulate of electro-magnetic theory is required for living organisms with their even more obviously persisting relatedness? It was reasoning of this kind, which led the writer and H. S. Burr (1935) to put forward the electro-dynamic theory of life — the theory that an understanding of biological organization is to be found if we conceive it from the standpoint of the postulates of electro-magnetic theory.

If this hypothesis be correct, it follows that electro-metric experimental methods should detect systematic, organic, electrical properties of living organisms. Guided by this hypothesis, H. S. Burr, in conjunction with C. T. Lane and L. S. Nims (1936), developed a new experimental apparatus to put this theory to an empirical test. This apparatus has been applied

to many different species of living organisms. In every case
it has been found that systematic, distributed, potential differences exhibit themselves over any living organism considered as a whole. The details concerning these findings have
been published elsewhere (1937). A more recent experiment
shows that at last in this theory we have the type of epistemic
correlation between the postulated structure of physical theory and the directly inspected natural history data of organization which our previous analysis of the scientific method for
handling postulational physical theory has shown to be required for any trustworthy scientific solution of the biological
problem.

The experiment is as follows: On a fertilized egg of amblystoma in one of its early stages of embryonic development,
when no directly inspectable differentiations of the natural
history type were observable, H. S. Burr found, with his
experimental apparatus, a definite organized pattern of potential differences. Using dyes, he designated an inspectable
pattern on the surface of the organism corresponding to the
postulated potential differences designated by his apparatus.
When the organism was allowed to grow, later, inspectable,
natural history differentiations appeared at precisely the loca-
tions which his dyes, as guided by his electro-metric readings,
had indicated. This suggests quite definitely that electrical
differentiation is at the basis of the developing differentiation
of the natural history data. It indicates, also, that the requirements of sound, scientific method for solving the problem of biological organization are satisfied. That is, epistemic
correlations have been established between the postulated
electrical distinctions of physical theory and the directly
observable data of the natural historians' inductive observation of biological organization.

It would appear, therefore, that in the relationship between
the fundamental concepts of chemical theory, thermo-dynamical theory, and the electro-magnetic theory of field physics, a

scientific theory for the solution of the problem of organization in biology is to be found. Chemical theory provides
the postulated entities at the basis of the material constituents
of living organisms; thermo-dynamics provides an understanding of their dependence on energy factors from without;
and the electro-dynamic theory provides the irreducible
relatedness necessary for an understanding of the organization of the constituents as worked upon by the energy.

This chapter is reprinted from *Growth Supplement* 1940 with the kind
permission of the Editor. It was presented originally in the Second
Symposium of the Society for the Study of Growth and Development at
Salisbury Cove, Maine, on June 25th, 1940.

J. H. Woodger. *The Axiomatic Method in Biology,* Cambridge
University Press, 1937.

Nicolas Rashvesky. *Mathematical Bio-Physics: Physicio-Mathe-
matical Foundations of Biology,* The University of Chicago
Press, Chicago, 1938.

P. A. M. Dirac. Quantised Singularities in the Electromagnetic
Field," *Proceedings of the Royal Society of London,* Series A,
133, 1931.

Albert Einstein. *The World As I See It,* Covici Friede, New
York, 1934, p. 60. "Considerations Concerning the Funda-
ments of Theoretical Physics," *Science,* 1940, 91: 487 and 489.

J. H. Jeans. "Activities of Life and the Second Law of Thermo-
Dynamics," *Nature,* 1934, 133: 174.

F. G. Donnan. "Activities of Life and the Second Law of Thermo-
Dynamics," *Nature,* 1934, 133: 99.

F. G. Donnan and E. A. Guggenheim. "Activities of Life and
the Second Law of Thermo-Dynamics," *Nature,* 1934, 133:
530.

J. C. Maxwell. *Scientific Papers,* Cambridge, 1890, Vol. i, p. 193.

H. S. Burr and F. S. C. Northrop. "The Electro-Dynamic Theory
of Life," *The Quarterly Review of Biology,* 1935, 10: 322.
"Evidence for the Existence of an Electro-Dynamic Field in
Living Organisms," *Proceedings of the National Academy of
Sciences,* 1939, 25: 284.

H. S. Burr, C. T. Lane, and L. F. Nims.   "A Vacuum Tube Microvoltmeter for the Measurement of Electrical Phenomena,"
Yale Journal of Biology and Medicine, 1936, 9: 65.

F. S. C. Northrop.   *Science and First Principles,* New York, 1931,
Chapters III-V. "The History of Modern Physics in Its
Bearing upon Biology and Medicine," *Yale Journal of Biology
and Medicine,* 1938, 10: 209, 227.

CHAPTER IX

THE FUNCTIONS AND FUTURE OF POETRY

Poetry is one of the arts. Any art functions in two ways, either in and for itself, or as the means to an end defined by some other subject or science.

It is a characteristic of the arts when they function in and for themselves that they are concerned with immediately experienced materials. This is especially evident in the case of painting. In conveying color and form the painter places before us the immediately experienceable blues and reds and greens. It is true, also, of music. The composer may work with black marks arranged on horizontal bars ordered at intervals much after the manner of the symbols of the mathematician. Yet he would hardly be called an artist were not the symbolic form of his score embodied in and presented with the sensuous content of the immediately heard sounds at the symphony concert.

Literature, in the form either of written poetry or prose, may seem upon first thought to be an exception to this rule. When the literary masterpieces are not read aloud the artist has presented merely the symbols on the page and not the actual people or elements of experience to which the symbols refer. A closer examination of his artistry will indicate, however, that he achieves the status of an artist only if, by means of these symbols, he succeeds in bringing into concrete vividness in the reader's imagination that which he purports to convey with all the freshness of color, the vital movement of the emotions, and the sensitivity of feeling which an immediate experience of the imagined subject matter, were it possible, would exhibit.

This becomes clear if we note the difference in the treatment of the same phenomenon, for example, a flowing brook, by the poet and by the scientist. The poet refers to it as the "babbling brook." If he achieves his purpose with us by his use of these words in the context of his verse, we experience ourselves in imagination, immediately confronted with the rippling sounds and the broken, flashing surfaces of the waves of shining water as they flow over the stones and incline gradually between the banks of the stream to disappear into an immediately felt vagueness in the periphery of our consciousness. The scientist, on the other hand, referring to the same phenomenon, would speak of molecules falling from the top of one stone to a stone below and moving in a path which is a parabola, compounded out of an inertial force with a constant velocity in a horizontal straight line, and an accelerated motion perpendicular thereto defined by the constant gravitation. There would be further statements concerning the angle of deflection which defines the paths of the molecules as they bound from the second stone to inaugurate another parabolic path on their way to the sea. It is quite clear even to an observer immediately confronted with an actual brook that neither these individual paths nor the particles themselves are seen. What one immediately observes are the babbling sounds and the shining, moving surfaces which the poet portrays. Were science the mere description of what is immediately observable, poetry, rather than physics, would be the better science of the brook. These considerations make it evident that the poet, even though he operates mediately through symbols, provides no exception to our general rule that the arts when they function in and for themselves are concerned with immediately apprehendable materials.

It becomes clear, also, that the symbols of the artist and the symbols of the physicist, even when they refer to what may be termed, speaking somewhat loosely, the "same" phenomenon, are different in kind. It is important that we have names and precise definitions for these two kinds. Symbols, like those used by the poet, when poetry functions in and for itself, we shall term concepts by intuition. *A concept by intuition is one the complete meaning of which is given by something immediately apprehendable.* "Brook," in the sense of the babble of sounds and the sequence of shining surfaces, is an example of a concept by intuition. Symbols, like those employed by the physicist, when science has experimentally confirmed, deductively formulated theory rather than mere natural history description, we shall call concepts by postulation. *A concept by postulation is one designating something in whole or part not immediately observable, the meaning of which is prescribed for it by the postulates of the scientific theory in which the symbol occurs.* "Brook," in the sense of the collection of molecules moving in paths with the form of the parabola, is an example of a concept by postulation. Electrons, electro-magnetic waves, and Einstein's tensor equation for gravitation are additional examples, since what these scientific concepts designate is not immediately observable and can be known only by theory, which is experimentally confirmed, in a somewhat complicated but none the less trustworthy manner, through its deductive consequences.

This distinction between concepts by intuition and concepts by postulation shows that what in some sense is the same world is known by man in two different ways. It is important that we have names for the two aspects or components of reality which these two ways of knowing anything give us. *That factor of anything which is denoted by a concept by intuition* we shall call *the aesthetic component of reality,* or *reality in its aesthetic aspect;* that designated by *a concept by postulation, the theoretic component,* or *reality in its postulated or theoretical aspect.*

Since these two components are in some sense components of the same thing, it is important to designate the relation

between them which defines this sameness. The common-
sense man, most literary critics, and even scientists who are
not too critical and informed in their analysis of what they
are doing, suppose that this relation is one of identity. It is
easy to fall into this error because linguistically scientists and
laymen use the same symbol to designate the radically different types of concepts. For example, the word "blue" is used
both for the concept by intuition, which is the immediately
sensed color presented by the painter, and the concept by
postulation, which is the number for an unobserved wave
length in electro-magnetic theory postulated by the physicist.
It is clear, however, that the relation between these two factors is not one of identity. Even the scientist and the man
of common sense appreciate this. Both realize it to be nonsense to assert that the wave length is blue. It would be
equally meaningless to say that electrons are noisy. Such
nonsense always occurs when concepts by intuition and concepts by postulation are treated in the same sentence as if
they belonged to a single rather than to two different worlds
of discourse.

But if the relation between the immediately apprehended,
aesthetic, and the scientifically postulated and experimentally
confirmed, theoretic components of reality is not that of
identity, then what is it? The answer is epistemic correlation. *An epistemic correlation is a relation,* preferably, but
not always, one-one, *joining a theoretically-known factor
designated by a concept by postulation to its immediately
apprehendable, aesthetic correlate denoted by a concept by
intuition.* This relation is termed epistemic, from the word
"epistemology," referring to knowledge, because it relates
items of reality which are known in two different ways.
These epistemic correlations both (1) distinguish the aesthetic component of reality denoted by the concepts by intuition
with which the poet operates from the theoretic component
of reality designated by the concepts by postulation which

only the scientist and the scientific philosopher are competent to determine and (2) relate these two diverse factors.
In short, epistemic correlations both separate and connect the
real as known aesthetically with immediacy and the real as
known scientifically through deductively formulated, experimentally verified theory.

In this dual rôle of the epistemic correlations, art in its
two functions has its basis. By distinguishing concepts by
intuition from concepts by postulation and thereby preventing the identification of reality as scientifically and truly
thought with reality as immediately and aesthetically intuited,
the epistemic correlation permits the aesthetic, purely empirical component of reality to be treated by itself and thereby
makes possible the pursuit of art in and for itself without any
dependence upon or reference to scientific theory or philosophical, political, or religious doctrine. By relating, but
not identifying, concepts by intuition with concepts by postulation the epistemic correlations also indicate that the aesthetic component of reality points beyond itself to the theoreti-
cally-postulated. Thus, providing the epistemic correlations
are made one-one, they permit the poet to convey analogically
in terms of immediate experienceable materials, the unobservable theoretic component of reality which can be
literally expressed only by the technical concepts by postulation of science and scientifically formulated philosophy.
Thus arises art in its second function as the instrument or
handmaid for metaphorically and analogically conveying a
theoretical doctrine, the truth of which can be determined
correctly only outside of art by some other subject or science.

The poetry of the babbling brook illustrates art in its
first function. Clearly this poetic treatment of the sequence
of sounds and shining surfaces is quite independent of any
scientific theory concerning molecules. The concept by
intuition denoting the aesthetic component of reality is here
treated by itself apart from the epistemic correlation which

joins it to the theoretic component. This is art in and for itself.

Art in its second function is exemplified in Dante's *Divine Comedy*. Here, as in the poem of the "babbling brook," the artist is using concepts by intuition conveying vivid, immediately experienceable elementary emotions and impressions. Up to this point it is art in and for itself. It can be so treated as mere poetry. But there is more in the poem, and it is this additional factor which gave this poem its influence in its period and its importance in Western culture. Dante had studied the *Summa Theologica* of Saint Thomas. This opus in eight volumes is a theoretical treatise in science, philosophy, and theology formulated technically in dry, formal definitions and with syllogistic reasoning in terms of concepts by postulation. Its propositions made the theological doctrine of the Catholic Church articulate in terms of the science and purely scientific metaphysics of Aristotle. This Aristotelian, inductively verified, scientific and philosophical theory defined the conception of the theoretic component of reality as determined by the scientific knowledge acquired up to its time.

But the theory, like all scientific and philosophical theories, was technical, difficult for anyone but the expert to comprehend, and required for its appreciation a tremendous amount of empirical knowledge in mathematics, physics, astronomy, and especially biology, in which Aristotle excelled. The problem was to convey this doctrine which defined the idea of the good for informed scientific and philosophical minds to the general masses, who were incapable then, as they are now, of grasping the fundamental ideas of systematic scientific and philosophical theory literally. The general public, like all but a few of our contemporary professors of psychology and education, are incapable of using concepts by postulation with their technical definitions and logical deductions; they must have bells rung for them while they salivate, and have vivid images instead of postulationally prescribed scientific concepts. Dante solved this problem for his time by epistemically correlating the vivid images denoted by the poet's concepts by intuition with the technical concepts by postulation of Saint Thomas' *Summa*. Then he moved the images about as the technical doctrine of Saint Thomas related their correlated concepts by postulation. Thus in his poem, to people who could not grasp the technical doctrine literally in terms of its concepts by postulation, Dante conveyed an analogue of this doctrine metaphorically in terms of the vivid, immediately apprehendable aesthetic materials denoted by the poet's concepts by intuition. This is art in its second function as the instrument or handmaid of some other subject or science.

If the distinction between art in its two functions is now clear, we are able to evaluate the rôle of poetry in our culture. This will prepare us for an understanding of the future of poetry.

The primary task of poetry, arising out of art in its first function, is to convey the aesthetic component of reality in and for itself apart from all postulated doctrine and theory. Put more concretely, it must keep men continuously aware of the freshness and the ineffable beauty and richness of the immediately apprehended.

This is a function which must be provided. Otherwise we lose the riches and values of life which are immediately before our senses.

One of the most deadening influences upon human living arises out of the need to move on beyond the aesthetically immediate to postulated common-sense objects for the purposes of practical life and to postulated scientific objects and philosophical systems for the satisfaction of our intellectual curiosity and the attainment of more complete and manageable human knowledge. Both of these movements are necessary and good. Nevertheless, by themselves they tend to cause us to treat the ineffable beauty and the soul-sustaining freshness of the aesthetically immediate merely as a means to an end, thereby overlooking the contemplation of it in and for itself.   As we hurry down the street of an evening the worries of practical living so overwhelm us, or, — if we are more scientifically and philosophically minded — we become so engrossed in our theories of the internal molecular constitution of the stars that we do not see and become refreshed by the beauty of the sunset which is immediately before our eyes.   Unless we are protected by poetry and the other arts functioning purely in and for themselves, reality in its theoretical aspect is sought at the cost of losing its equally real aesthetic component, and the mind of man becomes over-stimulated while his spirit dies.

There is a factor of the nature of things which can be known only by science and by theory with its recourse to concepts by postulation, and there is another important part pressing on the very threshold of our senses denoted by concepts by intuition which is equally essential for calm and complete living.   The tragedy of the neglect of poetry and its sister arts treated in and for themselves is that we lose those riches of life which are available to everybody, rich and poor alike, immediately before our ears and noses and eyes.   It is as if a man has part of the riches for which he is searching, present in his own yard and being so concerned about what is on the other side of its fence, goes off seeking in a far country.

The character of anything immediately apprehended merits more meticulous examination.   Any item which is immediately felt or sensed is ineffable.   One can look at a blue for hours and not quite intuit all its depth and richness.   Also, if one's friend has never sensed a blue, no amount of discourse by the poet or the scientist can convey that datum to him. This is the character of anything immediately apprehended — that it has to be immediately experienced to be known.

If to be unstatable and hence ineffable is the characteristic of the mystical, then, contrary to popular opinion, the mystical and the ineffable is not off in some far distant speculative heaven, but in immediately apprehended fact directly before our eyes.

This ineffable character of the immediately observed, with which the artist or the natural history scientist who has not arrived at deductively-formulated theory concerns himself, has one other, somewhat shocking, consequence, when art is compared with science.   It is usual for the popular mind and occasional uncritical, scientific minds to assert that science is concerned only with fact in the sense of what can be observed and that it has nothing to do with theory.   A careful examination of the symbols of science and art, the barest elements of which we have given above, together with an analysis of specific scientific theories, will indicate that the situation is, in point of fact, the exact reverse of this.   If it is pure fact, apart from all theory, which one wants, then it is not to science but to the arts when they function in and for themselves that one must go.   The brook which is the immediately observed brook — the fact apart from any theory about it — is the babble of sounds denoted by the poet's symbols, not the trajectories of moving molecules designated by the physicist's experimentally confirmed, postulationally formulated theory. The fact is the immediately heard sounds denoted by the poet's "babbling."   The colliding molecules and even the common-sense brook considered as an external material object are given only by postulated theory, confirmed through its deductive consequences.   Thus the brook of the scientist is not fact in its purity; it is instead known only by indirectly-confirmed theory.   It is the brook of the poet when poetry functions in and for itself which is fact attempting to devoid itself of all theory.

The knowledge of the man of common sense stands in the same relation to the immediately sensed sounds and colors of the artist as does the knowledge of the physicist. At this point Berkeley and Hume have something very important to teach us. Their inquiries show that even the common-sense public objects, such as tables and chairs and other persons, are, in the strict sense of the word, postulated objects and not immediately observed materials. All that one immediately observes are the deliverances of introspection and of the senses, and these are colors and sounds and feelings which are local, private things, varying, as color blindness shows, from individual to individual. They are not public, external objects or persons. And this which Berkeley shows to be true for common-sense physical objects, Hume, by the same type of analysis, demonstrates to be true for the persistent self also. Knowledge of the subject as well as of the external object is by postulation, not by immediate apprehension.

This reflection throws considerable light on the status, as art, of the development of impressionism and the appearance of a work such as James Joyce's *Ulysses,* which treats events, whether they refer to actual objects on the streets of Dublin or to items of the imagination, on the same level, moving continuously back and forth from one to the other with little attention to what is externally real and what is only in the imagination. Berkeley and Hume remind us that art which talks about brooks and buttercups is really not art in and for itself, but art which has in part become the handmaid of the postulated theories and objects and practical concerns of common sense.

An art which restricts its symbols to the meanings given by common-sense objects, assigning all the immediately apprehended forms and sounds and colors to them, cuts itself off in two directions. It limits itself with respect to the postulated by preventing the designation of a more adequate and necessary scientific and philosophical conception of the theoretic component of reality. It also restricts itself in the region of the immediately apprehended by treating immediately experienced materials not in and for themselves, with all their potentialities of relatedness and assignment left open, but merely as predicates of a certain restricted set of postulated common-sense objects. It may be said, therefore, that the art of our time, in freeing itself from common-sense realism, has made art truer to itself.

It is important, also, to remind ourselves that this is what the soul of man needs. His daily life takes his attention from the ineffable richness of the immediately experienced and concentrates it upon the practical utility of the external persons and objects of which the colors and sounds and forms are mere signs. One of the things which makes our lives drab and empty and which leaves us, at the end of the day, fatigued and deflated spiritually is the pressure of the taxing, practical, utilitarian concern with common-sense objects. If art is to release us from these postulated things and bring us back to the ineffable beauty and richness of the aesthetic component of reality in its immediacy, it must sever its connections with these common-sense entities.

Never, in recent generations at least, has this been more needed than it is today. The world of common-sense things, both physical objects and persons, is a sorry and painful sort of place. If our spirits are to get the food they need to nutrify and preserve themselves through these years of torture and tragedy, the poet must take up his primary function of directing our attention to immediately experienced materials in and for themselves. There is, for today at least, no peace and no paradise in the utilitarian, postulated, practical world of common-sense things. There is always, however, something ineffably rich and sustaining, and, because it is part of the real nature of things, also intrinsically true and valuable, in the immediacy of the aesthetic unmixed with the intrusion of the postulated. To say that the aesthetic factor is real is not to maintain, however, that the theoretic component is not real, also. This brings us to the second function of poetry as one of the arts.

It is the characteristic of any immediately experienced material that it functions not merely in and for itself but also as a symbol pointing beyond itself to another aspect of reality knowable only by postulated theory. This happens because of its status as a term in the epistemic correlations which join it to the postulated. In the case of the postulates of common sense this is so evident that we hardly realize that it occurs. Although we immediately apprehend only the data of sense and introspection, these guide us on unconsciously, naturally, and instinctively to postulated external, physical things and persons so effectively that all but the most philosophically sophisticated suppose we immediately observe these objects. When we come to examine the immediately apprehended systematically and in detail through the sciences, it happens that the postulates of common sense, while adequate for everyday, ordinary purposes, are quite inadequate to take care of all the immediately inspected sensuous items. Thus science finds it necessary to replace the gross postulated objects of common sense with the more refined, microscopic and systematically related entities of biological, chemical, astronomical, and physical theory. When this occurs, our conception of the theoretic component of reality is modified.

Each one of us trying to piece together, from our limited experience and our scattered knowledge of the sciences, the different postulated items of our knowledge, partly consciously, for the most part unconsciously, arrives at a certain rough working conception of the whole. This is our philosophy. It defines what is, for us, the theoretic component of reality, which in turn determines our idea of the good.

This philosophy, to be dependable and adequate for the whole of human experience, can hardly be taken as trustworthy if it is summed up merely by one of us upon the basis of his own private and necessarily restricted observation and reflection. It is necessary, if man is to have a philosophical conception of the theoretic component of reality which can claim public validity and be adequate to all the observable facts, that he take as the criterion of what is postulated, that which the sciences in their more systematic, comprehensive, and thorough inspection of the immediately apprehendable find it necessary to introduce. When this happens the objects of common sense are replaced by the more sophisticated objects of science, and more and more technical concepts by postulation are introduced. In this manner common-sense philosophy passes over into scientific philosophy.

This means, as over the centuries observations increase and the major postulates of knowledge have to be changed, that the meaning of human existence and our conception of the theoretic component in reality changes also. For this reason poetry in its second function, which conveys such scientific and philosophical doctrine analogically in terms of intuited materials, is dated in its appeal.

"What is so rare as a day in June" is an immortal line, saying something which will always be true, since, regardless of changes in scientific and philosophical theories of the postulated component of reality, the association and sequence of lights and shades and fresh fragrant odors in all their immediacy which these poetic words conjure up for us will always be with us. Similarly, Dante's *Divine Comedy* as pure poetry, apart from its philosophical and theological message, has the same wizardry and immortality, but Dante's *Divine Comedy* in its second function as the analogical conveyor of Saint Thomas' and Aristotle's theory of the postulated component of reality is strictly dated. It belongs to the Middle Ages. For our time, notwithstanding its appeal to our imagination as sheer poetry, this poem has lost its message.

The reason for this is to be found outside poetry in the development of Western science and philosophy after Aristotle and Saint Thomas.

With Galilei's scientific analysis of the motion of cannon balls, Aristotle's physics revealed its inadequacy. Since Aristotle's philosophy was reared upon this science, and Saint Thomas' theology was formulated in terms of Aristotle's philosophy, it forthwith became evident to informed minds that Saint Thomas' and Aristotle's conception of the theoretic component of reality must be replaced by a new postulated and more empirically adequate scientific and philosophical theory.   This is the basic reason why Dante's *Divine Comedy* has lost its message for the Modern World.

The new conception of the theoretic component which replaced Aristotle's and Saint Thomas' was formulated for modern science and philosophy by Sir Isaac Newton and John Locke.   If the reader is interested in seeing how this theory in its turn is conveyed analogically by modern poets, he will find it instructive to read Kenneth MacLean's *John Locke and English Literature of the Eighteenth Century.* Kenneth MacLean's study shows that Pope and other poets of his time did the analogical task for Locke and Newton which Dante accomplished for Saint Thomas and Aristotle.

These considerations make it evident that it is never the poet or any other artist who is in the position to determine, when he operates in his second function, whether the doctrine which he conveys analogically is the correct one or not.   This is the task of the scientist and the philosopher, not the artist. It is because they are instruments for conveying a doctrine found by someone else, and because poetry in its second function does not have the capacity within poetry to determine whether the doctrine which it conveys analogically is true or not that poetry, prose, painting, music, and sculpture are called arts rather than sciences.

This is the reason, also, why a society tends to become

demoralized when it tries, as the recent modern world has done, to base its theory of the good life upon the arts and the humanities, rather than upon the sciences and a scientifically determined philosophy. There is no criterion within the arts or the humanities to determine whether one theory rather than another of the theoretic component of reality which an artist may convey analogically is the correct one. This is also the reason why it is a very dangerous thing for contemporary professors of English to set themselves up as competent teachers and judges of a philosophy of life.

This point provides the basis for Plato's warning concerning the danger of poetry. Providing that one recognizes that the concepts by intuition with which the poet works are merely epistemically correlated with, and not *identical* with, the concepts by postulation which only expert training in science and philosophy can enable one to understand and evaluate, no harm is done by the poet in conveying scientific and philosophical doctrine concerning the theoretic component, analogically. But when these intuited materials are presented as if they were the theoretic component of reality, and when the poet's concepts by intuition are treated as if they were the concepts by postulation of the scientific and philosophical doctrine, then positive harm is done. The conveying of the theoretic then becomes corrupted by the intrusion of and confusion with the aesthetic, just as art in its first function of presenting the aesthetically immediate becomes corrupted with the intrusion of the theoretical.

Nothing is more important, if Western culture is to escape from its present demoralization than that professors of the arts should learn the proper functions of the arts and restrict themselves to those functions. At this point the primary fact to keep in mind is that art in its second function is art and not science. It is not the business, nor is it within the capacity of the poet, or any other artist, to determine the truth of any doctrine of the theoretic component of reality which he may use his immediately experienceable materials to convey analogically. This is the business of the scientist and of the philosopher who uses the investigations of science to enable him to choose by objective criteria between one possible theory of the theoretic component of reality and another. Art in its second function must follow, not precede, or assume the rôle of science and philosophy.

The timeless character of poetry in and for itself leaves its future secure. The present need for bringing our attention back to the ineffable beauty and richness of the aesthetically immediate has been indicated. It is the fate of poetry in its second function that raises a question. The historical considerations to which we have previously referred show that its doctrine is dated. Is there a present need for this second type of poetry?

The need is greater than ever before. We have noted how the common-sense notion of the postulated component passes over into the scientific. Such a transition takes one from the more concrete to the more abstract. In similar fashion with the accumulation of positive knowledge in the passage of time one scientific conception passes over into a more adequate one. This movement also is toward greater abstractness.

But this very fact makes the contemporary scientific philosophy of the theoretic component of reality all the more difficult for anyone but the expert scientist and philosopher to comprehend literally in terms of its concepts by postulation. A four-dimensional space-time continuum defined by Einstein's tensor equation for gravitation and Ψ-functions definable only in terms of the primitive concepts of pure mathematics and formal symbolic logic are replacing the trim atomic models of the old physics. The real as conceived by contemporary science is not even such that it can be grasped by the imagination, to say nothing about it being sensed; only formally by the intellect can it be known.

Nevertheless, comprehend it we must. Otherwise our philosophy of the theoretic component and our conduct flowing out of it will be false to the nature of things. Even for the purposes of common sense this is necessary, since these scientific conceptions through technology are determining the character of every item in our everyday experience. If we are to comprehend the character of ourselves and our universe, and if democracy is to cope intelligently with the basic ideas which are creating the problems and producing the reconstruction in our culture, not merely the expert but the majority of us must come to terms in some way with the exceedingly abstract contemporary scientific and philosophical concept of the theoretic component of reality.

It is often said that men are moved by their emotions and not by abstract scientific and philosophical theory. The tremendous rôle of scientific theory operating through technology upon men's lives gives the lie to this claim in so far as it applies to the experts. Unfortunately it is all too true for the masses. But even this does not alter the fact that the philosophy of the theoretic component of reality embodied in the unreflective, emotional reaction of the masses is the false and inadequate one, and that the conception formulated in the verified postulated theories of the scientist and the scientific philosopher is the more correct one, and the only one at present known by mortal minds which has any chance of enabling us to resolve the conflict between the feelings and the thoughts in our own souls or to solve the problems of our culture. Thus, even in the case of the primarily emotional reaction of the masses, there can be an uninhibited emotional life only if the emotions are brought into a working agreement with an adequate conception of the theoretic component in oneself and the universe. Fortunately, by art the emotions of men can be moved. Consequently, the fact that the reactions of the majority of men are ruled by their emotions rather than by trustworthy scientific and philosophical theory, while suggesting the nature of the difficulty, also indicates precisely how it can be met.

It is at this point that the future of poetry in its second function begins to define itself. What cannot be grasped by everyone literally in terms of the concepts by postulation of the scientist and scientific philosopher, can be suggested and presented analogically with vividness and moving power, by recourse through epistemic correlation to the concepts by intuition of the artist.

Here the art of the future will find its new message for men. Its task will be to take the new conception of the theoretic component of reality which philosophical analysis of the experimentally verified theories of contemporary science is now making articulate, and to convey this conception metaphorically, by recourse to epistemic correlations, in terms of the vivid aesthetic materials given in immediate intuition. Then and not until then will there be poetry in its second function which meets the emotional, moral, aesthetic and intellectual needs of contemporary men.

Never has the poet faced a more difficult task. Not only is the gulf between the aesthetic and the theoretic components of reality greater than it has been before, due to the extreme abstractness of contemporary scientific and philosophical theory, but also the number of people in high places whose emotions are still epistemically attached to outmoded conceptions of the theoretic component is probably greater today than at any time since the beginning of the seventeenth century.

The reason for this can be put very briefly. We have noted how the poetry of the eighteenth and nineteenth centuries gave expression to the outlook of Newton and Locke. In 1905 this theoretical outlook came to its end with the appearance of the physics of Einstein. The basic scientific and philosophical concepts by postulation which defined the

conception of the theoretic component of reality for the
modern world and which determined the problems of modern
science and culture are now outmoded. Yet the emotions,
not merely of the masses, but of all of us, and especially all
humanists, are still geared to the old conceptions.

Thus it happens that we find ourselves in the tragic position of feeling emotionally uncomfortable before the sole
idea of the good, defined by the new scientific philosophy of
the theoretic component of reality, which is our only constructive means of salvation. Our emotions, still correlated
with an outmoded doctrine, have yet to be reconstructed in
terms of the new intellectual outlook.

Until the aesthetic component of reality which art in its
first function conveys is weaned away from its old theoretical
attachments and brought by art in its second function into
epistemic correlation with the new theoretic component of
reality which contemporary scientific philosophy is defining,
so that the one reinforces and sustains the other while each
retains its own independent validity and vitality, man's feelings and his reason will be at cross purposes, and there will be
no peace either in the world or in the souls of men. Such is
the difficulty, and by the same measure the importance, of
the task of the artist of the future.

It is inevitable at those periods in human history when an
old conception of the theoretic component of reality is breaking down and before the new scientific philosophy which is
taking its place has been made articulate, that the artist, the
practical man, and the purely historically minded intellectual
become demoralized. Not only does the artist tend to insist
that art in and for itself is his sole function, but he also feels
himself to be morally neutral or apathetic, if not positively
evil. This, as Archibald MacLeish's essay *The Irresponsibles*
eloquently indicates, is the condition in which the poet finds
himself today.

The reason for this moral apathy the artist himself can

never explain.   Art in its second function never discovers but merely conveys its metaphorical message.   Hence it can never tell when that message ceases to be valid or what the new one is which must take its place; this only science, subjected to philosophical analysis, can do.   Consequently, it is impossible to tell by examining the arts or humanities themselves whether their loss of confidence in symbolic references is a mere passing mood of the moment or a sign of a more fundamental breakdown in our intellectual outlook and our philosophy.   Only by examining our philosophy with respect to its adequacy to take care of known, positive, scientific findings can we gain unequivocal evidence that our demoralization has a real and fundamental basis.   That this is the case today we know.   For at those points in science where we can put our traditional, modern, postulated theory to a crucial test, we find that it fails.   Our traditional conception of the theoretic component of reality must be replaced by a new one.   This means that the movement of contemporary poets away from the traditional poetry with a message to art in and for itself represents a genuine and healthy advance.   It means also that all attempts of my generation to take the younger generation out of their present moral apathy by appeals which try to reconvince them of the vitality of traditional doctrine and ideals are doomed to failure.

There will be no poetry in its second function with a vitality sufficient to meet our intellectual and moral needs and thereby provide a new and effective idealism until a philosophical analysis of the new postulational theory which contemporary science has verified and put in the place of the old makes articulate a new and more adequate philosophical concept of the theoretic component of reality.

This, I take it, is the fundamental challenge and task of our time.   *It is ours* not to try to reconvince ourselves of the truth of an old morality, whether it be that of Tennyson and Browning and the Modern World, or of the later T. S. Eliot and the Medieval World, but *to start afresh with the immediacy of experience as it has forced the scientist to new and more adequate theory, and, in terms of this theory to make articulate a new philosophy joining the theoretic and aesthetic components of reality, thereby defining a new meaning for human existence and hence a new morality, which it will be the privilege of some Dante of the future to express metaphorically and embody aesthetically in the feelings and emotions of men.*

The creative artist of the younger generation who possesses the sensibility and the skill to refer concepts by intuition unambiguously to immediately apprehendable aesthetic materials, thereby becoming expert in poetry in and for itself, and who has the intellectual capacity to master the scientific philosophy of the immediate future in terms of its technical concepts by postulation, can, by joining the aesthetic and the theoretic through epistemic correlation, command the poetry and perhaps, in major part at least, even the culture of the future.

One final consideration is to be emphasized. Our two functions of poetry are pure, limiting cases, rarely realized in fact. Most actual poems are combinations of and compromises between these two pure and opposing aims. Hence poetry in all its exemplifications must be thought of as a spectrum in which these two unmixed types are end terms.

When these end terms are considered in their possible combinations they define the mean points in the spectral series with which the various types of actual poetry are to be identified, and when they are treated in their purity, by themselves, they constitute two norms for evaluating the degree to which any specific poem fulfills one or the other of the two purposes for which poetry exists. In this manner our definitions of the two major functions of poetry would provide criteria of both the actual and the ideal.

This chapter is reprinted from *Furioso,* Vol. I, No. 4, 1941, with the kind permission of the Editor.

CHAPTER X

BODY AND MIND

Analysis of the methods of the natural sciences has shown the importance of the distinction between two fundamentally different kinds of scientific concepts. There is evidence that the concept of body and the concept of mind are confused because each is used in two different senses without the shift in meanings being recognized, due to the failure to distinguish sharply between these two basic types of scientific concepts.

They are appropriately called (1) concepts given by intuition and (2) concepts given by postulation. The characteristic of any concept given by intuition is that, in logical terms, its meaning is purely denotative, that is, its meaning is given always by pointing to something or by apprehending something that is presented with immediacy. For example, we can sense the whiteness of this paper and then abstract it from its context to gain thereby the concept "white." In so far as any science is purely empirical and descriptive it uses concepts by intuition.

But there is another kind of concept used in science. The major theories of physics are stated in terms of them. These are concepts by postulation. A concept by postulation is one the meaning of which, to use the terminology of logic, is connotative rather than denotative, and hence is designated, not by looking at anything immediately observable, but by means of the basic assumptions and postulates of the scientific theory in which it occurs. An electron or an electro-magnetic field serves as an example. One cannot understand what a physicist means by such a scientific object by looking at anything after the manner in which one understands what is meant by the word "white." An electron is not observed; it is designated by the postulates of electron theory. Similarly one means by an electro-magnetic field nothing which one can observe but precisely what the scientist postulates it as being in his electro-magnetic theory. The scientist can define these unobserved scientific objects in any way that he pleases providing he specifies their properties and behavior unambiguously in the postulates of his theory so that rigorously logical deductions can be made therefrom and providing he does not regard his theory as true until these deductions stated in terms of concepts by postulation are checked experimentally or empirically by appeal to directly observable fact, that is, to factors denoted by concepts by intuition.

It is precisely at this point, namely, experimental or observational verification of the deductive theory, that Dr. Kurt Goldstein's emphasis upon the need of a scientific psychiatry facing epistemological questions becomes important. For the fundamental problem in scientific verification, whether in physics or psychiatry, is how one can confirm theories concerning unobserved postulated entities and processes like electrons, electro-magnetic waves, reflexes, frustrations, hydrogen ion concentrations, etc., when all that observation can give one are immediately apprehendable things like colored patches in the sky, colored lines on a photographic plate, spots before the eyes, feelings of uneasiness, pains, etc., all of which are denoted by concepts by intuition — a problem which, since it involves the relation between two different types of concept for the same subject matter, and between inferred entities and observed factors, is epistemological.

It is to be noted that mere observation and experimentation do not provide a trustworthy criterion of the verification of a scientific theory, since observation and experiment alone give only concepts by intuition whereas what is present in a scientific theory are concepts by postulation. What is required in addition is some unambiguous relation joining the two.

The success of physical science is due, not merely to the fact that it possesses deductive theory expressed in terms of concepts by postulation, and insists upon observation and experiment which give immediately apprehended data denoted by concepts by intuition, but also that it has specified *epistemic correlations* joining the one to the other. Whenever, as seems to an outsider to be the case in psychiatry, there are, on the one hand, most suggestive theories and, on the other hand, a wide range of data, without the two getting together effectively to command assent from all experts concerned, a logician and epistemologist can merely suggest upon the basis of the analysis of the method of natural science, that perhaps the neglect to distinguish clearly between concepts by intuition and concepts by postulation and the resultant failure to designate unambiguous epistemic correlations joining the one to the other may have something to do with the matter.

The presence and essential importance of epistemic correlations in the method of natural science have been obscured by a bad symbolism. The symbol "blue" is used both for the concept by inspection which refers to the immediately sensed color and the concept by postulation which refers to the unobserved wave-length of a certain type of electromagnetic propagation, with the result that what are two quite different things joined by an epistemic correlation are often taken for one thing, an identity.

Epistemic correlations are not to be confused with the usual correlations in social and physical science, such as that between pressure and volume in physics. The latter may be termed empirical correlations. The distinguishing characteristic of an empirical correlation is that it holds only between scientific concepts of the same type. Thus, empirical correlations join either a concept by inspection to another concept by inspection or a concept by postulation to another concept by postulation.   The distinguishing characteristic of an epistemic correlation is that it joins a concept by postulation to its corresponding concept by inspection, or conversely, thereby making empirical verification referring to unobservable postulated entities possible.

If these distinctions are clear we are in a position to consider the problem of body and mind.   We shall examine first a case where body is being considered.   Then a query concerning parallelism.   And thirdly an example bearing more directly on mind.

Consider a psychiatry which would attempt to formulate its theory wholly in terms of neurological and other physiological concepts, which in turn are defined in terms of chemical and physical concepts.   All such concepts are concepts by postulation, not concepts by intuition.   Consequently, the first point to be emphasized is that if one means by body what such a psychiatry means by body, then it is with a postulated, indirectly verified thing, not with something immediately apprehended, that one is concerned.

A second consideration has to do with parallelism.   In speaking of the parallelistic theory of the relation between mind and body, it is frequently asked why the parallelism does not show in respect to non-cortical factors.   When we recall, however, the distinction even for physical science between concepts by intuition and by postulation and realize that the epistemic correlations parallel nature as denoted by the one type of concept with nature as connoted by the other type of concept, then we may say that a parallelism does show for non-cortical and cortical factors alike.   But the parallelism, more exactly termed epistemic correlation, is not between body and mind but between the person as immediately apprehended as an association and continuous sequence of sensuous aesthetic qualities denoted by concepts by intuition and the

person as theoretically conceived as a neurological physio-
chemical system designated by concepts by postulation.

The same considerations apply to "mind." One may
mean by "mind" what is given directly to consciousness.
This is a concept by intuition. But "mind" in this sense as
the Far Eastern Taoists and Zen Buddhists have noted, is not
one whit different from immediately sensed body or immediately sensed nature. All such directly apprehended factors
are ineffable and part of one differentiated continuum given
in immediate awareness. In other words, if one restricts
oneself to concepts by intuition when using the words "body"
and "mind" then there are not two different realms or two
different entities given; instead there is one continuum of
diverse factors presented with immediacy. No line can be
drawn in the realm of the immediately apprehended between
a pain which we are wont to speak of as psychical and the
yellow patch in the sky denoted by the symbol "sun" which
we sometimes refer to as physical. Both factors are denoted
by concepts by intuition, and are for that very reason abstractions from a single continuum of directly apprehended
fact. One feels a pain as one apprehends the yellow patch in
the sky now. The realm given by concepts by intuition
denotes one continuous world, not two diverse worlds, even
when one concept by intuition bears the tag "mental" and the
other concept by intuition bears the tag "physical."

Newton, in the Scholium at the beginning of his *Principia*,
points out that sensed time and sensed space (i.e., denoted by
concepts by intuition) are not to be confused with "true or
mathematical" time or space (i.e., designated by concepts by
postulation) with which physics is concerned. One reason
for the difference is that whereas the time of physical theory
is postulated as flowing uniformly, the time given to the
senses flows unevenly. He goes on to add that anyone who
confuses the two is guilty of a vulgar ignorance.

It is to be noted also that sensed time, sensed space, and sensed objects are just as ineffable as self-consciousness or a pain or any other so-called psychical disturbance. In the realm of the immediately-given, denoted by concepts by intuition, there is no inner and outer, no subjective and objective, no distinction between the mental and the bodily; there is merely the all-embracing aesthetic continuum with its aesthetic qualitative differentiations.

There has been a second meaning of the symbol "mind." It goes back to Descartes and Locke. This is "mind" in the sense of a mental substance. "Mind" in this second sense is a concept by postulation. As Hume showed, "mind" in this sense is just as different from "mind" in the sense of that which is immediately apprehended as sensed space and sensed time and sensed objects are different from the "true and mathematical" postulated space, time and masses of Newton's physical theory.

These considerations make it evident that when discussing the problem of the relation between "body" and "mind" we must be perfectly clear about the possible meanings by the two words, since each has two quite different meanings, one of which is given by immediate apprehension, the other by postulation indirectly verified. The futility of most previous discussions and investigations of this problem is due in great part to a muddling of these diverse meanings.

Consider "mind" in the sense of a mental substance designated by a concept by postulation. The trouble with "mind" in this sense is that when one applies to it the scientific method appropriate for postulated entities, the method, namely, of deduction, the concept is so empty and ambiguous that nothing of any definiteness can be deduced from it. Also, as the development of modern psychology and philosophy following Descartes and Locke made clear, no one has been able to formulate clearly, within a single deductive theory, how the postulated mental substance is related to the postulated material substances of physiology and physics. These are the main reasons why the concept of a mental substance has tended to be discarded by physiologists, psychologists and philosophers. When this occurs, one is left with "mind" only as a concept by intuition. The symbol merely denotes what is immediately apprehended when one introspects.

That "mind" in this sense is important for medicine and psychiatry is shown by the fact that it is the pain or uneasiness or depression that one introspects which sends one to the physician, and it is the concepts by intuition which one uses to denote one's feelings which provide the physician with the first clues to his diagnosis of the patient's ailment. Consequently, although "mind" in the sense of a mental substance given by a concept by postulation must be thrown away, "mind" in the sense of a concept by intuition, or some other word meaning the same thing denotatively, must be retained.

But at this point a new difficulty arises. A large part of contemporary diagnosis refers to neurological, chemical and physical factors. The chemical factors involve postulated molecules and atoms, i.e., concepts by postulation. Certain classifications of psychiatrical types are at the same time based, in part at least, on mere description and upon introspectively given data, that is, appeal is made to concepts by intuition. A scientific psychiatry must sooner or later attempt to bring these diverse bits of knowledge into some working relation with each other. But to combine them in their present form is to put concepts by postulation in the same world of discourse with concepts by intuition and thereby so to muddle fundamentally different types of scientific concepts as to talk nonsense.

This consideration suggests that "mind" in the sense of a concept by intuition must find epistemic correlates in the physico-chemical concept by postulation world of discourse for all and not merely some of its immediately apprehended manifestations. Since concepts by postulation designating physico-chemical entities and relations are unavoidable, nonsense can be escaped only by completing the entire postulation theory in terms of such entities and relations. In this manner consciousness and its immediate data are accounted for in terms of concepts by intuition and the mental substance-material substance difficulties in the traditional postulational theory are avoided. Concepts by intuition referring to immediately introspected data will still remain as ultimate and irreducible, as is the aesthetic component of the self which they denote, but they will be used in deductively formulated theory only to denote the data for which the deductively formulated theory must account; they will not be used to define the entities or relations of the latter theory itself.

The great advantage of a postulated physiological and physical theory of all factors denoted by concepts by intuition, whether they be given through the senses or introspectively, is that one keeps all postulated entities within a logically connected theory. The trouble with the postulation of "material substances" to account for certain immediately apprehended factors and "mental substances" to account for other directly inspected factors is that, being so completely different from each other and having nothing in common, there is no way of getting them into working relationship with each other in a single deductive scientific theory.

This is the strong argument for a postulated physiological and physical theory of the so-called subjective, as well as the so-called objective, factors which are immediately apprehended. If one is going to work with deductive theory at all in psychology and psychiatry, as is inevitable when one introduces the postulated entities and processes of chemical and physical theory, then it is necessary to bring the different entities and relations into connection with one another.

To use the language of the mathematical logician, a sound set of postulates for any scientific theory must possess not merely consistency, independence and completeness, but also connexity. But if connexity is to be present, then the basic relations of the scientific must apply to all the entities and not merely to some of them. This will not be the case if some of the entities which we postulate as having spatial relations are physical and others are mental, not having spatial relations.

It appears, therefore, when one passes to postulated theory in psychology and psychiatry, that one must introduce the same kind of entity as the epistemic correlate of introspected emotions and feelings as one introduces for the equally immediately given and equally ineffable redness of sensed bodily blood which it is usual to think of as in some sense designating the physical. In other words, the ultimate dualism is not between "body" and "mind," but between the immediately apprehended component of the person denoted by concepts by intuition and the theoretic component of the person designated by verified scientific theory which is stated completely in terms of concepts by postulation. The two components are related by epistemic correlations to make empirical verification possible. Hence the one component is as ultimate and real as the other component. The complete person in his unity is these two aesthetic and theoretic components joined by the two-termed relation of epistemic correlation.

This chapter is a reprint, with the modification necessary for independent presentation, of remarks made in the *Symposium on Mind and Body* of the Association for Research in Nervous and Mental Disease in December 1938 and published in Vol. XIX, pp. 99-104 of their Proceedings by the Williams and Wilkins Company of Baltimore, in 1939. Permission from the Secretary of the aforementioned Association for this republication is gratefully acknowledged.

CHAPTER XI

THE CONCEPT OF PROBABILITY IN QUANTUM MECHANICS

A striking characteristic of contemporary science is its emphasis upon probability. This is especially notable in quantum mechanics.

There is a respect in which probability is the same for all scientific theories. Verifiability requires that any theory predict certain numbers which can be compared with the numbers gained by actual operations of measuring. In actual practice these numbers, which we shall term theoretical measurables and operative measurables respectively, never correspond. It becomes necessary, therefore, for the scientist to specify when the deviation between them is such that verification occurs. These specifications are defined by the theory of errors in which the concept of probability has an essential place and a specific meaning. But the theory of errors is the same for all applications; hence, probability as defined by the theory of errors is the same for all scientific theories.

There is another use of probability which varies in meaning from theory to theory. This happens because it is defined in terms of the basic concepts and principles of the theory in which it occurs. It is essential that we have different names for these two uses of probability. Probability which is defined in terms of the theory of errors and which is concerned with the actual operations by means of which any theory is verified we shall call operative probability. Probability which is defined in terms of the basic concepts and principles of the specific scientific theory in which it occurs we shall call theoretical probability. Every verifiable scientific theory uses operative probability; only certain scientific theories use theoretical probability. It is with theoretical probability and theoretical measurables only that this chapter is concerned.

Our question is this: What is the philosophical significance of theoretical probability in quantum mechanics?

The importance of this question is indicated by the following considerations. Because of its unique use of theoretical probability, quantum theory has been appealed to as evidence for the conclusions (1) that ontological contingency exists in nature, (2) that the principle of causality has been dismissed from science, and (3) that all propositions in science assumed to hold categorically and to express necessary connections have been replaced by more modest statements expressing merely what happens on the average or with a certain degree of probability. Certainly, these conclusions, if true, are important for philosophy. But, if so, they also merit a much more specific and technical designation of their essential connection with the fundamental concepts of quantum mechanics than has been given to date.

How is this essential connection to be determined? The meaning of the theoretical probability prescribes the method to be pursued. By definition, theoretical probability depends for its meaning upon the basic concepts and principles of the specific scientific theory in which it occurs. It follows that our task is twofold: we must determine the fundamental concepts of quantum mechanics, and we must designate precisely how its particular use of theoretical probability arises out of those concepts.

The following analysis draws heavily upon R. B. Lindsay and H. Margenau's *The Foundations of Physics,* and in particular upon many private discussions of critical points with Professor Margenau. It differs from theirs in manner of presentation and in the number of postulates introduced, since the concern is with fundamental concepts and assumptions only as necessary to determine the precise meaning of theoretical probability in quantum theory.

Quantum mechanics in its present systematic form is a very unusual scientific theory. The best approach is (1) to appreciate the empirical and logical predicament in which physics found itself before quantum mechanics was systematically developed, and (2) to apply the method used by scientists to escape this predicament.

The predicament was as follows: Physicists knew, in the sense in which experimentally verified theory permits one to know, that physical systems behave as if they were particles. Physicists also knew, in precisely the same sense, that the same physical systems behave as if they were not particles but waves.

The method which physicists used to escape this predicament is a very old, but theoretically-unformulated, one. When exactly described, it may be called the method of acting as if one does not know what one does know. For the benefit of those who insist upon an abstract and more dignified title we shall call it the method of simulated ignorance.

It consists in doing what its name prescribes. One proceeds as if one does not know what one does know, and to do this most effectively, one leaves the world of experimental physics and retires into one's study where one constructs the following abstract system function F. A system function is a body of abstract, purely logical or mathematical forms, devoid of material content; sometimes called a system form or a doctrinal function.

This system function F contains a number of elements s. Nothing is known concerning these elements except that they have certain unspecified properties o. Different properties o we shall designate with different small letters, q, p, m, and e. The system function F also contains certain operators O.

Different operators O are designated by different capital letters.   In addition to the elements s with their properties o, and the operators O, there are functions ϕ or ψ.   Concerning the specific properties of these functions, we know as much as we act as if we know about everything else, which is theoretically nothing.   This ignorance upon our part is exceedingly fortunate for it permits us to choose almost any purely formal mathematical function for ϕ or ψ.   Only certain very general restrictions are prescribed.   Moreover, these restrictions are almost, but not entirely, independent of the elements s in the system function F.   Let us define the very general restrictions upon them formally by the postulates of another system function which we shall call F′.

The postulates of F′ could have been included in those of the system function F.   I have separated them in order to distinguish very general properties from more restricted and technical ones; also, for reasons of emphasis which will appear later.   In point of fact, our physicist, turned mathematical logician, knows, as physicist, precisely what the definition of F′ must be.

But his method of acting as if he does not know what he does know will not permit him to express this knowledge in stating the postulates for F′.   Moreover, there is an exceedingly good reason why this is the case.   For if he based his system function F′ upon what he knows he would be rearing it upon those concepts which lead to the contradiction from which he is trying to escape.

Hence, he makes a guess at how F′ is to be defined, and since there is no more reason for one guess than another, he picks one by chance and writes down the postulates for F′ which his knowledge would have told him to be correct had he forgotten that he does not know what he does know.   To be sure this does not seem to be quite fair.   But he will assure you that it is, for he could have written down a different set of postulates for F′ and then gone on to complete the system function F.   He would have found in the end when he returned to the laboratory that the deductions from such assumptions. did not accord with observation.   This would have forced him to try the method of simulated ignorance over again.   Finally, by this process he would eventually arrive at the proper postulates for F′.   This being the case, I am sure you are not merely satisfied but relieved that he guessed correctly the first time.

Having designated the base of the system function F, he now proceeds to designate its postulate.   Postulate I asserts that to any property o of an element or elements s of F there corresponds an operator O.   The precise correlation is found again by the method of simulated ignorance in conjunction with trial and error.

The purely formal properties of O are such that an interesting consequence follows, which we shall term Theorem 1. Theorem 1 asserts that an operator O for a given property o generates a sequence of real numbers o_λ according to the equation

$$O\psi_\lambda = o\lambda\,\psi_\lambda,$$

where the o_λ and the ψ_λ are what pure mathematicians term characteristic numbers and characteristic functions respectively.

The essential point in this theorem is that the operator O generates a definite set of o_λ numbers which are in correspondence with the ψ_λ functions.

One more consequence of the system function F is needed for our purposes.   It can be deduced from the properties of the function ϕ by purely mathematical principles.   We shall designate it as Theorem 2.   This theorem asserts that the equation $\phi = \Sigma\ a_\lambda\ \psi_\lambda$ holds, where a_λ is another set of numbers, also in correspondence with the ψ_λ functions.

It follows, therefore, from Theorem 1 and Theorem 2, because of the transitive property of this relation of correspondence, that the o_λ and a_λ numbers are in correspondence with each other. This consequence, we shall call Theorem 3. There is another interesting consequence of our system function F which we shall term Theorem 4. It will be mentioned later.

We will gain from these technicalities everything essential for the purpose of this chapter, if we concentrate attention upon the following simple fact: The few abstract assumptions of our system function F are sufficient to generate two sets of numbers o_λ and a_λ which are in correspondence with each other. The following important properties of these two sets of numbers should be noted.   The o_λ numbers are real numbers. The a_λ numbers satisfy the equation $\Sigma \mid a_\lambda \mid^2 = 1$.   This last fact we shall call Theorem 5. Strictly speaking, this theorem is not true unless certain additional assumptions are made.   Great aid in concentrating attention upon the crucial factors, and no weakening of our final conclusion, results from our omission of such technical details, for, as the reader will see in the end, our conclusions would be reinforced rather than weakened were these additional assumptions included.

We must admit that our method of acting as if we do not know what we do know has not done so badly by us.   Actually, its full potentialities have hardly been touched.   But let us be satisfied with what we have, cast our simulated ignorance aside, and consider again what we do know.   In other words, let us leave the seclusion of our study and return with our abstract system function F to the concrete world of the physicist's laboratory.

Can we find any factors in the latter world of observation which can be identified with the factors in our abstract system function F?   Let us look around.

The world of physics contains certain observed systems; our abstract system function contains certain entities.   Suppose we identify the two.   This transforms the abstract system function F into the concrete physical system F^p.   As a result, the entities s of F become the "systems" which physicists refer to as molar masses, electrons, protons, photons, etc. Similarly, the properties o of s become the physical properties, such as coördinate position, momentum, angular momentum and energy of physical systems. Quantum physicists call these properties o, observables.

Postulate I of our abstract system informs us that to every "observable" or physical property o of any system s there is a corresponding operator O. Hence, if the world of experimental physics provides an interpretation of our system function F there should be operators corresponding to the properties of physical systems. This happens to be the case. The position property q has a corresponding coördinate operator Q, the momentum property p a corresponding momentum operator P, the angular momentum property m a corresponding angular momentum operator M, and the energy property e a corresponding Hamiltonian, or energy, operator H.

It remains to identify our abstract system function F′ which formally defines the functions ϕ or ψ. Our abstract system function F informs us that the ϕ or ψ functions are operated on by the operator O. In the world of physics it is permissible to assume that the element upon which the energy operator operates is the state of the physical system in question. Hence, the functions ϕ or ψ become identified with the physical states of physical systems, and are called state- or eigen-functions. Similar considerations will show that the system function F′ formally defines the extremely general conditions imposed upon the function ϕ, the arguments of which are to be identified with the coördinates of what the physicists term configuration space.

It appears that there is an exact correlation between our abstract system functions F and F′ and the states of physical systems and the configuration space of the more concrete world of experimental physics. Does this permit us to say that our theory has been verified?

In one sense the answer is in the affirmative. Certainly, perceived factors correspond to the abstract factors in our system function. But in another sense the answer must be in the negative. So far, the correspondence is purely qualitative. A theory does not meet the requirements of experimental physics unless the correlation is also quantitative. To satisfy this requirement the theory must (1) imply certain numbers which (2) may be identified with quantities whose presence can be determined by actual operations of measuring.

Does our abstract system function provide us with numbers? We know that it does. In fact, it somewhat embarrasses us in this respect for it provides us with two sets of numbers, the o_λ's and the a_λ's.

Can either of these sets be identified with the theoretical measurables to which operations of measuring refer? A simple consideration causes us to select the o_λ set. The theoretical measurables to which operations of measuring refer must be real numbers; our o_λ numbers are real numbers. Hence, we identify the two. As a result the o_λ numbers, which the pure mathematician calls characteristic numbers, become identical with the theoretical measurables which the physicist calls eigenvalues.

The identification of the a_λ numbers is not so obvious. However, Theorem 5 of our abstract system function gives a clue. This Theorem informs us that the sum of the squares of all the a_λ numbers is equal to unity. What customary things in the world of experimental physics have this property of summing up to equal unity? A little reflection suggests that probabilities behave in this way. The suggestion arises, therefore, that the a_λ numbers are to be identified through their squares with probabilities. Experience has shown this surmise to be correct.

When these identifications between the aggregate of o_λ numbers and the theoretical measurables and between the

$|a\lambda|^2$ numbers and probabilities are made, it happens that the concept of physical state takes on an entirely new meaning in physics.   It is in this consequence of our system function F that the unique character of quantum mechanics consists. Instead of defining the state of a physical system, as did Newtonian mechanics or Gibbs' statistical mechanics, in terms of a single set of theoretical measurables, quantum mechanics defines the state in terms of an aggregate of such quantities each of which has a certain probability of being observed in a given theoretical measurement of the state in question. For example, in Newtonian mechanics the state of a system was empirically defined when six theoretical measurables for position and momentum were prescribed; in Gibbs' statistical mechanics this happened when theoretical measurables for temperature, volume and pressure were given.   But in quantum mechanics the definition of state is quite different. Theorem 1 gives not one set of numbers o_1 but an aggregate of such sets o_λ.   More concretely, this means that in quantum mechanics a state function for an electron gives, not one sharp set of values for position and momentum, but a whole aggregate of sets of such values.   Similarly, Theorems 3 and 5 correlate with each o_λ number, an $|a_\lambda|^2$ number. Put concretely, this means that in addition to the aggregate of sets of theoretical measurables for position and momentum, the state function for an electron also assigns to each theoretical measurable o_λ in the aggregate, another specific number $|a_\lambda|^2$ which specifies the theoretical probability with which that particular theoretical measurable will be observed if the theory is correct.   Conversely, one determines experimentally that an electron is in a given specific state by finding not one set of values for the defining property or properties in question, but by designating an aggregate of sets of such theoretical measurables, together with the theoretical probability with which each is observed.

At last we have found the precise sense in which the con-

ept of theoretical probability enters into quantum mechan-
.cs. Our findings may be summarized as follows: First,
from the very general assumptions of our abstract system
function F two sets of numbers o_λ and a_λ can be derived
which are in correspondence. Second, when the elements s
in the system function F are identified with physical systems
and the function ϕ is identified with the physical state of any
one of these systems, then the o_λ numbers define an aggregate
of sets of predicted theoretical measurables for the state in
question and the $|a_\lambda|^2$ numbers define the theoretical
probability with which the corresponding o_λ numbers will be
theoretically observed. In other words the two sets of num-
bers o_λ and $|a_\lambda|^2$ in correspondence define a theoretical
probability aggregate which uniquely defines the physical
state of the physical system in question.

A theoretical probability aggregate is an aggregate of
theoretical measurables each with its correlated probability.
This aggregate composed of theoretical measurables must not
be confused with the quite different aggregate composed of
measurements to which it is related in the a posteriori or
operational definition of probability. Since only the former
type of aggregate enters into this chapter it is not necessary for
us to use some other word than aggregate to designate one of
these two classes of things, as von Mises and Lindsay and
Margenau have done. It happens that they have reserved
the expression "probability aggregate" for the class of measurements, and use the expression "probability distribution"
for what we have termed a "theoretical probability aggregate."

It may be added that this physical theory predicts every
verified theoretical measurable predicted by previous theories
together with important new ones in addition while escaping
the predicament in which traditional theories involved us.

We are now able to appreciate the importance of the scientific method of acting as if we do not know what we do know.
It reduces to a minimum the number of physical assumptions

necessary to give the maximum number of quantitative predictions for the subject matter in question. Difficulties arose in traditional physics because physicists insisted upon conceiving of perceived physical phenomena in certain concrete ways. The result was not merely a contradiction in our physical theory, but also an inability to account for the quantitative measurables actually observed. By acting as if we do not know what we do know we free ourselves from accidental characteristics of what we do know, and from physical conceptions holding only for a restricted range of phenomena, and, thereby, make it possible to pass to the realm of abstract logical and mathematical forms where we find definite conceptions with the generality sufficient to account for all observed phenomena without the previous contradictions. Such is the method and the achievement of quantum mechanics.

Our analysis has indicated the fundamental assumptions of quantum mechanics and the precise manner in which these assumptions lead to its concept of theoretical probability. The essential point to remember is that the theory generates for any physical system a theoretical probability aggregate which uniquely defines the state of that physical system.   We are now in a position to answer our fundamental question: What is the philosophical significance of the concept of theoretical probability in quantum mechanics? Space permits consideration of but two points: (1) Its bearing on the status of causality and (2) its presuppositions.

In discussing the scientific concept of causality it is necessary to define one's terms. Historically, three different factors have entered in part or whole into this concept. They are (1) the state of the physical system at a given time, (2) the manner of defining this state, and (3) the relationship between states at different times. In quantum mechanics, item (1) is given by the general state function ϕ as restricted by the system function F', item (2) by the theoretical probability aggregate identified with a given state function ϕ, and item (3) by the Schrödinger time equation.

Any definition of causality involves the notion of state and of relationship between states at different times. Certain definitions also prescribe the precise manner in which a state must be defined. Laplace's famous definition is of the latter type. It asserts not merely that a uniquely defined state at one time uniquely determines a uniquely defined state at any later time, but also that a unique state must be defined solely in terms of one sharp set of numbers for the position and velocity of the mass particles constituting the system.

If this is what we mean by causality there can be no doubt that quantum mechanics has rejected the concept. For it does not insist that only coördinate and momentum properties are permissible in defining the state of a system. Also, as we have indicated, it does not define a state for any property in terms of a single set of predicted measurable quantities; instead it uses a theoretical probability aggregate of such measurables.

But we may well ask whether the particular way in which one happens to define the state of a given system is essential to the concept of causality. Whether a state is defined, as it is in Newtonian mechanics, in terms of a single value for position and momentum, or, as it is in Gibbs' statistical mechanics, in terms of a single value for temperature, pressure and volume, or, as it is in quantum mechanics, in terms of a single probability aggregate for any sufficient properties, may be said to be irrelevant so far as causality is concerned. The essential notions in this concept are (1) that the state at a given time be uniquely defined in some manner which appeals to measurable quantities, and (2) that given such a uniquely defined state at one time, the theory predicts one and only one similarly defined state at any later time with absolute and unqualified exactness and certainty. Certainly, quantum theory requires this conception, for it introduces many operations, all on an equal footing, with no justification for giving the position-velocity operations a privileged position.

It becomes necessary, therefore, to strip the scientific definition of causality from the accidents with which its formulation in conjunction with Newtonian mechanics associated it. The following definition results: A given theory in physics introduces the concept of causality when it permits the definition of a unique state function at a given time, and given such a state function predicts with exactness and absolute certainty a unique state function for any later time.   In other words, given uniquely defined states, whenever the relationship between states at different times is necessary and exact we shall say that the law expressing this relationship is a causal law; and whenever it expresses merely the theoretical probability that the later state will occur, it is a non-causal or statistical law.

As Henry Margenau has indicated (1934), when one judges quantum mechanics by this definition of causality, an unexpected conclusion follows: Quantum mechanics retains the concept of causality in physical science.   This becomes evident when one examines the Schrödinger time equation which defines the relationship between the states of a physical system at different times.   This equation prescribes that given a uniquely defined state function ϕ at one time, a uniquely defined state function ϕ' at any specified later time is exactly and absolutely determined.   We have previously indicated that the measurements of an aggregate of quantities which are observed to occur, each with specified frequencies, uniquely define a state function.   Thus the two requirements for causality are satisfied by quantum mechanics.

It will clarify the present status of this concept in physical science if we compare Newtonian mechanics, Gibbs' statistical mechanics and quantum mechanics.   In such a comparison three factors are significant: First, the physical properties in terms of which the state of a system is defined. Second, the presence or absence of theoretical probability in defining the state of a system. Third, the presence or absence of theoretical probability in defining the law relating states at different times. With reference to the first factor, Newtonian mechanics permitted only position and velocity; Gibbs' statistical mechanics emphasized volume, temperature and pressure, and quantum mechanics permits the use of any properties which are sufficient. With reference to the second factor, only quantum mechanics uses theoretical probability in the definition of a unique state of a system. In other words, quantum mechanics defines the state of a system uniquely in terms of a theoretical probability aggregate of measurable quantities, whereas both Newtonian mechanics and Gibbs' statistical mechanics require a single set of quantities. With reference to the third factor, only Gibbs' statistical mechanics uses the concept of theoretical probability in the definition of the law relating states at different times. Both Newtonian mechanics and quantum mechanics reject theoretical probability in defining the time relation between states. It appears, therefore, that the key to the presence of causality in science is not, as so many contemporary scientists and philosophers have supposed, the mere use of the concept of theoretical probability, but its use in the definition of the law relating states at different times. Hence, Gibbs' statistical mechanics rejected causal law by introducing theoretical probability into the time equation, whereas quantum mechanics brought causality back into physics by shifting the concept of theoretical probability from the definition of the law relating states at different times to the definition of a unique state at any one time.

It may be noted that the status of causality in quantum mechanics is in no way changed if one considers groups of particles instead of a single particle. This merely expands quantum dynamics for a single particle into quantum statistics. In both cases the state of the system is uniquely defined, and the law relating states at different times holds exactly and without any qualification.

However, the transition from quantum dynamics for a single particle to quantum statistics does affect the theoretical probability aggregate. Up to this point we have introduced the minimum number of assumptions necessary to indicate how theoretical probability enters into quantum mechanics. These assumptions also give Theorem 4 of which the famous Heisenberg uncertainty principle is a special case. If no additional assumptions are introduced it happens when we pass to quantum statistics, that the probability aggregate is the one defined by the classical Maxwell-Boltzmann distribution law.

It can be shown, however, that a state function thus defined will not predict correctly for neutral atoms and photons. When the postulates of quantum mechanics are modified to care for this discrepancy the result is an entirely different probability aggregate defined by the Bose-Einstein statistics.

In similar fashion it can be shown that these assumptions will not provide for the observed behaviour of charged particles. In order to remove this deficiency the Pauli exclusion principle must be assumed as a postulate. The result is a new theoretical probability aggregate defined by Fermi-Dirac statistics.

These additional technicalities have been introduced in order to establish the second and major conclusion of this chapter: the concept of theoretical probability has no scientific meaning by itself, and takes on such meaning for the scientific theory in which it occurs only if the concepts and categorical principles, many in number, used in its definition, are assumed to hold exactly and without variation. This is evidenced in the changes which occur in the theoretical probability aggregate, from the Maxwell-Boltzmann through the

Bose-Einstein to the Fermi-Dirac statistics, with modification in the basic postulates of quantum mechanics. It is shown also in the different meanings which theoretical probability has in Gibbs' statistical mechanics and quantum mechanics.

The philosophical significance of this conclusion is indicated by one consideration. It has been customary since Hume's attack upon causality and upon relations or laws expressing necessary connections in nature, for certain students to suppose that it is possible to reconcile Hume's empirical philosophy with the existence of science by recourse to the scientific concept of theoretical probability. Our study of quantum mechanics shows that this is a mistake. No escape from the need for propositions expressing causal or necessary connections between natural factors is to be found by an appeal to the scientific concept of probability; instead, if anything, one merely increases the number of universal propositions expressing necessary connections which must be assumed to hold absolutely and exactly. Otherwise, in quantum mechanics for example, the probability aggregate would be in such a state of flux that no prediction could be made, and the theory would be utterly useless in science.

In order that there may be no ambiguity upon this point, let us indicate the universal, exact propositions asserting necessary connections, which we have shown to be the very minimum necessary to define the concept of theoretical probability as it appears in quantum mechanics. First the one-one correlation between a physical property o and its operator O, which is expressed in Postulate I, must hold without exception. Second, all the identifications between physical factors and formal factors which we have made must be assumed to hold without exception. If the assumptions necessary to guarantee these identifications were stated in the form of postulates at least two more postulates would be added to our system. Third, all the propositions necessary to define the system function F' must hold with equal rigidity.

These propositions are not inconsiderable in importance or in number. In the first place, they must include all those necessary and sufficient to define Euclidian geometry for the configuration space. In the second place, the law that the number of dimensions in configuration space is equal to the number of degrees of freedom of the physical system considered must also hold. Finally, the Schrödinger time-equation expressing a causal relation between states at different times must hold categorically. If, in addition, one wants to provide for photons, electron-spin, etc., then additional similar propositions, such as the Pauli principle, are necessary. It appears, therefore, that the person who hopes to reconcile the principles of Hume's philosophy with the existence of science by recourse to the concept of probability would do well to stay away from quantum mechanics.

The situation is no better if one appeals to Gibbs' statistical mechanics in which the causal type of law relating physical states at different times is replaced by a law of the statistical, non-causal type. For the number of propositions asserting necessary connections required to define theoretical probability is just as great whether one uses theoretical probability to define the time relation between state functions, as Gibbs' mechanics does, or to define a single unique state function, as quantum mechanics does. Hence, a general rule concerning the universality of statistical laws in nature can be stated. This rule is that if there are certain laws in science which are statistical then there must also be laws in that science which are not statistical. Otherwise the concept of theoretical probability essential to the meaning of the statistical law in question cannot be defined.

Our conclusions may now be summarized. First, a distinction must be drawn between the numbers predicted by a specific scientific theory, and the numbers gained by the actual operations of measuring in verifying that theory. The former numbers we call theoretical measurables, the latter, operative measurables. Second, theoretical measurables and operative measurables are never identical, even when scientific theories are said to be verified. This lack of identity is in kind as well as quantity. For, as we have indicated, the theoretical measurables predicted by quantum theory are real numbers, whereas the operative measurables given by actual operations of measuring are always natural numbers. Moreover, the real numbers which are the theoretical measurables cannot be defined in terms of the natural numbers which are given by operations of measuring since actual operations of measuring give only a finite number of natural numbers in any given case, and it is impossible to follow Dedekind and Cantor's method of defining real numbers in terms of classes of rationals which are in turn defined in terms of classes of natural numbers unless one has an infinite number of naturals. It appears, therefore, even for the relatively few concepts in any given scientific theory which are associated directly with operations, that the operational theory of the scientific concept gains what plausibility it has, only because its proponents overlook the fundamental distinction between theoretical measurables and operative measurables. Third, a similar distinction must be drawn between probability referring to theoretical measurables and probability referring to operative measurables. The former type of probability we call theoretical probability, the latter type operative probability. Fourth, quantum mechanics, *qua* quantum mechanics, refers only to theoretical measurables and to theoretical probability. Operative measurables and operative probability are the subject matter of the theory of errors, and are associated with each specific theoretical measurable in the aggregate of theoretical measurables of quantum theory, in exactly the same way, as they are associated with the specific theoretical measurables of any other scientific theory. Fifth, the abstract assumptions of a certain system function F generate two sets of numbers o_λ and a_λ in correspondence, which in quantum physics constitute a theoretical probability aggregate that uniquely defines the state of a physical system. Sixth, this use of theoretical probability in the definition of the state of a physical system, instead of in the definition of the time relation between states, permits quantum mechanics to retain the concept of causality. Seventh, the concept of theoretical probability, as actually used in physics, has no meaning by itself and presupposes in its definition a large number of principles expressing necessary connections which must be assumed to hold exactly. Hence, the existence of statistical laws is impossible without the existence of non-statistical laws.

It appears, therefore, that one solves no philosophical problems concerning the status of necessary connections in science by appealing to the concept of theoretical probability. Instead, when one replaces a proposition asserting a necessary connection with one asserting merely a probable connection, one introduces more assumptions concerning necessary connections than would have been required to state a necessary relationship in the first place. Apparently, the reason for this is that the concept of probability is an exceedingly sensitive concept because of its necessary definition in terms of a very large number of assumptions in any given scientific theory; hence, unless these assumptions hold exactly and constantly, the concept of theoretical probability becomes so fluid as to be scientifically useless.

This chapter is reprinted from *Philosophy of Science*. Vol. 3, No. 2, 1936, with the kind permission of the Editor and the Williams and Wilkins Company. It was read originally in the Symposium on *Probability* before the Eastern Division of the American Philosophical Association at Baltimore in December, 1935.

R. B. Lindsay and H. Margenau. *The Foundation of Physics*. New York, 1936.

H. Margenau. *Philosophy of Science*. 1934. pp. 133ff.

CHAPTER XII

CAUSALITY IN FIELD PHYSICS IN ITS BEARING UPON BIOLOGICAL CAUSATION

The concept of causality as it appears in a specific scientific theory involves two factors: (1) the relation of necessary connection between the states of a system at different times, and (2) the definition of state at a given time.

The first of these two factors is necessary if causality is to hold for a given theory, but the more interesting point philosophically is the second factor, since it tells us what initial conditions of a given system a given branch of science finds it necessary to assume in order to be able to deduce by means of the relation of necessary connection, a future state of that system.

Consider a few concrete examples. You will recall Laplace's famous statement to the effect that were an all-seeing Providence provided with a knowledge of the positions and momenta of all the particles in the universe at a given instant of time, He would be able with the help of the Newtonian equations to predict any future state of the universe to the minutest detail. In this dramatic expression the two factors are present in the form in which classical particle physics employed them. The definition of state at a given time is given in the knowledge of the positions and momenta of the particles of the system, and the relation of necessary connection is provided in the form of the Newtonian equations together with the relation of formal implication as applied to them in mathematical calculations.

In the previous chapter, it was noted that if one means by

causality not merely the relation of necessary connection between the states of a system at different times but also the
particular definition of state which Newton gave, then most
certainly causality does not hold in quantum theory.   But if,
on the other hand, one means merely the relation of necessary
connection between states at different times, as would seem
more appropriate, then quantum mechanics is to be regarded
not as a rejection of causality but as an indication of the
radical change in the definition of state at a given time which
must be made in order to retain the concept.   The relation
of necessary connection between states at different times is
given by the Schrödinger time-equation.   The difference
from Newtonian mechanics centers merely in the fact that in
order to retain the relation of necessary connection as prescribed by this equation, it has been necessary to identify the
state of a system at a given time with a function ϕ which is
defined not merely in terms of positions and momenta or other
measurable quantities but also in terms of certain numbers
correlated with these quantities which designate the probability in any observation that a given observable value will
be found.

It is to be noted that the retention of causality is not purely
nominal due to an ambiguity in the definition of state at a
given time.   A state is none the less uniquely and unequivocally defined because two sets of numbers, rather than one,
have to be given in order to determine it quantitatively and
experimentally.

Recently a book upon quantum mechanics by the physicist
A. Landé has appeared in which this validity of causality is
put in a slightly different but perhaps more intuitively com-
prehensible way.   Starting with the complementarity principle of Bohr, according to which any process may be expressed in the two independent parallel languages of wave or
of particle and photon, A. Landé maintains that causality
holds in both languages and only seems to break down when,

due to the operational approach to the problem, one fallaciously muddles the two worlds of discourse, by bringing a process, such as the diffraction of electrons, up to a crystal screen in particle language and then completes the process from the screen to the plate in wave language. When this is done causality obviously fails since it is impossible to deduce a later state of a system defined in wave terms from an earlier state defined in particle terms, but carry the whole process through in either language, A. Landé suggests, and the connection follows necessarily.

This is usually accepted for the wave language. Of the particle language A. Landé writes: "If the picture of particles is adhered to, then there *is* a mechanical causal explanation." In evaluating this statement it is important to distinguish two senses of the word "particle." There is (1) particle in the sense of classical particle physics, i.e., an entity persisting continuously in space and time with a position and momentum at every instant, and (2) particle in the sense permitted by quantum mechanics. Of particle in the former sense one may say, speaking loosely, that causality does not hold in quantum mechanics for it, but the only precise way to state this point is to say that particle in the sense of classical particle physics does not exist for quantum mechanics and hence to ask whether causality holds for it in quantum mechanics is meaningless. There is, however, the other sense of the term "particle" which does have meaning in quantum theory, that, namely, of the entity to which certain quantities in the state function may be spoken of as referring when one chooses, quite unnecessarily, to express formal quantum mechanics in the language of discrete entities. Depending thus upon the state function for its own definition, and causality holding for the time relation between state functions, causality may be said to hold for the "particle language" as thus defined. Landé seems to be using the term in this, its proper, sense when he writes: "It is only if one insists on clinging to the old mechanical models that one comes to such contradictory ideas as ... 'failure of mechanical causation.' " Elsewhere it is not clear, however, that he avoids falling back into the classical meaning of the term. It would seem wise, therefore, either to drop the wave or particle language entirely, using only the formal exposition of quantum theory, or else to introduce two different words for the two different senses, perhaps reserving the term "particle" for the entity of classical particle physics and introducing some other term for the particle of quantum mechanics.

Although A. Landé's analysis is illuminating in indicating why certain people reached the conclusion they did with respect to the status of causality in quantum mechanics it is not as trustworthy a way to put the matter as the more purely formal one of the previous chapter. The reason is that the Bohr complementarity principle is not required, since the formal statement of the theory in which all attempts at wave or particle pictures are dropped, thereby making the complementarity principle unnecessary, gives a more general analysis of the status of causality and takes care of the experimental data with a smaller number of formally precise initial assumptions. Also, the danger of falling back upon the rejected mechanical models by surreptitiously using the particle and wave of quantum mechanics in the sense of the particle and wave of Newtonian mechanics and hydro-dynamics is avoided.

Up to this point we have emphasized the respect in which quantum mechanics retains the concept of causality by introducing a definition of state different from the one used in Newtonian mechanics. It remains to direct attention to a respect in which quantum mechanics represents a return to the definition of state used by Newton. This brings us to the concept of causality in field physics.

Ever since 1861 when Maxwell published his second famous paper on electro-magnetics, entitled "On Physical Lines of

Force," there have been two major branches of modern physics, the one associated with Newton, Laplace, Dalton and Ampère and called particle physics, the other identified with Faraday, Maxwell, Larmor, Lorentz and Einstein and termed field physics. It has been one of the most grievous errors of philosophical thought and of scientific thought outside of theoretical physics to identify the whole of modern physics with nothing but particle theory.

The validity of causality in field physics as well as particle physics has been generally accepted. Both express their laws in terms of differential equations. Certainly there has been far more furor over the threat to causality in quantum mechanics than ever occurred in connection with field physics. Nevertheless, the first alteration in the definition of state at a given time, in connection with the retention of causality, was not made in quantum mechanics but as long ago as 1861 when Maxwell laid the foundations of modern electro-magnetic theory. Moreover, this new definition of state introduced by Maxwell and carried on by Einstein, is in certain respects, although not in all, a much more radical departure from the Newtonian definition of state than quantum mechanics makes and to this extent a much more serious threat to causality.

Nevertheless, causality holds in field physics as in particle physics and in quantum mechanics, for the result of Maxwell's new definition of state is not to invalidate causality but to designate more precisely the action of the past on the future in a peculiar way.

Again the relation of necessary connection between states at different times is retained. The difference is that it is defined by Maxwell's differential equations instead of Newton's or the Schrödinger time-equation, and the states which it relates are given in a unique way in each of the three cases.

We must turn, therefore, to the definition of state in field physics. The crux of the matter centers in what the physicists term retarded potentials. A potential, let it be recalled, is a function from which can be derived a direction and intensity of a force at a point in a field. A field conversely is a continuum of matter or of force, every point of which is defined by two factors differing usually from point to point, one of which designates the direction of the force at that point, the other of which specifies its intensity.

It might seem that the only alteration in the definition of state required to pass from particle to field physics would be the designation of the potentials, i.e., the direction-intensity quantities, at every point in the field of the system, instead of the positions and momenta of all the particles of the system. This would be the case if field physics followed particle physics in assuming the action of forces instantaneously at a distance.

It is the rejection of this idea for that of force propagated from point to point in the field with a high but finite velocity which complicates the definition of state in field physics by requiring the introduction of retarded potentials. Only at the point in the field where the observer is located at the present time t_0 do non-retarded potentials, i.e., directions and intensities of the forces at the time t_0, occur. At all other distant points the potentials which enter into the definition of state at the present time t_0 are directions and intensities of the forces at those points, not at the time t_0 but at an earlier time t_{-n} such that these forces, leaving the distant points at the time t_{-n} and traveling with the finite velocity c, arrive at the observer's position at the present time t_0. Such potentials applying only to points in the field distant from the observer and determined not for the present time t_0 for which the state of the system is being defined but, nevertheless, entering into this definition even though determined for the past times t_{-n}, are called retarded potentials.

The reason for their use, be it noted, is that the rejection of action at a distance prevents the definition of state at a given present time t_0 in terms of the instantaneous relation to each other of the forces at distant points in the field and requires its definition in terms of the forces at different points related to each other by a finite velocity. But to relate the force where the observer is located to forces at distant points in the field by a finite velocity is to prescribe that the potentials of the latter points for the state of a system at the observer's present time t_0 must be those, not at the time at which the finite velocity of propagation arrives at the observer's position, but at the earlier time t_{-n} at which it leaves the distant position. Hence, the need for retarded potentials in the definition of state in field physics.

Let us now consider the status and meaning of causality in field physics in the light of this definition. Causality holds in the sense that given a state at the present time t_0 as thus defined in terms of retarded and non-retarded potentials, Maxwell's equations in their earlier form, or in the invariant form provided by Einstein's special theory of relativity, permit one to deduce a determinate future state at the later time t_{+1} defined in precisely the same way. Providing that one permits each theory to define the state of a system at a given time in its own way, the relation of necessary connection between states at different times holds in field physics as it does in particle physics and in quantum mechanics.

If we concentrate attention, however, not upon the definition of state in field physics at the given time t_0, but upon the distinction within this definition between retarded and non-retarded potentials then certain unique factors appear. First, there is no meaning in field physics, either theoretical or operational to simultaneity of action of the forces at all the points in the field at the present time t_0. To admit such a meaning would be to smuggle back the rejected notion of forces acting simultaneously at a distance. This entails that the causal action of the past with respect to the future is not with respect to the whole spatial field of force in the present for a given observer but merely of that point in the present where the observer is located. Thus, strictly speaking, the causal action of the whole spatial field of nature in the temporarily extended past upon the whole spatial field of nature in the temporarily extended future is for a given observer with respect to but one point in the spatial field of force in the present, namely, that point, designated by non-retarded potentials, where the observer is situated. It is to represent this peculiar relationship graphically that the familiar light cone illustration has been used.

This is well known. It was treated by Hermann Weyl in 1926 in his paper before the Sixth International Congress of Philosophy at Harvard. It has received full popular exposition from A. S. Eddington and meticulous treatment by Hans Reichenbach in his Philosophie der Raum-Zeit-Lehre.

It is reconsidered here for different purposes: First, to demonstrate that the necessity of a radical modification of the definition of state in order to retain the concept of causality in physics did not originate in quantum mechanics but occurred as long ago as 1861 when Maxwell laid the foundation of electro-magnetic theory. Second, to show that there is a respect in which the definition of state introduced by quantum mechanics marks a return to the definition of state used by Newtonian mechanics. This becomes clear when one fact is noted: Quantum mechanics does not prescribe the use of retarded potentials in its definition of state. This entails that it admit a meaning for the relation of every point in the spatial field of force of nature at any present instant of time and hence, return to the Newtonian concept of causal action of past upon future for a given observer by way of the whole spatial field of force of nature in the present.

It is precisely because of this return to the Newtonian concept of simultaneity for all points in the spatial field of force that ordinary quantum mechanics is at present incompatible with the relativity theory and that the resolution of this conflict is the basic problem confronting contemporary physics.

To be sure P. A. M. Dirac has relativized quantum mechanics for the simple case of one electron, but not for general quantum theory which applies to atoms with many electrons.

The third reason for reexamining the definition of state in field physics arises because of its bearing upon causation in biology. This brings us to an aspect of the definition of state in field physics which must now be considered.

So far as biological systems are concerned the distinction between retarded and non-retarded potentials may be ignored, since the size of an organism is so small and the velocity of electro-magnetic propagations is so large that for all theoretical and practical purposes it is as if we had action at a distance and only non-retarded potentials at every point of the field of the system. Consequently, for living organisms field physics differs from particle physics in its definition of state only in its substitution of force directions and intensities at every point in the field of the system for positions and momenta of all the particles of the system.

But in this little word "only" there is a tremendous difference. This begins to become evident when one recalls that alterations in the definition of state at a given time represent differences in what the scientist finds it necessary to assume in the initial conditions in order to account for the subject matter he is studying.

The restriction of the definition of state to positions and momenta means that any subject matter for which particle physics is adequate is to be understood as the mere effect of the compounding of the motions of its constituent particles. Applied to a living organism this leads to the notion that its observed form and organization have no primary status or causal significance in themselves but are instead the mere effect of the motion of its atomic parts. In practice this produces a state of mind, very common among contemporary experimental biologists and physiologists, which regards any reference to the form of the organism as a whole as very superficial and which supposes that if the chemical components are determined all relational factors will be taken care of automatically as mere by-products.

The net result is that the central difficulty of biology, — the problem of organization — is ignored, or, if you prefer, solved by an arbitrary act of faith. Certainly no one has determined experimentally the positions and momenta of the trillions upon trillions of particles in even the smallest of living organisms. Nor would it do one very much good, so far as the deduction of biological organization is concerned, were all this empirical information obtained, for no mathematician has learned yet how to solve Newton's equations for three or four particles to say nothing about trillions upon trillions of them.

The position is little better with the modern alternative theories which emphasize the primacy of the formal factors by introducing such notions as holism, gestalt, emergent evolution or entelechy. Being largely intuitive and purely qualitative in character these concepts provide most excellent theories of biological causation when presented to the imaginations of mixed audiences in psychological and philosophical congresses, but unfortunately they turn out to be of little use when applied to the concrete bodies of the living creatures to which they are supposed to refer. In the hands of the working biologist they lead nowhere except to futile debate.

These futilities will not be worthless, however, if they cause us to look elsewhere and remind ourselves that there are other conceptions of causation in physics than the one provided by particle physics. For the significance of the shift in the definition of state in passing from particle to field physics is that it completely reverses the status of relatedness and particles with respect to their primacy in the initial conditions which science must postulate to account for a given subject matter. To put the matter over-simply but none the less correctly in general: whereas particle physics postulates the discrete atoms with their positions and momenta defined experimentally and then deduces the field and its relatedness, field physics postulates the field and its relatedness defined experimentally in terms of the directions and intensities of its forces at every point and then in part at least derives the local actions of ponderable masses.

The point, moreover, is not merely that physics has found this to be an alternative way of understanding nature, but that it is the only way if one would have a universe such as this one with interfering polarized light waves and the other electro-magnetic waves of the wireless in it. To put the matter mathematically, as Maxwell showed long ago, particle physics cannot derive the wave equation, and without the wave equation Young's and Fresnel's experimental proof of the interference and polarity of light and Hertz's discovery of the electro-magnetic waves other than light which Maxwell's field theory predicted, cannot exist.

The time has come, however, to allow Maxwell to speak for himself upon the relative status of relatedness and particle in field theory. It is to be remembered that the accepted theory of electricity and magnetism when Faraday and Maxwell carried on their investigations was the rigorously mathematical one provided by particle physics. In his first paper in electro-magnetics entitled "On Faraday's Lines of Force," Maxwell says of Ampere's theory that its basic "assumption is no doubt warranted by the universal consent of men of science in treating of attractive forces considered as due to the mutual action of particles." Then, in the same sentence, Maxwell adds, "but we ... are proceeding on a different principle, and searching for the explanation of the phenomena, not in the currents alone but also in the surrounding medium."

This medium he conceived, tentatively following Faraday, as a continuum of lines of force having their termini, if any, in what he called "sources" and "sinks." It is natural to identify these "sources" and "sinks" with particles of the system. It is to be noted, however, that the lines of force and the field are completely defined by the designation of the direction and intensity of the force at every point. Hence, any theory concerning the mechanism of the "sources" or the "sinks" or the medium is quite irrelevant for the precise formulation or experimental application of the theory. What is important is merely the relatedness of the forces throughout the field given directly by the direction intensity quantities.

This becomes explicit in Maxwell's third paper on "A Dynamical Theory of the Electro-magnetic Field" in which he drops the previous physical models and presents his famous equations. "We ought to be able," he writes, "to write out all the consequences of its [the field's] motion, provided we know the form of the relation between the motions of its parts." Two paragraphs later he adds, "The phenomena of the induction of currents has been deduced from their mechanical actions by Helmholtz and Thomson. I have followed the reverse order, and deduced the mechanical action from the laws of induction," that is, from "the form of the relation between the motion of the parts." As Albert Einstein has expressed it in a paper written upon the hundredth anniversary of Maxwell's birth, "It was clear that the equations themselves were all that was essential, and that the field intensities that appeared in them were elementary, not derivable from other simple entities."

The relevance of this to biology is evident. Were field physics applicable to a living organism as a whole it would provide an experimentally determinable and quantitatively expressible definition of that "form of the relation between the motions of the parts" which is the organization of a living system. It would also designate the difference between this organic relatedness from species to species and individual to individual. In addition, a scientific basis would be provided for that theory of biological causation which conceives the form of the system as a whole as in part at least an irreducible causal factor, rather than a mere effect of the atomic constituents. This follows, be it noted, from the fact that the field intensities which define "the form of the relation between the motion of the parts" are, to use Albert Einstein's language again, "elementary, not derivable from other simpler entities," at least so far as field physics is concerned.

The crucial question, therefore, arises: Is field physics applicable to living organisms? Are they electro-magnetic systems? Do they when examined with the experimental apparatus of a field physicist exhibit potentials at every point of their form as a whole? This question is not answered by the experimental work upon the so-called brain waves or upon action-current potentials in other parts of the body. Such evidence is suggestive but it demonstrates merely that certain parts of the organism at certain times have electrical concomitants; it does not show that the continuous field of the organism as a whole is characteristically and persistently an electro-dynamic field both spatially and temporally.

In 1932 in his experimental study of the reorganization of the developing nervous system in young growing amblystoma, my Yale colleague H. S. Burr noted phenomena which he found most natural to conceive in terms of field factors. The question immediately arose concerning their character, and the hypothesis suggested itself to him that this field was physical and not purely biological in character. Meeting with little encouragement from his scientific colleagues, he consulted a philosopher. The reply was, among other things, that since particle theory has to be supplemented, at least, with field theory in physics, it would be exceedingly surprising if this were not the case also in biology where the primacy of the relational factor is even more self-evident. H. S. Burr suggested, therefore, that a joint paper be written in which the philosopher would designate the general considerations from physics and the philosophy of science, and the anatomist would indicate the more concrete factors from biology, which make it likely that living systems are physical systems in the sense prescribed by field physics. This paper entitled "The Electro-dynamic Theory of Life" appeared in 1935.

Meantime H. S. Burr attempted to secure the apparatus which would put this theory to a test. No available apparatus of the physicists was satisfactory, since one could not be sure that any potentials which appeared were not contributed by the apparatus rather than the organism. Finally, through the joint efforts of the anatomist and expert mechanic H. S. Burr, the physicist C. T. Lane, and the physical-chemist L. F. Nims, an apparatus called forth first by general scientific and philosophical theory, and shown to be possible theoretically by Maxwell's mathematical electro-magnetic theory, took on material form in fact in the Burr-Lane-Nims microvolt-meter. With this, one could be sure that any potential differences which were found belonged to the specimen.

In 1935 it was applied to the living organism. Since then tens of thousands of observations have been made on different forms of life from the egg of amblystoma, a few millimeters in length, to the gross bodies of dogs and monkeys and men. Not only do the electrodes pick up potential differences on the organism as a whole, but also in decreasing intensity at a distance from the surface of the organism, equal in some cases to one-ninth of its length. Moreover, the patterns of these potential readings persist in time and remain remarkably constant through changes in many local chemical factors.

There are two strains of mice which to ordinary observation appear to be identical except that the one strain develops cancer when bred, in a very high percentage of the offspring, and the other strain, only in an exceedingly small percentage. These two strains have different field patterns. This establishes the point suggested earlier in this paper that field physics provides not merely an experimentally determinable definition of organization in general but also a criterion of the difference in the formal factor from one organism to another.

There are many other findings of great clinical and theoretical interest. I shall refer to but one. The exact time of ovulation in many different organisms, including the human, exhibits itself in a variation in the potential readings. This solves a problem upon which clinicians have been working for decades. It is also important theoretically. One of the unique characteristics of living things is that they reproduce themselves. The detection of ovulation by electrical methods shows, therefore, that an important part of one of the most distinctively biological processes is electro-dynamic in character.

From all these findings it may be concluded, consequently, that living creatures are electro-magnetic systems and that field physics applies to them. The Burr-Lane-Nims microvoltmeter enables one to define the state of a living system at a given time t_0 in terms of the force directions and intensities at every point in the surface field of the system. Certain of the conditions requisite for the validity of the concept of causality of field physics are satisfied. It follows, therefore, since field physics in its definition of state postulates the relational factor as in part, at the very least, irreducible, that biological causation must be viewed in the same way.

This chapter is reprinted from the *Philosophy of Science*. Vol. 5, No. 2, 1938, with the kind permission of the Editor and the Williams and Wilkins Company. Originally it was read in the Symposium on *Causality in Physics* before the Eastern Division of the American Philosophical Association at Princeton University on December 29th, 1937.

R. B. Lindsay and H. Margenau. *The Foundations of Physics.* New York. 1936.

A. Landé. *Quantum Mechanics.* New York and Cambridge 1937.

H. Weyl. *Zeitverhaeltnisse im Kosmos.* Proc. 6th Int. Cong. Philosophy, 1926. New York, 1937.

A. S. Eddington. *Space, Time and Gravitation.* Cambridge, 1921.

H. Reichenbach. *Philosophie der Raum-Zeit-Lehre.* Berlin, 1928.

M. Faraday. *Experimental Researches in Electricity.* 3 vols. London, 1839-1855.

J. C. Maxwell. *Scientific Papers.* 2 vols. Cambridge, 1890. Esp. Vol. I. 193, 533.

J. J. Thomson, A. Einstein and Others. *Clerk Maxwell 1831-1931.* Cambridge, 1931.

H. S. Burr. *Electro-dynamic Theory of Development.* J. Comp. Neur., 56: 347-371. 1932.

H. S. Burr and F. S. C. Northrop. *The Electro-dynamic Theory of Life.* Quar. Rev. Biol., 10: 322-333. 1935.

H. S. Burr, C. T. Lane, and L. F. Nims. *A Vacuum Tube Microvoltmeter for the Measurement of Electrical Phenomena.* Yale Jour. Biol. and Med., 9: 155-158. 1935.

H. S. Burr and C. T. Lane. *Electrical Characteristics of Living Systems.* Yale Jour. Biol. and Med., 8: 31-35. 1935.

F. S. C. Northrop and H. S. Burr. *Experimental Findings Concerning the Electrodynamic Theory of Life and an Analysis of Their Physical Meaning.* Growth, 1: 78-88. 1937.

F. S. C. Northrop. *The History of Modern Physics in Its Bearing upon Biology and Medicine.* Yale Jour. of Biol. and Med., 10: 209-232. 1938.

R. E. Zirkle. *Particle Physics Approach to Biology.* Scientific Monthly, Vol. LXIV. No. 3. March, 1947. 213-217.

H. S. Burr. *Field Theory in Biology. Ibid.* 217-225.

Henry Margenau. *Particle and Field Concepts in Biology. Ibid.* 225-231.

CHAPTER XIII

THE METHOD AND LIMITED PREDICTIVE POWER OF CLASSICAL ECONOMIC SCIENCE

Were a benign and omnipotent being to appear before the vast body of creative contemporary economists, in religious fervor assembled, promising the answer to one request, the prayer offered up would probably be as follows: Most Needed and Welcome Being, give us a scientific theory of economic dynamics.

By "theory" would be meant a deductive system designating the primitive concepts in terms of which all other concepts in the science can be defined, and the primitive propositions or postulates from which, by formal logic or its special branch — pure mathematics, all other propositions in the science can be deduced as theorems. Such a theory would be scientific if, in some manner, its adequacy were tested by appeal to the empirical subject matter of the science. By a scientific theory of economic dynamics is meant such an empirically verified deductive system, providing primitive concepts and postulates defining the present state of an economic system in such a way that, once its quantitative values were determined empirically, the theory, through its postulates and theorems, would enable one to deduce a future state of the system without any further appeal to empirical factors. In short, a theory of dynamics exists for a given science when its concepts are sufficient to designate the specific state of a system at a given time and its postulates permit the deduction of a specific state for any future time. A most spectacular and typical example is Newton's mechanics.

Economists recognize that they do not possess such a dynamics. Lionel Robbins writes, "Economic Science knows no way of predicting . . . the configuration of the data at any particular point of time." Our purpose here is to attempt to throw some light on the possibility of a scientific theory of economic dynamics, by analyzing logically contemporary economic theory with respect to its primitive assumptions and its method of verification, in the hope of revealing precisely what it is, in its basic concepts or postulates and in its method, which prevents its attainment of an economic dynamics. This will be facilitated by making a similar analysis of Newtonian mechanics. It is to be emphasized that this chapter restricts itself, as did Lionel Robbins' important treatise on The Nature and Significance of Economic Science, to classical Austrian economic theory.

One caution must be noted. In saying that economics does not have a theoretical dynamics we are not asserting that economists do not study and possess important empirical knowledge concerning economic changes in time. The statistical studies of Wesley Mitchell and his group and the work in economic history and in the sociological approach to economic factors are well known. These studies, however, constitute only the first of the two stages in the normal development of any empirical science. Having gathered its empirical natural history data, a science then passes to the construction of deductively formulated theory, in which a system, for its subject matter, is postulated, from which it follows by logical deduction that the natural history data should be what they are. It is this deductively formulated theory of the natural history data — not the natural history data themselves — which we are asserting to be lacking at present in the case of economic changes with time. In economic statics, on the other hand, economics possesses, in its classical theory, not merely the natural history data but also the deductively formulated theory. Our question, therefore, is whether it is possible to generalize the present deductive theory for economic statics so that one can get from the present empirical state of an economic system to a future state, not by the speculative extrapolation of the empirical curves of past economic events, as the purely empirical economists are forced to do, but by logical implication as a deductive consequence of the concepts and postulates of one's theory.

Let us begin, therefore, with an analysis of certain features of the contemporary theory of economic statics. Our attention must be focused upon two factors: (1) its basic concepts and postulates, and (2) its empirical method of verification.

An examination of an older treatise, such as J. S. Mill's *Principles of Political Economy*, shows that it divides into three parts entitled Production, Distribution and Exchange. Under Exchange, the first concept is that of Value. Of it Mill writes that "of the two departments of political economy, the production of wealth and its distribution, the consideration of Value has to do with the latter alone; and with that only so far as competition, and not usage or custom, is the distributing agency."

A similar study of a contemporary treatise, such as Wicksell's *Lectures on Political Economy*, reveals an important shift of emphasis. The initial chapters treating of the basic principles of the entire science have the title "The Theory of Value." Upon this point such diverse economists as Menger, Wicksteed, Schönfeld, Pareto, Marshall, Hicks, Knight and even Marx are in agreement. As Lionel Robbins has put it, "The most important propositions of economic analysis are the propositions of the general theory of value . . . no matter what particular 'school' is in question" and "no matter what arrangement of subject-matter is adopted."

These considerations indicate that the development of contemporary economic theory has resulted in the shift of the concept of Value from the status of a secondary concept, dealing only with one portion of the science, to that of the primitive or basic concept of the entire science.   It is upon this concept, therefore, that we must concentrate our attention.

Its distinction from ethical value must be noted.   In economics anything has Value if it is a service or any other possible object of human interest which is wanted.   Whether these wanted objects are "good" or "bad" is not the concern of economics.   Ethics, on the other hand, asks, with respect to these economic valuations, whether it is "good" or "bad" for people to want the things in question.   Politics, similarly, in its aspect of social ethics and in its laws, condemns the wanting of certain possible objects of human interest and encourages the pursuing of others.   Instances of Value in the economic sense we shall term Valuations; those of Value in the ethical sense, Values.

A valuation, or an economic value, reflects the want of some individual for some object or service.   This means that the subject matter of economics is not the physical object or behavior itself but the desire of the individual for that object. Consequently, an economic good is not an externally observable object or behavioristic activity, but is, instead, a relation between such an object or activity and an individual person — a relation, moreover, which exhibits itself introspectively in the person's interest in and desire for that object.   Lionel Robbins has indicated this most dramatically by Winston Churchill's description of war materials on the day of the Armistice in 1918.   Lionel Robbins writes, "After years of effort, the nation had acquired a machine for turning out the materials of war in unprecedented quantities.   Enormous programmes for production were in every stage of completion.   Suddenly the whole position is changed.   The 'demand' collapses.   The needs of war are at an end. . . . What is relevant is that what at 10.55 a.m. that morning was wealth and productive power, at 11.5 had become 'not-wealth,' an embarrassment, a source of social waste.   The substance had not changed.   The guns were the same.   The potentialities of the machines were the same. From the point of view of the technician, everything was exactly the same. But from the point of view of the economist, everything was different. Guns, explosives, lathes, retorts, all had suffered a sea change." In short, what constitutes an economic good is not the guns and lathes as objective, physical entities, but the desire for them or the wanting of them by individual persons.

Any deductive theory in any subject whatever must possess relations as well as elements among its primitive concepts. The fundamental entities of economic theory are economic goods, or wants, or valuations. Its fundamental relation is that of "preference."

In any properly formulated deductive theory the postulates are expressed in terms of the basic, or primitive, concepts. Contemporary economic theory measures up to this logical criterion of excellence. For its first and fundamental postulate is that economic wants arrange themselves in an order by virtue of the relation of preference. As Lionel Robbins has expressed it, "the foundation of the theory of value is the assumption that the different things that the individual wants to do have a different order." Given this fundamental postulate of the theory of Value, he then adds that "the idea of the substitutability of different goods, of the demand for one good in terms of another, of an equilibrium distribution of goods between different uses, of equilibrium of exchange and of the formation of prices" can be deduced as theorems.

To gain the theorems which are the economic laws of the theory of production, it is necessary to add a second postulate to the effect that "there are more than one factor of production." Similarly, to get whatever theory of dynamics contemporary economics possesses, a third postulate is required. It is that "we are not certain concerning future scarcities.". . .

The character of the last postulate should be sufficient by itself to indicate the incapacity of contemporary economic theory to attain an adequate dynamics. A much more fruiful analysis, however, will result if we concentrate attention on the more basic, first postulate of the science, and especially upon its primitive concept of economic goods.

We have noted that this basic concept identifies the subject matter of economics, not with an objectively verifiable physical object or the behavior of physical individuals, but with a relation between such an object and the individual, which exhibits itself in an introspectively given interest in, want of, and desire for the object. This entails that the subject-matter to which economic theory refers is not objective in the sense either of the immediately inspected sense data or the verfied inferred common-sense objects. As Lionel Robbins has put it, "There is no quality in things taken out of their relation to men which can make them economic goods. There is no quality in services taken out of relation to the end served which makes them economic. Whether a particular thing or a particular service is an economic good depends entirely on its relation to valuations." This consideration has caused Professor Frank H. Knight to refer to the economist's materials as "data of a different character from factual observations." It is to be emphasized that this is as true, as Lionel Robbins has indicated, of the "indifference systems of Pareto and Messrs. Hicks and Allen" as it is of "the simple want systems of Menger and the early Austrians." The question then arises how a deductive theory referring to such a subject matter can be empirically verified. This brings us to our second topic.

It might be supposed that the verification is like that of natural science, except for the minor difference that natural science appeals to empirical data given through the senses, whereas economic science uses empirical data given introspectively. This would dispose of the matter, providing economic science held only for the introspective data of a single individual. But upon this basis one would expect a different science of economics for each individual. It is

clear that economic science does not conceive of itself in this
fashion.   It claims for its theory the same validity for everybody that natural science claims for its laws and verified
propositions.

But how, by appeal to introspection rather than to the
senses, can one get any criterion for public validity?   Moreover, since valuations are the very subject matter of the science, and these, as they enter into economics, are relativistic,
personal things, how can publicly valid meaning for the postulates of an economic theory using such valuations as its basic
concept be obtained?   Clearly this is the fundamental difficulty which the economist had to face in attempting to attain
a publicly valid science.

The way in which he solved this problem is exceedingly
interesting and quite different from that of natural science.
He gained the public validity by ignoring the specificity of
the private valuations which vary from person to person and
by basing his science upon the generic property of the concrete immediately inspected wants apart from their content
and concrete specific character.   In short, he postulated
merely that any individual inspects wants of some kind and
that these wants take on an order because of the individual's
preferences.   Although the particular valuations are relative,
varying from person to person, and thus do not have public
validity, the fact that any individual does make valuations of
some kind, which in every instance do order themselves, is
not a private, relativistic fact but a fact which is true for
everybody.   In this manner a science which found its subject
matter to be constituted of private, introspected, relativistic,
personal valuations nevertheless attained a theory which is
publicly valid.

Note the difference, as compared with the objectivity of
natural science.   In the latter field one's data are the deliverances of sense awareness.   As Berkeley has shown, one does
not immediately apprehend even common-sense, public ob-

jects, to say nothing about the scientific objects of physics such as electrons and electro-magnetic propagations. What one immediately apprehends are colors and sounds. It is well-known, especially in the case of color-blindness, that even these vary from person to person. Consequently, the natural scientist also, in his immediately apprehended data, is confronted with factors which are personal and private and relative. Had he attained publicly valid theory by dropping attention upon the specificity of sense data and by rearing his theory upon the thesis that any individual has sensations of some kind which can be ordered, the publicly valid theory of natural science would be identical with that of economic science.

It seems to be the case that sense objects do point beyond themselves to postulated factors such as tables, chairs, persons, electrons, electro-magnetic propagations, and a space-time manifold which is public, whereas the private wants, interests, valuations, etc. of individuals, insofar as they enter into economics, do not. At least this has been the conclusion of economists as a result of their study of these introspectively given valuations. Otherwise they would have attained publicly valid theory by proceeding to specific postulated objective valuations the same for everybody, instead of by the method which they have actually pursued, of ignoring the specificity of the private valuations and concentrating attention merely upon the generic fact that individual people have valuations, which become ordered by virtue of the relation of preference.

It is not that one subject is empirical whereas the other is speculative, but that the empirical sense data of natural science do suggest public postulated objects with *specific* as well as *generic* properties, the existence of which is confirmed through their specific deductive consequences by appeal back to the immediately inspected sense data, whereas the equally empirical private introspective data of economic science, at least as they enter into economics, do not point beyond themselves by hypothesis to publicly existent valuations or factors. Consequently, there being no public, objective, specific economic valuations to provide the ground for publicly valid theory, the economist had no alternative but to ground the public validity of his theory upon the generic fact that each individual has wants and that these order themselves. This means that insofar as the economist has empirical information concerning the specific character of his subject matter, this information provides concepts which hold only for the individual, and insofar as economics has publicly valid propositions, these propositions assert merely what is true because the subject matter is an economic subject matter and not because it is one of a specific instance.

Let us now consider the bearing of this procedure upon the possibility of an economic dynamics.   An examination of the theoretical dynamics of Newtonian mechanics indicates that a dynamical theory involves at least two main factors: first, the definition of the state of a system at a given time, and second, a relation of necessary connection or formal implication between the specificity of the state of the system at one time and the specificity of its state at any later time.   In Newtonian mechanics the state of a system at a given time is designated completely when the momenta and positions of all its masses are determined.   What is to be emphasized for our present purposes is that these basic concepts of momenta and position define not merely the *generic* properties of any state whatever, but its *specific,* particular properties also.   In short, the basic concepts of Newtonian mechanics refer not merely to characteristics of the state of a system, regardless of what state it is, but also to all the characteristics necessary to distinguish one state of a system from any other.

The first reason for the failure of contemporary economics to attain a theoretical dynamics now becomes evident.   The initial requirement for such a dynamics is a theory providing concepts which define the state of a system at a given time, not merely with respect to its generic but also its specific properties. The method by which contemporary economics attained publicly valid theory forced it to take as basic a postulate referring only to the generic properties of its subject matter. Consequently it is unable to meet the first requirement for a theoretical dynamics.

Even if this were not the case, contemporary economic theory will fail to attain a dynamics. This brings us to the other requirement for such a theoretical science: the relation of necessary connection joining the specific state of a system at one time to a unique specific state at any later time. This relation was present in Newtonian mechanics only because the law of the conservation of momentum was empirically valid in that science. Even though its concepts of momentum and position define the specificity of the present state of the system, Newtonian mechanics would be quite unable to deduce a future state and thereby obtain a theoretical dynamics, if the total momentum of an isolated physical system changed with time.

This conclusion can be generalized for any dynamical theory whatever. To assert that a science has a theoretical dynamics is to maintain that the principle of mechanical causation holds for it. This principle asserts that a knowledge of the present specific properties of the state of a given system enables one to deduce all future states. This presupposes that all future effects are the result of causes or properties of the elementary subject matter which are present now. Such can be the case only if the properties of the subject matter of the science in question remain constant in time. This is to affirm that this subject matter obeys conservation laws.

It is to be noted that every concept entering into the definition of a state of a system in Newtonian mechanics meets this requirement. These concepts are momentum and position. The law of the conservation of the momentum guarantees this for the former; the fact that space in Newtonian mechanics has Euclidian metrical properties which are constant through time insures it for the latter.

Let us now consider the fundamental concept of contemporary economic theory with respect to this requirement. This concept is "economic wants." It is quite clear that the total volume of these wants does not remain constant through time. They are in constant flux. In short, the basic subject matter of economic science, as conceived by contemporary economic theory, does not have the property of obeying a law of conservation. As F. H. Knight has written, "There is nothing in economics corresponding to either momentum or energy, or their conservation principles in mechanics" and "there is no definable economic space." It appears, therefore, that even if contemporary economic theory had concepts which define the specificity of the state of an economic system at a given time, it would still be unable to achieve an economic dynamics, because the second requirement for such a theory is not satisfied; its subject matter does not obey a conservation law and hence it cannot deduce a future state from a present state of the system.

We conclude, therefore, that a theoretical economic dynamics is impossible within the framework of classical economic theory. As long as valuations are taken as the fundamental concept of the science, an economic dynamics will be impossible for two reasons: (1) the subjective relative character of valuations necessitates the grounding of the public validity of economic theory on their generic properties merely, thereby leaving the state of a system at a given time unprecisely designated theoretically. Thus the first requirement for a theoretical dynamics cannot be satisfied. (2) The failure of the total quantity of valuations to obey a conservation law prevents the prediction of a future state, even if the present state were given specifically. Thus the second requirement for a theoretical dynamics is ruled out.

These limitations are associated with its scientific method. This method is surprisingly different from that of natural science. Physics, for example, does not verify the postulates of its deductive theory directly. Instead, as Chapters VI and VIII have shown, they are experimentally confirmed indirectly through the theorems which are their logical consequences.

There are several reasons for this. First, its postulates designate an objective systematic structure with parts, such as electrons, molecules and light quanta, possessing most specific properties. This increased postulated specificity permits the theory to deduce in its theorems more meticulous local phenomena which can be put to an exact experimental test in a laboratory. Consequently, the theorems usually refer to items which are more susceptible to experimental test than the postulates. Second, physics has a theoretical dynamics. This permits it to predict rigorously in time. These deduced predictions appear as theorems. Hence the theory can be experimentally tested only by checking a theorem. Third, physics, as we previously noted, attains publicly valid theory by postulating more than the data of sense give. In short, it gained the public electrons and light propagations which provide the public validity of its postulates not by observation but by postulation. This means that its postulates do not refer solely to directly observable factors and hence they cannot be empirically tested directly. The only alternative is to test them indirectly through their deductive consequences. This is a more complicated process than is usually supposed, involving epistemic correlations as well as formal logic and experiment, but these complications need not concern us here.

None of these three considerations applies to contemporary

economic science. Consequently, it has had to devise a different scientific method.

We have noted its failure to possess a theoretical dynamics. Hence the testing of its postulates by deducing a future consequence is unavailable. Also, its method of obtaining publicly valid theory has provided only the generic fact that there are valuations of some kind which order themselves. This prevents both the postulates and their theorems from referring to the specific. Thus the deduction of a meticulous localized experimental situation is impossible. As Lionel Robbins has indicated, "It is ... clear that our belief (in the generalization of economic science) does not rest upon the results of controlled experiment."

But if the method of obtaining publicly valid theory in contemporary economics has rendered the indirect experimental testing of that theory through its theorems impossible, it has also made it unnecessary. By restricting itself to the generic properties of the introspected valuations, *economics has accomplished something unique in the method of empirical science; it has attained deductively formulated theory which is empirically verified directly through its postulates without the need of appeal to their deductive consequences.* As Lionel Robbins has written, "in Economics, ... the ultimate constituents of our fundamental generalizations are known to us by immediate acquaintance. In the natural sciences they are known only inferentially." These generalizations are, he adds, "so much the stuff of our everyday experience that they have only to be stated to be recognized as obvious."

The difference in scientific method is marked. Physics tests its deductive theory indirectly by empirically checking its theorems; economics, directly by empirically confirming its postulates. In physics one believes in the validity of its postulates because their deductive consequences, the theorems, are experimentally confirmed; in economics one believes in the validity of its theorems because they are the logical consequences of the immediately confirmed postulates. Lionel Robbins writes of certain theorems in economic theory, "these propositions are deductions from simple assumptions reflecting very elementary facts of general experience. If the premises relate to reality the deductions from them must have a similar point of reference." In speaking of a theorem in monetary theory, he adds that "This proposition is deducible from the most elementary facts of experience of the science, and its truth is independent of further inductive test." This, to be sure, does not prevent the economist from also empirically confirming the theorem, if this is possible.

It will be recalled that the second requirement for a theoretical dynamics, the capacity given the present state of a system to deduce a future state, is not obtainable within contemporary economic theory, because the total volume of economic wants does not remain constant with time. Clearly, in this case, the failure is due not to the scientific method by which the theory is obtained, but to the character of the subject matter to which its basic concepts refer. The difficulty is one of concepts and subject matter, not of method. In the case, however, of the failure to provide the first of the two requirements for a theoretical dynamics, — the specific definition of state at a given time, — this is by no means the case. Contemporary economic theory cannot achieve this because its primitive concepts refer only to the generic properties of the state of a system. But the primitive concepts have this limitation because of the scientific method used in obtaining publicly valid theory. It follows, therefore, that *a theoretical dynamics is impossible,* not merely within the assumptions but also *by the method of contemporary economic science.*

This does not imply that a theoretical economic dynamics is impossible upon any basis or by any method whatever. Our analysis, if correct, proves merely that this is the case within the assumptions or by the method of contemporary economic science. This, however, has important implications. It means, if an economic dynamics is possible at all, that the problem is not that of gaining more and more empirical information about more and more variables within the framework of contemporary theory, as so many empirical economists have supposed, or of generalizing the concepts of contemporary theory, as so many of their theoretical confrères have attempted, but of (a) basing economic theory upon radically different primitive concepts and (b) introducing a quite different scientific method.

Whether the empirical subject matter of the science permits this is an empirical question outside the province of this chapter. Our analysis has shown, however, that the contemporary concepts and method had their basis in the character of the subject matter. It reminds us also that a theoretical dynamics is possible only for a subject matter which obeys conservation laws. As logicians, we must add that there is no *a priori* reason why every subject should do this. Thus it must be seriously asked whether the quest for an economic dynamics may not have its basis in a dogmatic assumption, with respect to which our empirical knowledge already gives the lie. In any event, until someone presents a new theory and a new method for the science, it seems the part of wisdom to act upon the basis of the theory we possess and to learn precisely what it can and cannot do. With respect to this our analysis gives definite specifications.

Contemporary economic theory has suffered from two extremes; either too much or too little has been claimed for it. Some, realizing it is obtained by a legitimate scientific method, but not analyzing this method to note its difference from that of physics, have supposed that, being scientific, it can do what physical theory does, namely, permit the deduction of future events. Others, finding that it cannot do this, have jumped to the opposite extreme and concluded that it is of no use whatever.   Our analysis corrects both of these positions.   In indicating precisely why contemporary economic theory cannot deduce the future state of an economic system, it also lays bare the factors which define what it can do. This is by no means inconsiderable.

First, it provides a theory of economic statics.   That is, given certain characteristics of the state of a system at a given time, it can deduce other characteristics of that system at that same time.   This is all that the theory of the statical moment developed by Archimedes and generalized by Leonardo da Vinci, Stevin and Galilei accomplished, yet one certainly considers it to be scientific and important.

Recently Oskar Morgenstern has set forth considerations indicating that, even in statics, contemporary economic theory is ambiguous in its definition of equilibrium.   In terms of our analysis, this may be due in part to the fact that its basic postulates refer only to the generic and not to the specific properties of the state of a system at a given time.   Even so, its deductive capacity to imply certain generic properties at a given time from others given at that time is important.

Second, even with respect to dynamical problems contemporary economic theory is of great aid.   When the generic properties of the economic system designated by its postulates and their deductive consequences are coupled with its specific empirical characteristics given by contingent empirical information undesignated by theoretical concepts, the theory does enable one to foresee in part the more probable economic developments.

The point is that for a person without knowledge of contemporary economic theory, not merely the specific but also the generic properties of the state of an economic system are on a purely empirical, and hence contingent, basis.   The advantage of economic theory is that it continually reminds one of certain generic characteristics which any economic system must have regardless of its specific character.   Just because it is an economic system, there are economic wants ordered by the relation of preference. From this generic fact certain others follow necessarily by logical implication. The latter are by no means so self-evident psychologically as the postulates from which they can be logically deduced. Hence, in considering the transition of an economic system from its state at one time to its state at a later time, while certain specific factors must always be determined and observed empirically, without specification from theory, and cannot be predicted theoretically, nevertheless certain other characteristics of the states at different times are not on such a purely empirical and contingent basis. Consequently, the person equipped with a knowledge of the theory is located midway between the position of the pure empiricist in economics, who must merely observe and can theoretically deduce nothing, and the theoretical physicist who, given the present state, can, by his theory, predict everything.

Furthermore, by supplementing the generic empirical properties of the present state of a system denoted by the concepts of his theory with empirical information concerning the specific content of the present state of the system not indicated by the concepts of his theory, he can gain the specific and generic properties of the present state of his system. Then if, on empirical grounds, he finds reason to believe that its specific content will remain constant in time, or if, watching developments with time closely, he observes the specific empirical content to remain constant, then partially by the deductive consequences of his theory and partially by trust that the non-theoretically designated content will on this occasion keep constant, he can make a reasonably probable forecast of the near future. Also, if a little later he observes that the specific empirical content does not remain constant, he will know that his forecast must be rejected or modified accordingly.

The comparative analysis of the theory of physical and

THE PROPERTIES TO WHICH THE POSTULATES REFER

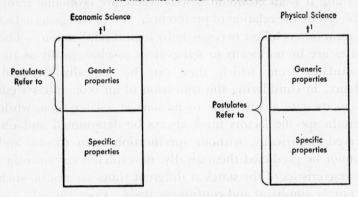

THE FACTORS BETWEEN WHICH THE RELATION OF FORMAL IMPLICATION ($\supset_x$)
JOINING POSTULATES AND THEOREMS HOLDS

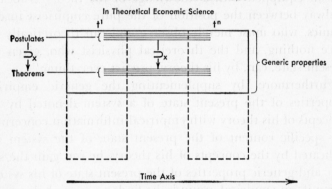

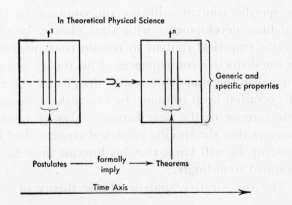

economic science which is at the basis of the preceding conclusions is summarized graphically in the above diagrams.
Each upright rectangle designates the state of a system at a
given time t^1 or t^n. The generic properties of these states
are designated by the upper portion of each rectangle and the
specific properties by the lower portion. Postulates and
theorems are designated by parallel straight lines. The symbol $\supset_x$ denotes the logical relation of formal implication.

The first pair of diagrams, referring only to the state of a
system at a given time, indicates why contemporary economic
theory is incomplete as compared with physics, even for
statics, and why it does not meet the first requirement of a
theoretical dynamics. The second diagram, referring to the
sequence of the states of a system in time, indicates why current economic theory fails to meet the second requirement
for a theoretical dynamics, yet nevertheless, when the lower
section of the rectangle of the initial state is filled in with
non-theoretically designated contingent empirical information, gives one a power with respect to the probable prognos-
tication of events over the near future, which otherwise one
would not possess.

These diagrams portray only the analysis of the deductive
aspect of economic theory. When to this is added the analysis
of the scientific method by which this theory is inductively
tested, we arrive at the following complete conclusion of this
chapter: It is impossible to attain a theoretical economic
dynamics within the assumptions or by the method of contemporary economic theory. Nevertheless, providing these
assumptions and this method are sufficiently analyzed logically, so that one knows precisely what it can and cannot do,
this theory is an invaluable aid, and because of the nature of
the empirical subject matter with respect to conservation
principles, perhaps the only possible theoretical aid, for the
following of economic changes in time. The importance
and necessity of any empirical science possessing an explicit

logical analysis of its concepts and method, if its principles are not to be misunderstood and misused, seems also to be demonstrated.

This chapter is reprinted, with the kind permission of the Editor, from the *Quarterly Journal of Economics* for November 1941, where it bore the title, *The Impossibility of a Theoretical Science of Economic Dynamics*. The new title is introduced to relate it to the other chapters of this book. It was read originally before the Economics Club of Yale University and shortly afterward before the Economics Club of Princeton University.

Lionel Robbins. *An Essay on the Nature and Significance of Economic Science*. Second Ed. Macmillan and Company, London, 1935.

J. S. Mill. *Principles of Political Economy*. Longmans, Green and Co., London, 1904.

Frank H. Knight. *The Ethics of Competition*. Harper and Brothers. 1935.

Risk, Uncertainty and Profit.

CHAPTER XIV

GENERALIZATIONS IN SOCIAL SCIENCE

An inquiry never starts unless some difficulty arises. If one looks at a homogeneous sheet of paper, no question is raised. Yet the plain sheet of paper is a fact. As Chapters I and II have emphasized, science does not begin with facts, with hypotheses, or even with a method, but with a specific problem. Social science is no exception to this rule.

Further, it is more important to pay attention to this rule in social science than in any other field. For social science, unlike natural science, faces two fundamentally different kinds of problems.

In natural science there are only problems of fact. Having found, upon the verification of Kepler's three laws of planetary motion, that planets move in an orbit which is an ellipse, astronomers do not face the normative problem concerning whether the planets should not do squads right in an orbit which is a rectangle.

But social institutions, being in part at least man-made, confront the scientist with two quite different questions: (1) What is the character of social institutions in fact? This is a question comparable to the astronomer's question with respect to the solar system; and (2) How ought social institution to be? Even though murder and unemployment exist, should one or the other or both be outlawed? Even though actual social organization in a given society be monarchical, should it not be replaced by social organization of a democratic, a socialist or a communist form?

The first of these two types of question is factual; the second is normative. Thus, whereas natural science faces only problems of fact, social science is confronted with problems of fact and with problems of value.

The generalizations appropriate for these two types of problem are fundamentally different. Also, the scientific method appropriate for determining the one type of generalization is quite different and very inappropriate for determining that of the other.

But unless it is realized that science begins with the problem or problems which initiate inquiry, not with facts or with some preconceived method, this basic difference between the two types of problem in social science is not noted, and the need for different scientific methods to resolve the different types of problems is not recognized.

When such oversights occur, confusion results. Normative theories presenting reforms are put forward as if they were factual theories of what is or will be inevitably the case. Or factual information or factual theories are put forward as if they were relevant for confirming or denying normative proposals. Or, what is most usually the case, the end-product is a theory which is neither a verified factual theory of what is the case nor a verified normative theory of what should be the case but a worthless hodge-podge of the two.

It is important to have different names for these two types of theory in social science. It seems appropriate to call them factual social theory and normative social theory respectively.

A factual social theory is one which is false if it is not in complete accord with what is the case. Such a theory of the present social order in the United States will be one that describes existing conditions as they are. It will involve hypotheses and go beyond mere description, but its unique characteristic will be that if there is even one fact out of accord with it, the factual social theory to that extent will not be scientifically verified.

A normative social theory designates what ought to be,

rather than what is. Classical Anglo-American democracy, British Labor Government Socialism, Roman Catholic Thomism and Soviet Russian Communism are normative social theories. None corresponds perfectly to any *de facto* state of affairs anywhere. They designate possible ideals, rather than the actual. Thus, by its very nature a normative social theory differs always in part and perhaps even *in toto* from what is in fact the case.

This means that the scientific method for determining normative social theory cannot be that of natural science applied to social facts. The latter method is appropriate for factual social theory. It is inappropriate for normative social theory.

But even with respect to factual theory, the method for verification in economic science is different from that in physics, as the previous chapter demonstrated. Also, in any one science, even when restricted to problems of fact, there are two stages — the natural history stage and the stage of deductively formulated theory — each with its unique scientific methods.

It is to be noted that factual social theory can include norms in its subject matter. A factual social theory of contemporary Russia would have to refer to its communist ideology. This, however, does not make the factual social theory normative. A social theory becomes normative when it restricts itself to the normative and passes judgment on its norm as compared with other normative theories. Hence, by the method for determining normative social theory is not meant a method enabling one to include norms among its factual data as a factual sociological theory can and probably must do, but the method by which, out of all possible normative theories which the imaginations of men have constructed or can construct, the scientifically correct one is to be determined.

Subsequent chapters will prescribe this scientific method.

But before normative social theory and the scientific methods appropriate thereto can be clearly understood, the different types of factual social theory must be distinguished and their respective methods designated.

The different kinds of factual social theory are best approached by way of the distinction between concepts by intuition and concepts by postulation made in previous chapters. A concept by intuition is one the complete meaning of which is given by something immediately apprehended. By their very nature such concepts can only be appropriately used by inductive methods. Concepts by intuition refer to factors which can be directly inspected. Hence, the scientific methods for handling them must be observation, description and classification. Factual science of this type is science in the natural history stage of development. Conversely, natural history science may be defined as science which restricts itself to concepts by intuition and the inductive methods of Bacon appropriate thereto.

This is the sense in which denoted or described facts come ahead of theory, where by theory one means deductively formulated theory stated in terms of concepts by postulation. One has concepts by intuition before one has concepts by postulation.

Much of contemporary social science is in the natural history stage. Witness most institutional economics, and the purely empirical statistical studies of Wesley Mitchell and his colleagues. The movement in German social science, including economics as well as sociology, called Historismus, falls within this stage. Like the evolutionary theory of Darwin in biology, it is description extrapolated over time, and, hence, due to the persisting use of concepts by intuition, it is of the natural history type.

Marxist economic, political and sociological theory, like Hegelian dialectical Historismus before Marx, is a peculiar mixture, and one must say hodge-podge and confusion (a) of natural history description with deductively formulated factual social theory, and (b) of the factual with the normative. This confusion and unscientific mixing of concepts belonging to different worlds of discourse and the identification of the factual and normative in one theory could never have occurred with Marx had he started with the character of social problems rather than with a natural history description of cultural evolution combined with certain questionable assumptions which he took over uncritically from Hegel.

Marxist materialism, as he and Lenin, following Feuerbach, emphasize, calls for a realistic epistemology. As Chapter III demonstrated, the notion of an external material object is a concept by postulation, not a concept by intuition. But description of evolving social institutions, following the Historismus natural history tradition, calls for concepts by intuition. To combine the two types of concept as Marx has done is to talk nonsense. It is like saying that electrons are pink.

The error slipped uncritically into Marx from Hegel's theory of all concepts as concrete universals. Hegel saw the particularity of the concept by intuition and the universality of the concept by postulation, but, overlooking the epistemic correlation, he saw only one concept, which he termed the concrete universal, when in fact there are two epistemically correlated. Thereby he made a hodge-podge of two distinct worlds of discourse.

Marx inherited a second error from Hegel — the Hegelian identification of the ideal or normative in society with the *de facto* actual. This identifies normative social theory with factual social theory and thus fudges the distinction between factual social problems and normative social problems.

The absurdity of overlooking this distinction showed itself in the case of Hegel in the identification of the ideal society with the *de facto* society of early 19th Century Germany. It shows itself in the case of Marx in the identification of the

ideal society not with any *de facto* society in the present, but
with the *de facto* society that is inevitable, supposedly, tomorrow.   Unfortunately, this supposed inevitability in the
case of Germany did not occur for Marx any more than it
did for Hegel.   The bourgeois democratic society of Germany did not move indubitably into communism.   It went,
instead, to Hitler and then, in the West, under an Anglo-
American ideology in part socialistic but in no part communistic.

Both Hegel's and Marx's identifications of normative social
theory with historical factual social theory have failed to be
confirmed by history.   Thus fact as well as the analysis of the
problems of social science support the distinction between
factual social theory and normative social theory noted earlier
in this chapter.   Furthermore, the distinction between the
natural history type of factual social theory of Historismus
with its historical method, and deductively formulated factual
social theory using concepts by postulation must be retained
also, to avoid mixing worlds of discourse and confusing
historical sequence which is contingent and a concept by
intuition with causal necessity which is a concept by postulation having meaning only in a deductively formulated theory
of history.

Causal necessity or determinism in history is only possible
in a deductively formulated social science which has a theoretical dynamics.   Hume made it clear that necessary connection or determinism is not given inductively in natural history data.

Chapter XIII has made it clear that economic science has
deductively formulated theory.   In this sense it is more
mature than biology among the natural sciences.   With
Pareto, sociology attempted deductively formulated theory
also.

It is to be emphasized that the achievement of deductively
formulated theory in social science involves much more than

the accumulation and extrapolation of natural history data, or the argument from analogy between cultures studied by the historical method after the manner of Arnold Toynbee; it entails the discovery of the key concepts in terms of which any and all natural history data are to be analyzed. The science of statics in mechanics made no progress until Archimedes formulated the concept of the statical moment and Leonardo da Vinci, Stevin and Galilei generalized this concept. Similarly, dynamics developed with Newton only because of Galilei's new definition of force. Likewise, Austrian economic theory achieve a deductive form when the natural history data of the market place were interpreted as the summation of individual wants ordered by individual relations of preference, as Chapter XIII has indicated. By regarding the countless diverse natural history data as but special cases of individual wants ordered by the relation of preference the logical simplicity and deductive fertility of a deductively formulated scientific theory was obtained in economics. Up to this point deductive theory in Austrian and Anglo-American economic science is like deductive theory in physics.

But besides the economy of thought and fertility which it introduces, a deductive theory must also be verified. It is at this point that deductive economics differs from deductive physics. The latter verifies itself indirectly by way of the theorems, as Chapter VIII has shown; the former verifies itself categorically by directly confirming the postulates empirically, as Chapter XIII has indicated.

For this direct verification, economic science pays a price. The price is a restriction to generic factors and the dropping of all specificity of wants and preferences. This renders a theoretical dynamics impossible, as Chapter XIII has demonstrated.

But even if its basic concepts defined the specific as well as the generic properties of the state of an economic system at a given time, the determinism of the latter state would not follow, since the total volume of wants in even an isolated economic system does not obey a conservation law, and without conservation laws, the deduction of the future state of a system from its present state would be impossible even in physics.

The total volume of wants in an isolated economic system is not like the total momentum of an isolated physical system. The latter remains constant with time. But in the economic system when people think prices are going up, their wants increase, and when they think prices are going down, they then tend to contract their wants. In short, economics has no conservation laws, and without conservation laws the deduction of the future state of a system from its present state is impossible.

These details have been repeated in this chapter for one very important reason. They explode the idea of the economic determination of even the economic portion of history, to say nothing about the economic determinism of the whole of social history.

Determinism is possible at all only in a deductively formulated science. Natural history science, as Hume showed, and as the failure of Hegel's and Marx's predictions confirm, can establish no necessary connections. Social science has obtained deductively formulated factual social theory only in the case of economics, and this economic theory is of a character such that in both its method and its assumptions it is impossible to deduce the future from the present.

It may be that the attempt to seek for a prediction of the future state of a social system in factual social theory is a mistake, and that the more fruitful place to look for it is in normative social theory. Since social institutions are in considerable part at least man-made, and normative social theories define the ends of human action, they might quite naturally throw more light on the future state of a social system than factual social theory would show. One empirical consideration supports this suggestion. Hegel and especially Marx, for all their failures with respect to prediction, threw more light on what happened than did the Austrian or classical Anglo-American economic science. And both Hegel and Marx, for all the latter's lip service to naturalistic economic factors, paid considerable attention to ideological factors such as bourgeois democracy vs. socialism and communism. In fact, the observation that social evolution proceeds through revolutions in which the normative social theory defining the traditional social institutions is negated, rather than by the gradualistic changes governing Darwinian evolution in biology, is one of the greatest contributions of Hegel and Marx to social science.

In any event, the need for distinguishing the diverse kinds of generalizations in social science is established. Normative social theory, both in character and method of verification, differs from factual social theory. And among factual social theories those of the natural history type using concepts by intuition are quite different from those of the deductively formulated type using concepts by postulation. And among existant deductively formulated economic theories, both the method of verification and the attendant limited predictive power marks them off sharply from deductively formulated theory in natural science.

It is to be noted that a science of statesmanship or diplomacy either nationally or internationally, and there is such a science both theoretically grounded and honourable, is impossible without both factual social theory and normative social theory. The statesman, when he acts scientifically and wisely, must think and operate literally in two worlds. He must know things as they are; he must also know things as they ought to be. To demand more of the normative in fact than possible changes in the factual will permit may mean the defeat of one's ideals completely, whereas to ask less than perfection may be to achieve more. Scientifically grounded wise statesmanship consists in possessing scientifically verified factual theory concerning what is the case, and scientifically verified normative social theory of what ought to be the case and then achieving as much of the ideal as possible changes in the factual will permit.

This chapter is based in part upon the writer's contribution to the Round Table on *Generalization in the Social Sciences,* under the Chairmanship of Morris Cohen, on December 2, 1939, in connection with the celebration of the tenth anniversary of the founding of the Social Science Research Building at the University of Chicago. See *Eleven Twenty Six: A Decade of Social Research.* Edited by Louis Wirth, pp. 227-273. The University of Chicago Press, 1940.

CHAPTER XV

PARETO'S GENERAL SOCIOLOGY

Pareto's purpose in his *General Sociology* is reasonably clear. He is attempting to establish a theoretical science of sociology, the fundamental concepts of which are justified in an objective manner by an appeal to a wide range of data.

Many have attempted this before him. Pareto believes they failed because they did not distinguish superficial phenomena from fundamental factors. The superficial phenomena, which appear as the reasons and theories people give for their conduct, he calls derivations; the more fundamental factors, which, according to him, are the "manifestations" of "instincts" and "psychic states," he terms residues. The common error is to conceive derivations like scientific theories, as referring to objective factors, when, in point of fact, their sole origin and basis are the "sentiments" which they satisfy. This leads him to draw the very important distinction between logico-experimental and non-logico-experimental theories. The former can be determined to be true or false by objective criteria; the latter are neither true nor false, and discussion of them in such terms is meaningless; they merely satisfy certain sentiments. They are important in sociology, nevertheless, since they indicate the presence of residues which are the significant factors determining the social equilibrium.

The inductive task of sociology, as Pareto practices it, is to collect and analyze derivations to determine the fundamental residues in which they originate. This is done by collecting groups of newspaper clippings and classical allusions bearing on "one same subject-matter," and "find-[ing] in them a constant element." The constant factor is the residue. This "inductive" examination of derivations and residues, together with a criticism of traditional theories in sociology and jurisprudence, concerns Pareto in the first three volumes. The result is six major classes of residues, among which "an instinct to combinations" is a typical example, "the improvident instinct ... in the United States" a more special case.

Pareto then turns to a theoretical formulation of his conception of society. This occupies the first sixty-seven pages of the fourth volume. From this abstract theory he proceeds back again to the empirical material, completing the work.

A preliminary remark may explain the technical and abstract character of his theory. Pareto was trained as an engineer, and investigated equilibrium in heterogeneous systems. This topic concerned Willard Gibbs when he constructed his monumental work in physical chemistry. Pareto carried Gibbs' ideas and method over into sociology. Gibbs' work was extremely abstract. This made Pareto realize that induction is not enough. Before one has mature science, fundamental concepts must be prescribed and a theory must be formulated in precise terms with specific methodological and logical connections to unambiguously determined, inductively given facts. Pareto's work is worth reading as a text in logic solely because of his account of these different aspects of scientific method.

Guided by these considerations from the natural sciences and by his own sociological materials, Pareto is led to conceive society as an equilibrium, composed of individuals termed "social molecules." These "social molecules" are "possessed of" or are "mixtures of" "sentiments" which "manifest" themselves as the "residues" already mentioned. These residues are of two types: those dependent upon, and

those independent of, other residues. The dependently related residues are joined by "ties." Residues, or the "instincts" and "psychic states" which they "manifest," in turn
"manifest themselves through derivations," which are "indi-
cations of the forces acting on the social molecules." They
give rise to changes of form in society which are called "real
movements." Movements which would occur were some
"tie" between "dependent residues" hypothetically sup-
pressed, are termed "virtual movements." In terms of "virtual movements" and "reactions" the crucial notion of "the
state of equilibrium" in a social system is defined: A given
state is a state of equilibrium of a given system if an artificial
subjected change in the system different from the change
which the system ordinarily undergoes, results in a reaction
which immediately returns the system to its normal state.
Physicists will recognize the source of this definition.

In addition to the residues, there are also the derivations.
The derivations do not determine the social equilibrium;
they merely indicate the direction, or the tangent at a given
point to the direction, in which the forces are acting, while
also manifesting the residues which are the significant forces.
By the compounding of residues (accompanied by their attendant derivations), the form of society results by a kind
of composition of forces. The analytical formulation of a
formal technique for representing these forces and their
compounding is one of Pareto's most important contributions.

The social system considered as a whole has certain "properties." One of these, Pareto terms "utility." It is a precisely defined concept replacing vague notions like "pros-
perity." The essentials in its definition are (a) a norm
arbitrarily chosen, and (b) an upper bound, in the mathematical sense of the term, for a series of quantities gained by
measuring certain factors which the society in question actually exhibits. In this connection, two points are to be noted.

First, Pareto admits into "scientific sociology," under the smoke screen of an attack upon metaphysics, the distinction between fact and value ("benefit"). His concept of "utility," together with the technical formal method developed in connection with it for handling the difficult question of "norms" and "benefits," is his second important contribution. Whether it is permissible in an "objective science" is a question which Pareto's disciples must fight out with their more empirically-minded colleagues.

In any event, his introduction of the concept of utility is suggestive. Important distinctions arise between utility for the individual, utility of and for the community, and utility for different individuals. Failure to observe them has certainly misled previous sociologists and reformers. The problem of combining utilities, Pareto regards as one of the major problems of the social sciences.

There is no abuse of statistics. He sees that numbers gained by social studies cannot be summed unless they refer to commensurable units. "The utilities of various individuals are heterogeneous quantities, and a sum of such quantities is a thing that has no meaning; there is no such sum and none can be considered." He sees also that if there is to be a science of sociology along the lines he proposes, a method must be found for reducing utilities to homogeneous quantities which can be summed.

In terms of this abstract system Pareto notes that there are two ideal extreme states: one, in which the equilibrium is determined entirely by "sentiments"; the other, in which logico-experimental theory holds sway. Animal societies are close to the former type; a scientifically controlled society would correspond to the latter type. The existence of a rational society now is a mere fancy of sentimentalists, Pareto holds. Prejudice prevents reason from operating even when known. Also the rational principles are not known, since the relevant data are the heterogeneous utilities and these are neither known nor capable yet of rational treatment.

This brief indication of the scientific substance of Pareto's work quite misrepresents the character of his treatise. His volumes make much more amusing reading than this review can indicate. The reason for this is that we are concerned only with Pareto the scientist, and in addition to him there is a more amusing but less trustworthy Pareto the sentimentalist who insists upon being in the foreground and occupying the greater portion of the space of the four volumes. This sentimental Pareto will be worth watching because he exhibits, in the name of science, the same uncritical devotion to those sentimental attachments that appeal to the typical South-European Latin mind, which his North-European cousin lavishes on the god of "progress." It is this same Pareto the sentimentalist who gives to Theodore Roosevelt, the unfortunate Senator Bérenger, Louis XVI, and countless others, that premature and spirited advice on concrete problems which Pareto the scientist regards as the curse of attempts at a scientific sociology. But it is hopeless for us to attempt to correct the false impression of Pareto's four volumes which strict attention to their scientific portions gives. If Pareto the scientist could not curb Pareto the sentimentalist short of 1,912 pages, it is useless for us to try within the scope of this chapter.

Unfortunately, however, the sentimentalism has flowed over into the inductive portion of the science. The application of Pareto's own criterion for sentimentalism to the inductive basis of his theory will make this clear. This criterion is that a sentimental theory is retained by its believer without objective evidence and when obvious inconsistencies in it appear.

Certainly Pareto assures us often enough that he is going to be scientific in precisely the same objectively verifiable sense in which the natural sciences are scientific. With equal vehemence he condemns introspective data. Nevertheless, on page 177 he writes that "on knowledge of such psychic states our research is based."

To be sure, Pareto tells us elsewhere that his "psychic states" have nothing to do with introspective factors. But what in actual practice does this mean? The word "such" in the last quotation gives the clue. It refers back to an immediately previous clause concerning the "psychic" states of people revealed in historical material. Thus instead of being even the first-hand psychic states given immediately to the trained introspective psychologist, they are the second- or third-hand characteristics assigned to people, mostly in the ancient past, who, at the time Pareto makes his "observations," exist only in his imagination as he reconstructs them from newspaper clippings and classical texts which are before him. Not once, be it noted, in getting his "facts" does Pareto leave the armchair in his study.

This in actual practice is the "scientific sociology" of Pareto, on its inductive side. Because the newspaper clippings and the classical texts are before him on his desk in the strict objective sense of the word, he believes for some mysterious reason that the societies and individuals (with their "psychic states" and "instincts to combinations," their "improvident instinct," and "their greater or less potency of the sentiments of uniformity") which he constructs in his imagination are objective in the same sense, and that by "basing" his research upon "such psychic states" he has made an objective science out of sociology.

Nor is this all. Even these imaginative reconstructions of people in the distant present or ancient past do not provide the fundamental concepts of Pareto's system. They give only derivations. As Pareto says, "derivations only are known to us." The fundamental factors are the residues. But there is no exact correspondence between derivations and residues. In fact, Pareto's fundamental contention is that derivations conceal the residues. The task, therefore, is to get from the deceptive derivations to the residues. To do this, Pareto says, "We have to collect large numbers of derivations associated with one same subject-matter, and then find in them a constant element that can be distinguished from variable elements." We are to presume that this is the residue. But what criterion is to determine which of many possible classifications is to define "one same subject-matter"? Furthermore, what specific rules of procedure are to determine whether a scientific sociologist, given a collection of newspaper clippings and classical allusions, does not, in the "common factor" which he "finds," confuse the objective "forces acting on the social molecules" with some whim of his fancy? Clearly the criterion for determining these specific rules of procedure must be found in the formal properties of the relation connecting derivations to residues. Unless this relation guiding one from the "given" derivations to the "inferred" residue is specific, there can be no scientific assurance in the objective sense of the term either that there are residues or that they are those which Pareto specifies.

Let us examine this relation. Pareto designates it by the term "manifestation." Residues are "manifestations" of "instincts" and "sentiments," and derivations are "manifestations" of residues. In the formal properties of this relation of "manifestation" we must look, therefore, for the clue to the precise methodological procedure which alone can ensure an objective scientific test for the existence of residues. Unfortunately, Pareto never defines this relation.

It appears, therefore, that Pareto's "objective facts" are spurious, and that even if this were not the case, the connection between them and the fundamental sociological concepts of his theory is so nebulous as to give the latter no scientific validity in the strict sense of the term. His theory on the inductive side gives high testimony to Pareto's astuteness in choosing his classical references and to his powers of suggestion; it is psychologically and sentimentally illuminating and interesting; it may be in part true, but, as Pareto the sober scientist would say, "Until some strictly logico-experimental test is given, who knows?"

These fundamental weaknesses on the inductive side must not be allowed to conceal Pareto's other accomplishments. His account of scientific method is excellent. His rejection of metaphysical theories which have their "criterion for truth outside experience," is equally sound. His recognition that systematically and precisely formulated theory is necessary in any science, and his attempts to draw upon the physical sciences to construct such theory for sociology, are important. His recognition of the need of the distinction between fact and value or "benefit" is noteworthy, and his development of a formal analytical technique for relating, while distinguishing, these two aspects of social phenomena, is even more important.

If future sociologists can take the formal properties of Pareto's abstract theory and replace his pseudo-objective clues with trained observers' first-hand observations of immediately present social phenomena of the type which Underhill Moore and his colleagues have finally succeeded in obtaining, it may well be that Pareto will mark the beginning of an exceedingly important advance in sociology.

This chapter is reprinted from the *Virginia Quarterly Review,* Vol. 11, No. 4, 1935, with the kind permission of the Editor.

Vilfredo Pareto. *The Mind and Society.* Edited by Arthur Livingston. Translated by Andrew Bongiorno and Arthur Livingston. Harcourt, Brace and Company, New York, 1935.

Underhill Moore and Colleagues. *Legal and Institutional Methods Applied to Orders to Stop Payment of Checks.* Yale Law Journal, Vol. XLII, 1933, pp. 817-862 and 1198-1235. Also *Law and Learning Theory: A Study in Legal Control.* The Yale Law Journal Company, 1943.

CHAPTER XVI

THE IDEOLOGICAL PROBLEMS OF
SOCIAL SCIENCE

If social science is to meet the problems of the present world it must contribute to the resolution of its ideological conflicts. Much of recent anthropological and sociological science is incapable of doing this because of its neglect of the rôle of the ideational factor in culture. Culture too often has tended to be thought of after the manner of nature, as an objective, completely deterministic, evolutionary process with respect to which man's social theories must be adjusted but itself conversely unaffected by these theories.

This conception fails to do justice to the revolutionary, rather than gradualistic evolutionary character of social changes in time, especially in the West, noted by Hegel and Marx. Also, it overlooks the manner in which the introduction of new economic, political, religious or philosophical doctrines leads to a reconstruction in social institutions. Unless this determination of social facts by the ideas or theories which one holds is recognized, social science is unable even to account for the ideological conflicts of our world, to say nothing about being able to resolve them.

The reason for this current incapacity is easy to understand. It goes back to the faulty conceptions of the initiation of scientific inquiry noted in Chapter I. Impressed by the success of the natural sciences, the social scientists hastily and uncritically assumed that the whole of social science can be put upon a scientific basis by applying the method of natural science to social facts. Since the methods of natural science are so determined by the problems of fact with which natural science is solely concerned that they give only theory which is completely in accord with what is in fact the case, the inevitable result was a social science in which social phenomena determined social theory and in which social theory never determined social facts. Hence the naive and erroneous assumption that social evolution is an objective, deterministic evolutionary process after the analogy of biological evolution, in spite of the fact that no social science has achieved the theoretical dynamics necessary scientifically to demonstrate historical determinism in social phenomena. Hence, also, the utter inability of natural history historians and social scientists alike to either comprehend or resolve the inescapable ideological social problems of our world.

The scientific cure for this incapacity of contemporary history and social science is equally evident. It is the prescription of Chapter II; Scientific inquiry in any field must begin not with some method taken over *a priori* from some other field, but with the character of the problems of its own field and the analysis of these problems. A subject becomes scientific not by beginning with facts, with hypothesis or with some pet method brought in *a priori*, but by beginning with the peculiar character of its particular problems.

In the social sciences and humanities, as Chapter XIV has demonstrated, these problems are of two fundamentally different types: (1) problems of fact and (2) problems of value. For the former the methods of natural science applied to social facts are appropriate. For the latter, the methods of natural science applied to social facts are inappropriate; a scientific method which gives verified normative social theory rather than verified factual social theory is essential.

With normative social theory, as well as factual social theory, the ideological conflicts of society can be understood, since an ideological conflict arises when two societies or two political or cultural groups in the same society hold and pursue different normative social theories. And with the scientific method for verifying normative social theory in a manner valid for everybody determined, a social science and humanism will be at hand which can not merely understand but also resolve the ideological conflicts of the world.

The crucial question for social science and the humanities, therefore, arises: What is the method for verifying normative human or social theory? An analysis of the ideological problems of social science should provide *one* approach to the answer to this question.

These ideological problems arise because of conflicting normative theories for society. Laissez faire Anglo-American democracy, socialism, communism, Roman Catholicism, etc., are competing for the allegiance of mankind as a model for the world's social institutions. Hence, if we are to understand these conflicts we must comprehend the different normative theories which define them.

Each one of these normative theories is understood when its specific economic doctrine, political theory, legal theory, religious doctrine and conception of art are specified. A doctrine in any field is specified when its elementary assumptions are indicated. These assumptions indicate the entities and relations taken as basic in terms of which the rest of the doctrine can be defined. But the primitive assumptions of the economic theory of a given culture are intimately related to the primitive assumptions of its political theory, its legal philosophy, its religious doctrine and its art forms. In short, a single culture is not made up of five independent economic, political, legal, religious and aesthetic assumptions but of a single set of assumptions of which the economic, political, legal, religious and aesthetic are parts. This single set of assumptions is the philosophy of a given normative culture. Thus, upon analysis, we find that every ideological conflict is at bottom a conflict between different philosophical theories.

When the different philosophical theories of differing cultures or ideologies are examined two possibilities present themselves. The ideologies may be different yet compatible, or the ideologies may be different and incompatible.

When the former possibility is the case, the problem of resolving an ideological conflict is relatively easy. It consists merely in enlarging the ideology of the one culture to include that of the other.

It is when the philosophies defining the different ideologies of two cultures are contradictory that the real difficulty arises. In this case the procedure of logicians and theoretical natural scientists provides a clue. It often happens in mathematical physics that the experimental evidence leads the physicist to two theories, both of which are required, yet the two theories are contradictory. The logician and theoretical physicist know that when such a situation arises, the problem can be met only by passing to a new set of assumptions which takes care of the data leading to the two traditional theories, without contradiction. This means that in the case of conflicting ideologies in the social sciences, such as exists at present between the ideologies of the traditional democracies and communist Russia, no real solution can be achieved without an analysis which passes to a new set of philosophical assumptions.

There is, however, one other clue. As we have noted, every cultural ideology, when made articulate, involves a basic philosophy in terms of which the economic doctrine, the political doctrine, the legal theory, the religious theory and the artistic forms of that culture are defined. The validity of any one such philosophy cannot be determined by appealing to the data of the humanities or social science. For the data reflect this or some other ideology. They are not objective like the processes of natural science. Thus to base one's normative social theories on the empirical cultural data is to beg the normative question.

Nature, however, is here independently of our theories of it. Nature does not undergo a revolution in its specific foundations when a physicist is led to a new theory of nature. Furthermore, an analysis of the verified theories and of the method of the natural sciences designates a philosophy of natural science. This philosophy is quite independent of normative social theories. Moreover, if properly determined by the appropriate method, the philosophy of natural science designated is uniquely determined. Thus by taking our empirical philosophy of the natural sciences as the criterion of the correct normative philosophy of the social sciences, we obtain an objectively verifiable philosophy of culture. Also, we secure a norm for culture in which man's scientific conception of himself and the good life is not in conflict, as is the case at present in the modern West, with his humanistic conception.

This chapter is the condensation of a paper read in 1946 before a group of anthropologists convened by The Viking Fund in New York City.

L. K. Frank. *Man's Multidimensional Environment.* Scientific Monthly, Vol. LVI, 1943.

David Bidney. *On the Concept of Culture and Some Cultural Fallacies.* American Anthropologist, Vol. 46, 1944, pp. 30-44.

Clyde Kluckhohn and William H. Kelly. "The Concept of Culture" in *The Science of Man in the World Crisis.* Edited by Ralph Linton. Columbia University Press, New York, 1945.

F. S. C. Northrop. *The Meeting of East and West: An Inquiry Concerning World Understanding.* The Macmillan Company. New York, 1946.

CHAPTER XVII

THE CRITERION OF THE GOOD STATE

Theories in social science differ from those in natural science. This occurs because the phenomena of nature give rise only to problems of fact whereas those of culture present problems of value as well. Of society we ask not merely concerning what the facts are but also how we can alter them to produce a more ideal state of affairs. Problems which raise questions of fact we shall call "factual social problems," and problems which raise questions of value we shall call "normative social problems." Similarly, social theories which propose a solution of social problems of fact we shall call "factual social theories," and social theories which propose solutions of social problems of value we shall call "normative social theories." Democracy is a normative social theory.

The question of the validity of democracy resolves itself, therefore, into the prior problem of determining the scientific method for designating the correctness of one normative social theory rather than another. What is this method?

The scientific method for determining factual social theory is well known. It is the application of the empirical and formal methods of natural science to social facts. This method prescribes that no theory treated by it can be correct unless it is completely in accord with all the facts in the situation to which it refers. A factual social theory for a given society may be defined, therefore, as a body of propositions designating a state of affairs which is completely in accord at every point with what actually exists. A normative social theory, on the other hand, is one designating a possible state of affairs for a given society which differs in whole or in part from what a correct factual social theory for that society would designate. The Declaration of Independence, the Communist Manifesto, and Hitler's *Mein Kampf* are examples. They do not purport to designate correctly the existing factual situation in any society. Instead, they define a norm for the social order toward which men may aim as an ideal quite different, in part at least, from any social situation actually existing.

It follows that the method for determining the correct normative social theory cannot be that of natural science applied to social phenomena. The method of natural science is so constructed that no theory will be designated by it as correct unless the theory is completely in accord with the factual situation to which it refers. Since by definition and because of its very purpose a normative social theory is one which differs in whole or in part from the factual situation, it follows that the scientific method for determining normative social theory cannot be that of natural science applied to social materials.

This is the methodological reason why one cannot get the "ought" or the "good" for a given society from the "is" for that society. When this point is overlooked, an error occurs which certain students of personal ethics term "the naturalistic fallacy" but which we, because problems of value arise in culture rather than in nature, shall term "the culturalistic fallacy." The fallacy is due not to a moral but to a methodological error. It consists in applying to normative social theory a scientific procedure which is appropriate only for factual social theory.

The prevalence of the culturalistic fallacy has not been appreciated. Under the misleading name of the naturalistic fallacy it has been emphasized in personal ethics by G. E. Moore and the idealists. They have seen quite correctly that the so-called "naturalists" in ethics are guilty of it in making immediately introspected pleasures and interests the criterion of the good. But even G. E. Moore and the idealists or phenomenological axiologists have not taken the fallacy with complete seriousness, as is evidenced by the fact that they do not recognize its even more flagrant presence in themselves. G. E. Moore's "good," given as an immediately apprehended ethical primitive which is indefinable, after the manner of the color yellow, is as excellent an example as can be found of identifying the criterion of the normative for man with the immediately intuited actual which he introspects in himself. The axiologists' "scale of values" gained phenomenologically by *reine Beschreibung* is an equally impressive instance. What all these traditional modern moral philosophers over-look is that the introspectively given factor to which they appeal, whether it be either a group of psychological items such as "pleasures" or "interests" or a primitive ethical item such as "intrinsic goodness," is culturally conditioned. We have the "interests," "pleasures," or sense of "intrinsic good-ness," which introspection at any time may reveal to us, be-cause we live in a democratic or a Nazi or a Communist com-munity. Thus to make any one of these items our criterion of the good is to beg the very point at issue in any social question concerning the validity of one of these normative social theories rather than another. Even in personal ethics any vital moral issue raises the question concerning whether our "interest," "pleasure," or sense of "intrinsic goodness" should be what it is. Thus to make any one of these the cri-terion of the good is not merely to beg the question but to commit the culturalistic fallacy by identifying the "interests," "pleasures," or sense of "intrinsic goodness" which one ought to have with the particular ones which one does have.

That this is a fallacy even the "naturalists" in ethics have no difficulty in seeing when it occurs in Hitler. That the Nazi normative social theory is more nearly in accord than any other normative social theory with the social facts in a good portion of Continental Europe at the present writing in 1941 cannot be denied. Most of the countries there are nazified. Yet none of our "naturalistic" moral philosophers would regard this as an argument for the correctness of naziism as a normative social theory, even where its proponents have made the social facts correspond to its ideal. It can hardly be denied either that Hitler is pursuing what seems to him in all sincerity to be "intrinsically good" or that he has the "pleasures" and "interests" and moral intuitions of the intrinsic rightness of his cause which he actually says he has. Insincerity concerning his own moral intuitions is, unfortunately, the least of his vices. He is too confoundedly sincere with respect to his psychological and moral introspections. His error is that he has made the actual interests and pleasures and the intuition of the intrinsic goodness of his cause, which he immediately experiences, the criterion of the correct normative theory in personal and social conduct. In short, he has committed the culturalistic fallacy. One must be equally suspicious of this practice when it occurs in one's self, and even when the normative theory which seems to be verified by this method is that of democracy. The democratic social ideal must find some other less fallacious and question-begging procedure than this for its justification.

But if the correctness of normative social theory cannot be determined by an immediate apprehension of the factual data of one's introspectively given psychological or moral sense or by the application of the method of natural science to social facts, how then can it be determined?

A partial answer is prescribed by one property of normative social theory: Its propositions are synthetic and not necessary. That they are not necessary is shown by the fact that there are several rival normative social theories, e.g., democracy, fascism, communism, etc. This prevents the truth of any one of them from being determined by the presuppositional method on Kantian a priori grounds. For the latter method to designate the verification of any theory to which it is applied, the theory must possess necessity and universality. No normative social theory possesses these properties. The fact that its propositions are synthetic rules out any guaranty of their truth within the propositions themselves, apart from their relation to facts outside them, on tautological grounds or after the manner of the primitive propositions of *Principia Mathematica* according to the earlier theory of Ludwig Wittgenstein. In short, the synthetic non-necessary character of the propositions of normative social theory necessitates that such theory can be verified only by an empirical method.

Nevertheless, as we have previously shown, when we make the data of one's introspectively given personal awareness or the facts of society the field of application of the empirical method, we gain factual rather than normative social theory and thereby commit the culturalistic fallacy. It would seem that we must use the empirical method and that we cannot use the empirical method.

Because of this paradoxical situation many positivistic contemporary students of ethics have concluded that normative theories have no scientific status whatever and are purely hortatory. Our analysis brings out even more conclusively than the positivists have done the basic reasons for the plausibility of their conclusion. Nevertheless, to acquiesce in it is to maintain that Hitler's ideal for the state has exactly as good a cognitive and moral status as Locke's or Jefferson's or Ghandi's. If we are to escape this conclusion, some way out of our paradox must be found.

It behooves us to examine the paradox more closely. It arises because essential properties of normative social theory (1) permit verification only by an empirical method and (2) necessitate the avoidance of the culturalistic fallacy. Verification by the empirical method is required because the propositions of normative social theory are synthetic; the

THE CRITERION OF THE GOOD STATE

culturalistic fallacy must be avoided because one cannot get
normative social theory, which by definition differs in whole
or in part from what is the case in actual society, by a procedure which can verify only factual social theory which is
completely in accord with what is the case.

This means that the paradox cannot be escaped by insisting
upon the first requirement of an empirical method while
ignoring the culturalistic fallacy, as the "naturalists" and
so-called legal "realists" have done or by emphasizing for
their opponents, while ignoring for themselves, the second
requirement of avoiding the culturalistic fallacy and then
rejecting the empirical method, as the "idealists" have done.
Both requirements must be satisfied.

Is this possible? One fact necessitates an affirmative
answer: The two properties of normative social theory
which entail the use of the empirical method and the avoidance of the culturalistic fallacy are themselves compatible.
Certainly there is no contradication in propositions being
synthetic and at the same time designating a possible form for
society which differs in whole or in part from what is the
case in any actual society. But compatible properties of a
set of propositions cannot entail incompatible methodological requirements for the verification of those propositions. One cannot deduce an incompatibility from a
compatibility. Consequently, the use of the empirical
method and the avoidance of the culturalistic fallacy can
be combined without contradiction.

The importance of this demonstration can hardly be
exaggerated. It shows that the problem of designating a
scientific method for solving problems of value in personal
ethics and social science has a solution. In trying to find
this method we are not, as the positivists maintain, attempting the impossible. The normative character of normative
social theory—i.e., its divergence from what is, in fact, the
case — does not preclude the use of the empirical method and

make verification impossible. Having put the argument for the nonverifiable and hence noncognitive, purely hortatory character of normative propositions in a more powerful form than that given by the positivists themselves, their thesis is nevertheless shown to be false. The attempt to avoid the culturalistic fallacy and at the same time attain verification by an empirical method is not self-contradictory. This our demonstration in the previous paragraph has established.

Our paradox has a solution which does not involve either rejecting the empirical method or committing the culturalistic fallacy. It remains to discover and to designate precisely what this solution is.

Evidently, in passing from the two compatible properties of normative social theory to their methodological prescriptions for verification, an unjustified assumption has slipped in surreptitiously. Find and reject this faulty assumption and the empirical method for testing normative social theory which avoids the culturalistic fallacy should exhibit itself.

Let us begin with the two important properties of normative propositions and move forward more cautiously to their requirements with respect to the method of verification.

The first property of normative social theory is that its propositions are synthetic propositions. This necessitates that normative social theory can be tested only by an empirical method. Two significant points must be noted: first, nothing is indicated concerning the kind of facts to which the empirical method is to be applied; second, it follows that the traditional statement of "the naturalistic fallacy" is erroneous. This statement as given by Kant, G. E. Moore, and W. M. Urban, prohibits taking *any* empirically given "is" as the criterion of the "good" or the "ought." Were this the case, normative propositions could not be synthetic propositions; also the paradox would be insoluble. If the culturalistic fallacy in the form in which it designates a demonstrable error were to prohibit the validation of normative theory by the empirical appeal to *any* "is" whatever, then, indeed, the requirements of (1) avoiding the culturalistic fallacy and (2) using the empirical method would be incompatible.

At last the surreptitious assumption producing our paradox reveals itself. It is the faulty traditional statement of the so-called naturalistic fallacy which, upon the basis of the demonstrable error of verifying normative social theory by appeal to introspectively given personal or publicly given social facts, asserts the *non sequitur* that it is a fallacy to test normative theory by an appeal to *any empirical data whatever.*

Our demonstration and previous precise statement of the culturalistic fallacy confirms this conclusion. The fact upon which the demonstration rests is that normative social theory, by definition, because of its very purpose designates a possible form for society which differs in whole or in part from what an empirically verified factual social theory for any actual society would indicate.   Consequently, the procedure for determining the correct normative social theory cannot be the empirical method applied to social facts, or, as we also showed, to introspectively given psychological or supposedly primitive ethical data.   Thus the precise statement of the culturalistic fallacy is not that it is an error to test the normative by an appeal to the factual but that it is an error to test the normative for society by an appeal to the factual in society or the normative for one's "pleasures," "interests" or "sense of goodness" by one's actual "pleasures," "interests," and "ethical intuitions."   In short, the avoidance of the culturalistic fallacy does not prohibit an empirical appeal to any facts; it merely prohibits an empirical appeal to certain facts.   Consequently, our paradox becomes resolved, providing that we, in our verification of normative social theory, apply the empirical method to facts other than those explicitly repudiated by the avoidance of the culturalistic fallacy in its precisely stated, demonstrably correct formulation.

Put positively, the steps of our analysis may now be summarized as follows: The synthetic character of the propositions of normative social theory necessitates that its correctness be determined only by an appeal to empirical evidence outside the theory. Yet, when we make the empirical data either of introspective awareness or of social phenomena the source of this empirical appeal, we gain factual rather than normative personal or social theory and thereby commit the culturalistic fallacy. In short, we must test normative theory by an empirical method applied to empirical facts, yet these facts cannot be either the subjective items of introspection or the public facts of actual society. Since no other facts exist except those of nature as verified by the data of immediate intuition and sense awareness, no alternative remains but to conclude that the scientific procedure for determining the correct normative social theory is that of applying the empirical method to the facts of nature. Only thus can the empirical method of verification required by the synthetic propositions of normative social theory be obtained and the culturalistic fallacy in the precise form in which it designates a demonstrable error be avoided.

But how, it may be asked, can the factual data of natural science provide an empirical criterion of the correctness of a normative idea of the good for social science? Are not the facts of nature one thing and man's social ideals for his culture a quite different thing? At first sight this seems to be the case. Further analysis, however, throws a slightly different complexion upon the matter. What do we mean by nature? Only an analysis of the method, the immediately apprehensible data, and the verified theory of natural science in their relation to one another can give us an answer to this question. Such an analysis shows that we mean by nature not merely the immediately apprehended data but also the postulated system of objects and processes which the experimentally verified, deductively formulated theories of natural science designate. The theories are held to be scientifically verified if deductions from them correlate correctly with the immediately inspected data. What must be realized, however, is that the theories designate a character of our universe and ourselves as a part thereof which goes far beyond the immediately sensed data by means of which the theories are verified. As a consequence our experimentally verified theories of nature provide us, when we analyze them with respect to their basic postulates and primitive concepts, with a tremendous philosophical conception of our universe and of ourselves. Our analysis suggests, therefore, that this philosophical conception in its epistemic correlation with the immediately apprehended data which provide its verification is to be identified with our scientific criterion of the correct normative social theory for culture. Our justification for this unexpected conclusion is that only thus can an empirical criterion for normative social theory be found which does not commit the culturalistic fallacy.

Our criterion of the good state is unorthodox only for recent ethical theory. It is the orthodox method used by Locke upon Newton's mechanics in arriving through his dualistic theory of material and mental substances at his normative theory of the state, and prescribed by Socrates in Plato's *Republic*. In vii. 533 Socrates says that "the power of dialectic alone can reveal this (the idea of the good), and only to one who is a disciple of the previous sciences." Examine these "previous sciences" which Socrates lists on the previous pages and the reader will find each one to be a mathematical natural science, thus supporting our thesis that it is only to the data of nature rather than to the humanities and culture that one must appeal for normative theory. Examine "dialectic" and one will find it to be a purely

288 LOGIC OF THE SCIENCES AND HUMANITIES

formal method applied to the scientific hypotheses to make evident their elementary, primitive concepts and postulates.

At last we come to the relevance of our technical analysis for our major topic, the philosophic basis of democracy. The relevance is this: Democracy is a normative social theory. Were democracy a factual social theory, its correctness could be determined by social scientists applying the methods of natural science to social phenomena without any contribution from philosophy. But, being a normative social theory, there can be no trustworthy, publicly valid criterion of its validity or invalidity apart from an analysis of the verified theories of natural science, which makes articulate on both their ontological-theoretical and their epistemological-operational side the philosophical conception of nature and of man in his relation to nature which these theories entail. This analysis it is the business of the philosopher of science to pursue, not adding new facts or interpretations, but merely making articulate the philosophical conception of nature and man which the verified scientific theory necessitates. Consequently, there can be no trustworthy determination of social ideals without such a philosophy of natural science.

The second major question now arises. What light does such a philosophical analysis of the verified theories of natural science throw upon the nature of the correct normative social theory which must define our social ideal for the immediate future? An adequate answer to this question would involve a technical analysis of the theories of contemporary science on both their ontological-theoretical and their intuitive-empirical side, taking us far beyond the scope of this chapter. Certain general considerations can, however, be indicated. As we have noted previously, natural science exhibits the character of nature to us in two ways: one, through the immediately apprehended continuum and its differentiated data exhibited by the senses to which natural science appeals for the verification of its theory; the other, through the systematically related, unobserved entities and processes designated by the postulates of that verified theory. Nature, therefore, as given by natural science, is partly known empirically by immediate intuition and the senses and partly known theoretically by the intellect and the imagination checked indirectly by experimental verification.

This continuity of the immediately apprehended is as inductively given and primary as the sensed qualities which differentiate the continuum. At this point contemporary scientific philosophy comes into agreement with the fundamental aesthetic intuition and religious insight of the Orient.

It is the character of anything immediately apprehended that it is ineffable in the sense of being indescribable to anyone who has not directly experienced it. The sun to which the astronomer appeals to verify his theory is not the three-dimensional spherical aggregate of particles to which his experimentally verified theory refers but is instead the two-dimensional colored patch which the artist paints. This reminds us that nature as immediately apprehended and sensed, even in the empirical verification of the scientist, is nature in its aesthetic character. Let us therefore designate this factor as the aesthetic component of nature.

Nature as designated by the verified scientific theory is a quite different thing, involving electrons with diameters too small for any possible observation to detect directly and velocities of an amount so great as to strain the most fertile imagination. Nature in this sense is not seen but thought. We shall call it, therefore, the theoretic component of nature.

We arrive, therefore, at this general concept of the idea of the good for our culture: That form of society is the good one which embodies in the emotions of men a sensitivity to nature in its aesthetic aspect and orders its education, its intellectual outlook, and its social institutions in the light of the latest verified, philosophically articulate scientific theory of nature in its theoretic aspect.

Note the remarkable manner in which this technical and abstractly determined normative social theory meets the specific problems and needs of our culture. If there is one thing more than anything else which has upset our traditional social, economic and political institutions and modified every phase of our personal and social lives it is the inroad of technology. Certainly no ideal can solve the normative social problems of our particular society unless this ideal includes within itself the fundamental ideas which have created these problems. The ideas behind modern technology are the fundamental principles of the experimentally verified natural sciences. These ideas the theoretic component of nature in our normative social theory provides.

There is a second problem in our culture. Our increased mastery of the theoretic component of nature made possible by the electromagnetic theory in modern science in particular has lifted the major portion of the work of the world off the muscles of the men and placed it upon the waterfalls. With this tremendous achievement the physical needs of mankind can be supplied by a relatively small portion of all men. Unfortunately, however, our monetary theory is still the the one that was defined by the normative social theory of the seventeenth and eighteenth centuries. According to this theory, one must do work in order to gain the money to buy the goods for one's needs. Yet in times of peace the work is not available for all, since a goodly portion of it is being done by the waterfalls. Thus, owing to the failure of our normative social theory to keep abreast of the scientific and philosophical advances at its basis, the American culture found itself, immediately before the present war, in the paradoxical position of having millions faced with starvation, while the food that would assuage their hunger rotted in the granaries. Such is the price which a society pays for failing to provide the philosophical analysis of the verified theory of natural science which is necessary to keep its normative social theory

abreast of the social changes wrought by its scientific technology. Our criterion of the correct normative social theory
would remove this deficiency, since it informs us that only
that ideal for the organization of the monetary, economic
and political life of the state is the correct one which proceeds
from the conception of man and nature which is specified in
the theoretic component of nature designated by a logical
analysis and philosophical articulation of the verified theories
of contemporary natural science.

There is a third problem in our culture arising out of
the second, to which we have just referred. What are men
to do with their time now that our mastery of the theoretic
component of nature has enabled the dynamo and the waterfalls to take a major portion of the work of the world off
the muscles of men? To this question also our normative
theory gives the answer. For it tells us that a truly good
state must cultivate man's sensitivity to the aesthetic component of nature and himself, as well as inform his activities
with the theoretical component. Thus to the degree to
which our mastery of nature in its theoretic aspect through
technology releases men from long-drawn-out labor, to that
extent they are left free to pursue nature in its aesthetic
aspect and thereby sustain our spiritual as well as our
material needs. The good state of the future must make
the cultivation of the arts a necessary part of its program.

It appears, therefore, that the fundamental moral issue
of our time is not so much between democracy as we now
know it and any of the rival ideologies which threaten its
destruction, as between the traditional social ideas in any
form and the more adequate ideal which it is our privilege
to actualize. Providing that we pursue the scientific knowledge and the philosophical analysis which are appropriate
for the correct determination of our normative social theory
and remodel our emotions aesthetically and our institutions
theoretically to bring both into accord with the aesthetic

and theoretic components of nature which this new normative social theory defines, then, come what may, we need have no fears for ourselves or for democracy.   By the fruits of our free but expert inquiry we shall have solved correctly the problems which confront our culture.

This chapter is reprinted from *Ethics,* Vol. LII, 1940, with the kind permission of the Editor.   It was read in part in the Symposium on *Philosophical Presuppositions of Democracy* of the Eastern Division of the American Philosophical Association at Vassar College on December 31, 1941.

G. E. Moore. *Principia Ethica.* Cambridge University Press, 1903.

W. M. Urban. *Valuation; Its Nature and Laws.* New York, 1909.

Ludwig Wittgenstein. *Tractatus Logico-Philosophicus.* Kegan Paul, London, 1922.

R. B. Perry. *General Theory of Value.* Longman's, Green and Company, New York, 1926.

K. N. Llewellyn. *The Bramble Bush: Some Lectures on Law and Its Study.* New York, 1930.

Moritz Schlick, *Fragen der Ethik.*   J. Springer, Wien, 1930.

C. I. Lewis, *Analysis of Knowledge and Valuation.* Open Court, 1946.

CHAPTER XVIII

PHILOSOPHICAL METHOD AND WORLD PEACE

The presuppositions of a culture determine its empirical manifestations and institutions. This is difficult to see in ourselves; it is easily evident, however, in a foreign culture. Certainly the predominantly Catholic society of colonial Mexico, with its baroque architecture, its hierarchical, monarchical political order, and its widely extended, deeply moving, religious sentiments, is not to be understood apart from the basic beliefs of medieval Spanish Roman Catholicism. It is clear, also beyond doubt in this instance that the beliefs of Aristotle, Saint Thomas and Las Casas came first and that the facts and institutions of colonial Mexico came afterwards. It is equally clear in the Mexican culture of the nineteenth century that the philosophical ideas of Voltaire and the French Encyclopaedists preceded the democratic, political revolution of 1810 and the subsequent nationalization of church property and secularization of education. In similar fashion, the social philosophy of Comte preceded and defined the pattern which determined social and political policy in Mexico between 1876 and 1910 under the dictatorship of Porfirio Diaz. Likewise, the philosophy of Marx, as conveyed to the Mexican intelligentsia and the masses by the paintings of Diego Rivera and David Alfaro Siqueiros, preceded by means of their influence during the 1920's and early 1930's the six-year plan of the Cardenas regime during the years from 1934 to 1940.

In no less striking fashion, the fundamental philosophy of Thomas Jefferson, John Adams, and the other founding fathers, going back in turn to the French political thinkers and behind them directly to John Locke, has determined the political pattern and social traits of the traditional culture of the United States.

One could repeat similar examples without limit. It cannot be denied that the philosophy of history of Marx and Lenin, with its predominantly economic emphasis and its presupposition of the evolving, dialectically determined form of the social historical process as primary, has had a great deal to do with the empirical facts and social institutions now exhibiting themselves in the Soviet Union.

In the Orient this basic and causely definitive importance of unique philosophical presuppositions in determining the facts of culture is equally evident. Starting from a philosophy which emphasized quietism, nonaction, intuition and contemplation, these peoples have given rise to religions expressed in the intuitive poetry of the Upanishads or the informal conversations of Confucius rather than in the formally constructed, logically reasoned doctrines of an Aristotle, a Saint Thomas, a Spinoza, a Kant or a Calvin. The Oriental peoples have also, by means of these philosophical assumptions and their attendant, more contemplative, pacifistic, less belligerent religious and political sentiments, kept their peoples out of bloody, nationalistic wars to the death to a degree which makes the fruits of Western religion in comparison look more like the product of Satan than of the Prince of Peace. For precisely the same reason Oriental nations, with the exception of Japan, which chanced to possess a discarded, tribal, and hence nationalistic, religion in Shintoism, have found it impossible to develop nations of the Western type without the importation from the West of quite alien philosophical and religious assumptions such as those of Christanity in the case of contemporary China. Only on this basis could the present Chinese leaders create a willingness of the individual to make moral principles applying over a nationalistic scale more important than the individual, so that the contemporary Chinese have become ready, recently, to reverse completely their scale of values by placing the soldier morally as well as actually at the top of the social scale instead of leaving him at the very bottom morally, where he had been for centuries.   As Generalissimo Chiang Kai-shek, in his recent letter to the Methodist Church in the United States, has written, "Today I find that I have taken a further step and have become a follower of Jesus Christ. This makes me realize more fully than ever that the success of our revolution depends upon men of faith, men of character who, because of their faith, will not sacrifice principle for personal safety under circumstances of difficulty and crisis. . . ."   With respect to the sentiments and the institutions of culture, the antecedent philosophical presuppositions are very important things.

Once this most elementary and fundamental fact is appreciated, the problem of the peace becomes evident and falls definitely into two parts: One, the designation of the basic presuppositions of the major cultures likely to determine the course of world affairs; and, two, the analysis of these with a view to finding a single set of assumptions defining our ideals for the peace, which will possess an adequacy and generality sufficient to permit the diverse, differing assumptions of the major cultures of the world to generate their own facts and institutions without conflict.   Since the subject whose business it is to study presuppositions is philosophy, its relevance for the peace now becomes evident.

Its first task is definite and straightforward.   It consists in taking the method of logical, accompanied by historical, analysis and applying it to an existent culture such as that of the Spanish Colonial Period or of the French Nineteenth Century Period of Mexico to trace the culture in question back to the antecedent economic, political, and religious doctrines, which in turn go back to the primary and more

elementary philosophical presuppositions upon which they
rest. Having done this for the major cultures of the world
that are likely to enter into the peace, the second task becomes
equally definite. It is that of finding a single set of assumptions more general and catholic than any of the traditional
ones revealed by the previous analyses which, so far as possible, gives meaning to all the basic assumptions of the traditional cultures of the world and at the same time relates them
so that, with the minimum repudiation of traditional beliefs
and values, all peoples can continue to be their traditional
selves without conflict with a similar expression of traditional,
indigenous assumptions and ideals upon the part of their
neighbors.

It may be added that this analysis provides a new definition
of ethics. The good is neither a fact nor a meaning; it is a
set of philosophical presuppositions. These presuppositions
have nothing to do with ethics, since, empirically and intellectually speaking, there is no such thing as ethics. There
are no purely ethical facts, as there are no purely ethical
meanings. There is only the nature of things and one's
basic theory concerning what it is. One's philosophical
presuppositions designate this basic theory. "Good" is
merely a single word for this basic theory. It is one's philosophy rather than, as modern ethical teachers suppose, an
item, either naturalistic or idealistic, within that philosophy.
For a given people any conduct proceeding from its basic
theory concerning the nature of things is good. Any theory
or attendant conduct not in accord with these presuppositions
or not given meaning by them is ethically meaningless, or
bad. Thus the problem of a good society is nothing more
than the problem of getting an adequate conception of the
nature of things. One knows what a given people regard as
good when one determines their philosophical conception of
the nature of things. This defines good for their culture.
We possess, however, an idea of the good which we have a

right to say applies to every culture, a good that holds for
everybody, when we have a set of assumptions which consistently, in terms of a theory of the nature of things, gives
meaning to all the diverse cultural assumptions, in so far as
this is possible.

This is much more possible than is usually supposed. A
given people, from its empirical inquiries, notes certain facts
in the nature of things, which lead it to conceive the whole
of reality in terms of the basic assumptions defined by these
facts, and forthwith builds its social habits and cultural institutions from this standpoint, valuing what its basic assumptions single out as fundamental and hence important. Another people, its attention called to different facts, proceeds
in a similar manner, arriving at a different assumption concerning the nature of things, and creating as a consequence
different practical social institutions, religious ceremonies,
and artistic forms. At first sight these different assumptions
and cultures seem to be a loggerheads with each other, since
one people affirms the nature of things and the attendant
good life to be of a certain character, whereas the other people
affirms them to be quite different. Actually, however, the
two sets of assumptions may be quite compatible. They
appear to contradict only because each people surreptitiously
makes the quite unjustified additional assumption that
nothing but its basic belief and attendant theory of the good
community represents the nature of things. When this quite
unjustified additional assumption, having its basis in what
may be termed "the fallacy of the nothing but," is removed,
it often becomes evident that peoples with radically different
theoretical assumptions and resultant ethical concepts are
merely giving expression to separate, equally valid, truths
and ideals about a perfectly compatible single world, rather
than to contradictory theses one or the other or both of which
must be wrong.

Notwithstanding the radically different assumptions and

attendant ideas of the good from which Eastern and Western civilizations proceed, there is no contradiction whatever between the two and convincing evidence that both are correct, the one supplementing the other. In fact, in so far as a given people, in arriving at their basic theoretical assumptions and attendant individual and social ethical aims, has allowed the facts of experience to determine those conclusions (and this, we may be reasonably sure to be the case for theories which have stood up for centuries in time both in theory and in practice sufficiently to define an old and vital contemporary culture), it is most likely if not inevitable that the theories must be in some way reconcilable, since the facts upon which they rest are facts of a single world.

Conversely, this would lead us to expect that in so far as the assumptions of two cultures are logically incompatible, even when "the fallacy of the nothing but" is eliminated, the incompatibility must arise because one or the other (or perhaps both) of the theories in question has made basic assumptions which are contrary to the facts in that portion of the nature of things to which the theories in question purport to refer. This consideration is very important because it provides an empirical criterion for deciding with respect to the goodness or badness of the ethical and institutional norms of two different cultures when these norms are inescapably contradictory. This criterion is to determine the philosophical assumptions from which the ethical norms proceed and to test these philosophical assumptions empirically against the immediately apprehended facts of nature to which they purport to refer. The philosophical and attendant ethical theory which passes this test is the correct one and the good one; the theory which does not must be repudiated and replaced with a set of basic philosophical assumptions concerning the nature of things, with their attendant ethical and cultural institutional consequences, more in accord with the facts.

That there are existent cultural theories with their ethical norms which are incompatible is evident. Certainly, the cultural aims of Hitler and of the Japanese warlords are incompatible logically with those of the Anglo-American democracies, Soviet Russia, and the young Chinese republic.

Our criterion has revealed to us, however, precisely how such conflicts resting in genuine contradictions are to be resolved. This is the third task of philosophy with respect to a constructive peace. Having analyzed each existing culture to determine its basic assumptions concerning the nature of things — its first task — and having related and reconciled those resulting basic assumptions which are compatible — its second task — there then remains the third task of distinguishing among all the assumptions of the major cultures of the world those which are valid and hence which are to be encouraged and built upon in the peace, from those which are invalid and which must be immediately and continuously repudiated without compromise.

But even with those peoples whose present culture proceeds from faulty philosophical assumptions concerning the nature of things, our procedure, while initially negative, must not be continuously so. In the place of the faulty assumptions which we must fight with all the instruments of reason, education, evidence, political pressure, and even military force, at our disposal, we must put positive correct assumptions concerning the nature of things which will permit the people in question to express their own talents and live with self-respect beside their neighbors in a common world. This can be done effectively only by building upon that portion of their traditional assumptions which is correct and upon those traits of their traditional culture and native capacity which are compatible with those of other people.

It would be folly, following the war, in the case of the Japanese for example, merely to repudiate their recent policy and to replace it with the ideology and practices of the Western Anglo-American democracies. The assumptions of the latter democracies are peculiar to a certain portion of the modern Western world. Only by long and painful effort can the Japanese hope to acquire these alien doctrines and the quite foreign ideals which they entail. Even then, the new beliefs must be worked out in ways that are peculiarly Oriental and uniquely Japanese, precisely as in contemporary China democracy has peculiarly Oriental accompaniments and is uniquely Chinese. Also, for decades these Western assumptions and their attendant values will seem exceedingly artificial. If they provide the only positive expression for Nipponese feelings and talents, the chances are likely that the Japanese, in order to be in some sense their own positive, spontaneous, traditional selves, will feel forced to revert, by underground methods if necessary, to their recent practices. In this case the present war will have to be fought over again later on. To avoid this unhappy event in the future we must build immediately following the war primarily upon those correct, theoretical assumptions and their attendant valuations which the Japanese already possess in part, adding Western correct theoretical assumptions and valuations as a secondary factor to be acquired by slow, patient effort over a longer period.

An analysis of Japanese culture indicates what these valid Japanese assumptions are. Before Perry's visit to Nagasaki Harbor in the middle period of the past century, the dominant religious and philosophical beliefs of the Japanese were those of Buddhism and Confucianism. These assumptions being Oriental in their inclusiveness and Chinese and Korean as well as Japanese in their influence, automatically reinforce peaceful relations between the Japanese, the Koreans, the Chinese and other Oriental peoples. Buddhism, for example, exists today in a remarkably pure form in Japan. It is only since the 1860's that it has been pushed into the background by the purely tribal Shintoism, because this was the easiest way for the Japanese to develop the nationalistic sentiments which the inroads of Western nationalism necessitated, without a break from their past.   Thus the return from Shintoism to Buddhism should not be difficult.   At the same time ways must be suggested for meeting the pressure of Western civilization and the inroads of its nationalism by means of philosophical assumptions and attendant ethical valuations compatible rather than contradictory, as was Shintoism, with those of the Western nations.

This should remind us, however, that all the readjusting in traditional assumptions and all the rejecting of existing traditional values are not to be made by the Japanese or even by the Germans.   The Japanese and the Germans are not the only peoples in the world to get into conflicts with other peoples.   The continuous series of wars throughout the entire history of Western civilization, in which every people in the name of both Protestant and Catholic Christianity has been involved, should make us take most seriously the fact that something must be wrong also with the theoretical assumptions and attendant intuitive valuations of each one of us.

There are other considerations which indicate this to be the case.   The ethical and political ideals of Western nationalism in its present form and the extremely individualistic and hence socially chaotic, intuitive ethical notions of the non-communistic or non-fascistic Western peoples, like all other cultural values, go back to a specific set of theoretical assumptions concerning the nature of things.   Although the way for these assumptions was in part prepared by the Protestant Reformation, they were first made articulate by René Descartes and John Locke.   They were made necessary because of the new physics of Galilei, Descartes, and Newton. At least up to the coming of the New Deal in 1932 and even at the present moment, if the recent reaction against Roosevelt is to be taken seriously, these scientific and philosophical assumptions concerning the nature of things of Galilei, Newton, Descartes, and Locke have defined the idea of the good for the culture of the United States.

To be sure, there have been philosophical and ethical additions from other sources, notably the idealistic, ethical theory going back to the *Critique of Practical Reason* of Immanuel Kant, but this idealism was purely formal and verbal and completely empty of content. Consequently, in practice it tended to be filled with the only content available. In Germany this was provided by the voluntarism of Fichte from which both the escapades of the Kaiser and those of Hitler, in part, stem. In France, Great Britain, and the United States, it was given by the scientific and philosophical doctrines of Galilei, Newton, Descartes, and Locke. More recently this has been supplemented in the United States by the pragmatic philosophy. But this also, because of its emphasis upon method, without the subsequent designation of the new philosophical theory of the nature of things to which this leads one, has been empty of content, producing a hit-or-miss political opportunism and normative chaos resulting in moral and social indifference, or else again has been filled in by the populace with the only content available, which is the common-sense doctrine defined by the scientific and philosophical theory of Galilei, Newton, Descartes, and Locke.

Every competent student of the latter doctrines knows them to be inadequate. No competent physicist living today believes that a correct conception of that portion of the nature of things with which physical science deals is given by the theoretical assumptions of Newton's physics. It has been replaced by the more fundamental and general physics of Einstein and by the quantum mechanics of Planck and Schrödinger as well as by the electromagnetic theories of Faraday and Maxwell. Rare indeed also is the philosopher, even in France, Great Britain, and the United States, who believes that Descarte's and Locke's dualistic, metaphysical theory of atomic material and atomic mental substances, from which the traditional formulation of the democratic theory of the state as a mere convention arises, can be any longer defended. Yet it is precisely upon these antiquated and repudiated scientific and philosophical theoretical assumptions that the content of our current individualistic, social, ethical norms in traditional French and Anglo-American culture rests. Not merely the Germans and the Japanese, but also the French, the British, and the citizens of the United States, must repudiate old, individual and political values and replace them by new ones with specific content resting upon the more adequate scientific, theoretical assumptions concerning the nature of things, which a competent philosophy at the present hour should make it its major task to render articulate.

The time has come for us to be done with the usual silly nonsense about science being the cause of the moral difficulties of our world, as if trustworthy knowledge were an evil, and to realize that one source at least of our moral apathy and the obviously evil fruits of our nationalistic and chaotically individualistic moral endeavors is in the inadequacy of our moral and religious philosophy itself. If we are going to require the Japanese and the Germans to repudiate the very ancient and intuitively satisfying values which they themselves cherish, because the theoretical assumptions from which these values proceed can be shown by inescapable evidence to be false, then by the same token we must reconstruct our own values also, notwithstanding their intuitive, apparent self-evidence, the emotional satisfaction attending them, and all the moral, political, and religious sanctions which they at present enjoy.

This is the major and the most difficult task of philosophy in connection with the peace. The philosopher with competence who faces this task must expect to find many of his colleagues and most of the contemporary moral and religious leaders of his culture against him initially. It is too much to expect of the majority of men immediately that they will give up their old philosophical assumptions and attendant political, ethical, and religious values without irritation and battle, especially when the old premises have given rise to intuitive values and sentiments ingrained in their emotions, with respect to which they have become attached. As Plato pointed out, when people are pulled out of the cave away from their old intuitive values produced by the traditional scientific and philosophical assumptions in the backgrounds of their minds and are brought out into the light again, where they face the evidence which determines the truth or falsity of these assumptions, they will assert that what is indicated is not good and rush back frantically into the cave. Nevertheless, as Plato saw, only by forcing them through this painful process can the correct idea of the good for the republic be found. This road the competent philosopher of the present must pursue, regardless of the irritation of his contemporaries and the inevitable misguided moral and religious indignation which will shower down upon his head.

The world is in a nasty mess. It is in this sorry state because each one of its cultures, operating from theoretical assumptions which are as a whole provincial and which are in part erroneous, has led its people to cherish moral, religious, and political sentiments which are in fact evil, and as a consequence has driven them on in the name of religion, patriotism and morality to lunge at each other's throats. What is Western nationalism but a political philosophy, an idea of the good, for which Protestant Christianity and modern moral philosophy is to a considerable extent responsible? What was the recent Spanish Civil War but a battle between conflicting traditional Western ideals for which the Pope himself and the Roman Catholic Church were similarly in part responsible? There is something wrong at the roots of the religion of both Protestant and Catholic Christianity as well as that of Japanese Shintoism. In all fairness it must be added also that the Jewish religion cannot expect to escape the need for reconstruction. A philosophy which meets its present duties, therefore, must root these wrongs out by designating the faulty philosophical conception of man and the universe upon which they rest and must then move on to repair the damage which is done by replacing traditional provincial and faulty doctrines with new theoretical assumptions more in accord with the nature of things as revealed by the advance of scientific knowledge and a more catholic inclusion of the insights of all peoples everywhere.

It appears, therefore, that philosophy has three tasks with respect to the peace: (1) An analysis of the major cultures of the Western and Eastern worlds which designates the basic theoretical assumptions from which the social institutions and practices that they value proceed. (2) The specification of a common, single set of assumptions possessed of the greater generality which permits the largest possible number of the resultant diverse, traditional assumptions which are logically compatible to be retained and acted upon without conflict. (3) The reconstruction of all the traditional assumptions to the extent that this is necessary, in order to bring them more in accord with the nature of things as this is revealed by contemporary as well as traditional philosophical and scientific knowledge.

This chapter is reprinted from *Approaches to World Peace*. Edited by Lyman Bryson, Louis Finkelstein and Robert M. Maciver (Harper and Brothers, New York, 1944) with the kind permission of the Editors.

CHAPTER XIX

TOWARD A BILL OF RIGHTS FOR
THE UNITED NATIONS

A Bill of Rights for all the nations cannot be based solely upon the traditional values and ideological assumptions of any one of the nations. If it is to capture the aspirations and ideals of all the peoples of the world, it must be rooted in at least some of the accepted institutions and social doctrines of each and every people.

The usual approach to the Bill of Rights or to the establishment of any other cultural value ignores the foregoing principle. It is customary, for example, to assume that the traditional modern French and Anglo-American concept of freedom and its attendant Bill of Rights exhausts the meaning of the concept. Precisely this assumption operates when anyone proposes to extend the governmental forms of the United States of America to a United States of Europe or a United States of the World. Such proposals have always left their recipients cold.

Yet the reason for such a reaction is surely not far to seek. The classical French and Anglo-American concept of freedom, which its Bill of Rights is designed to achieve, is conceived for the most part in, or after the analogy of, purely political terms. Freedom consists both politically, economically and even religiously in being left alone. Although this is perhaps somewhat of an exaggeration, Emerson's dictum that the best government is the minimum government tends, according to this conception, to hold. Furthermore, the economic freedom to have the work necessary to maintain even a minimum livelihood tends to be left to chance, as a mere by-product of the individual actions of men or groups who operate independently in a "free" market. Similarly, psychological freedom of the sentiments, the emotions and the passions, which the Spanish and Latin Americans cherish, is hardly even recognized as existing. And often in the religious field, because of a freedom to believe any faith, there tends to arise a culture in which people have no deep-going convictions about anything. In short, the price of a society rooted in the traditional modern Bill of Rights has tended to be a culture of laissez faire businessmen's values, with all the other values and aspirations of mankind left anemic and spiritually and ideologically unsustained.

A Bill of Rights written in terms of the contemporary Russians' values and ideology would have virtues and demerits different in content but similar in its neglect of the values of other cultures. The same would be true of a Bill of Rights grounded in Spanish or Latin-American values. For the latter Bill of Rights, the price which others would have to pay would tend to be a social system which escapes social anarchy at the cost either of monarchy or military dictatorship. A Bill of Rights formulated in terms of Oriental values would illustrate the same general thesis, as the difficulties of the contemporary Orient clearly indicate.

But to become aware thus of the inadequacies of a Bill of Rights defined in terms of the traditional values and ideology of any one of the nations or cultures of the world is to find the clue to the construction of an adequate Bill of Rights for a United Nations. The values and ideology of each nation or culture throughout the world must be determined and brought out into the open in terms of their basic assumptions. The existence of these different values and ideals must be frankly and honestly faced and admitted. In fact, the basic premise of this new Bill of Rights must be the right of any people to a world so organized socially that at least some of their values and ideals can have expression. A true Bill of Rights must guarantee a world in which there can be many ideologies, not merely one ideology. In short, the foundation of an adequate Bill of Rights must be conceived not solely in terms of political freedom but in terms of a plurality of cultural values.

More, however, is necessary. A designation of the diverse ideologies of the peoples of the world shows not merely that they differ but also that certain of them contradict one another. The latter is the case with respect to the ideologies of the present Western democracies and communistic Russia. Here we reach the real heart of the difficulty: An adequate Bill of Rights must guarantee the type of world in which there can be many ideologies; yet not even a catholic Bill of Rights can support a contradiction. For contradictories cannot be embraced. This means that an adequate Bill of Rights must both guarantee a world with a plurality of differing values and guarantee also a procedure by means of which peoples and nations can and must pass beyond their present ideologies when these ideologies are so mutually contradictory, as to threaten the peace of the world.

Unless this second guarantee is provided, a recognition and fostering of the existent ideological pluralism of our world will generate war rather than peace and destroy rather than create a united world. This follows because contradictories anywhere, if not transcended, destroy one another.

The prescription for guaranteeing a transcendence of the contradictory and conflicting valuations and social ideals of certain existent peoples and cultures of the world should be clear: Obviously one must go beneath the traditional ideologies to the considerations and methods which lead people anywhere to an ideology.

No conception of human values, no economic, political or religious ideology, as the history of human civilization clearly shows, comes *a priori*, perfect in every detail, God-given from heaven. Even the founding fathers of the United States and even Karl Marx were mortal men and not a perfect God. And being mortal men, they envisaged Utopia as the lessons of history and the finite empirical knowledge at their disposal at the time permitted them to envisage it. Thus at best they got facets of the truth, but not every facet.

Analysis shows that the basic assumptions of the political and economic Utopia of classical modern French and Anglo-American democracy are those for the most part of pre-Kantian British empirical modern philosophy. It is equally well known that the philosophical assumptions of contemporary communistic Russia are those of Karl Marx. Nor did the latter philosophical assumptions spring, with complete originality, into the mind of Karl Marx directly from the perfect omniscience of God. The philosophy of Karl Marx is a composite of contributions of his human historical predecessors, namely, Hegel, Feuerbach and the French socialists.

Nor were the contributions of the British empirical philosophers to the modern French and Anglo-American conception of human values and its Bill of Rights, or the contributions of Hegel, Feuerbach, the French socialists and Marx to the communistic Russian conception of a Bill of Rights as expressed in the Russian Constitution of 1936, mere philosophical speculations. Both sets of philosophical premises brought forward empirical, scientifically verifiable information in their support. This means that the philosophical premises at the basis of the diverse human values and ideologies of the peoples of the world are in part at least scientifically testable premises. Consequently, ideological conflicts are issues which can be discussed in the light of empirical and scientific evidence and treated by means of the methods of scientific inquiry. It follows, therefore, that any Bill of Rights which will guarantee effectively the processes for transcending the inescapable contradictory and conflicting ideologies of the contemporary world must prescribe freedom of scientific inquiry and of philosophical investigation of the underlying problem to which the existent diverse, and in some cases contradictory, ideologies are different answers.

An adequate Bill of Rights, therefore, must possess two basic guarantees: (1) The guarantee of a world in which all the differing ideologies of the world gain expression, each one in part at least.   (2) The guarantee of the freedom for, and the establishment of the scientific and philosophical inquiry into the basic premises of human and social ideologies necessary to provide the means for transcending and resolving the ideological conflicts of the contemporary world.

The minimum foundation for such a Bill of Rights is a political philosophy which is both a philosophy of all the world's cultures and a philosophy of science.   For unless this Bill of Rights is grounded in a philosophy of all the world's cultures, the first guarantee will not be met, and unless it is also grounded in a philosophy of science, the second guarantee will not be insured.

CHAPTER XX

EDUCATIONAL METHOD FOR
WORLD UNDERSTANDING

Education must fit men to understand and solve the inescapable problems of our time. Any consideration of the character of education, therefore, must begin with an analysis of these problems.

Even at the cost of becoming repetitious, it must none the less be reiterated that the most pressing problem centers in the atomic bomb. The presence of this bomb in our midst raises the question whether we will have any time to face the other presssing problems of our world. The next war will truly be a war to end all future wars, since it will be a war which ends all possible warriors.

Nevertheless, the atomic bomb itself is not the real danger. For the atomic bomb will not hurt civilization unless men direct it to such ends. This means that the problem centers not in scientific technology but in moral philosophy and the social sciences. It is the latter subjects which create social conceptions — economic, political, religious and philosophical — necessary to generate the social controls requisite for directing the use of scientific technology to constructive ends.

To note this, however, is to become aware that the problem confronting our world is even more serious than the presence of the atomic bomb might indicate. For when we turn to the economic, political, and religious doctrines defining the type of social organization which the different nations, peoples and cultures in the world deem good, we find not agreement but deep-rooted conflict. The Latin-American conception of the good society differs from the Anglo-American one; the American conception of appropriate economic and political organization differs from that of the Labor Government in Great Britain.   The ideology of the democracies west of the Rhine differs from the communist ideal of economic democracy of Soviet Russia, and the traditional culture of the West has been at loggerheads with the traditional culture of the East.   Everywhere in the realm of ideals to which we must turn if we are to control the atomic bomb, we find basic disagreement and conflict rather than agreement and mutual trust.

Furthermore, these differences in the social ideals to be used in setting up the social controls necessary to direct atomic energy to constructive ends are Oriental as well as Occidental in their character and focus.   It is no longer the case that war is likely to break out in a serious form only in Europe. The ideologies of the nationalistic nations of the West have now spread to Asia.   Thus nationalistic wars of the Western type are as likely to start in Korea or Java or Northwest China or India as in the Balkans or in the Rhineland.   Conversely, Oriental peoples and values are pressing upon the West for recognition in their own right.   The Japanese, Chinese, Indians and Javanese are insistent upon bringing their political, economic, and traditional cultural weight to bear upon the West as well as to receive values from the West.   This means that as time goes by, traditional Oriental ideological issues are more and more going to become Western issues also.

From these considerations certain conclusions follow immediately.   An education which would fit men to meet the problems of the contemporary world must acquaint men not merely with Western civilization but with all the major civilizations of our world.   Even within its treatment of Western civilization, it must do more than convey the economic, political, and religious doctrines of our particular culture and period in the Western world. This means, to be more specific, that a department of economics in any university cannot restrict itself to the economic science of Jevons and the Austrian School, rooted in pre-Kantian British empirical philosophy. It must also convey the theory of economics of Historismus, rooted in the historical philosophy of Hegel, and the labor theory of the economic science of Marx, rooted in Marxian dialectical materialism. Similarly, a department of religion must do more than merely convey one conception of religion, the theistic Western one, and within theism merely one type of theistic religion, namely Christianity, and within Christianity merely one form of that, namely, modern Protestantism or medieval Roman Catholicism.

What must be said with all the emphasis at one's disposal is that our very existence as human beings depends upon whether during the next ten or fifteen years we can learn to understand each other and resolve the ideological conflicts which divide us internationally. For this undertaking we must first thoroughly understand the differing cultures and their respective differing and often conflicting economic, political, and religious normative ideological theories. It is these theories which define what a specific culture regards as good and which prescribe the type of social organization to which it will agree in a conference of the United Nations. Consequently, if these conferences are ever to succeed, men in different parts of the world must receive an education which enables them to understand the other person's culture and ideology as well as their own, an education which gives a clear conception of the basic problem to which the conflicting ideologies are differing answers. Only if these basic problems, as thus clearly defined, are faced and then resolved, can a really constructive program for peace, grounded in understanding and knowledge rather than bickering and threats and verbal futile compromises, be achieved.

If this be accepted, a second question arises immediately.

What character must the curriculum in our educational institutions take on?   Obviously, everything which the sciences of anthropology and sociology tell us concerning the world's different cultures must be taught. This is obvious and axiomatic. Something more, however, is required.   A culture is not merely the facts which an anthropologist observes by a careful use of the objective methods of science.   It is also the concepts and theories by which these facts are understood by the people indigenous to this culture.

It is with respect to the concepts and theories in terms of which the people of a given culture themselves understand their own empirically present cultural practices and institutions that contemporary anthropology and sociology are weak. This, moreover, is a serious weakness so far as the present situation in our world is concerned.   For the failure of peoples from different nations and cultures to agree on social controls to avoid the present dangers, centers not in the fact that their empirical practices and institutions are different, but centers instead, in considerable part, in a difference in the normative theories from the standpoint of which they judge their own and all other empirical social institutions. Thus the normative theories indigenous to the respective cultures are at the heart of the difficulty, and an anthropological and sociological science which neglects these normative theories misses the fundamental problem of the contemporary world.

This fact is so important that it may be worth our while to indicate precisely why this weakness in the anthropological and sociological sciences has occurred. The reason is that these sciences have arisen in the modern culture of the modern Western world.   They have brought to the formation of their own methodology and their own conceptual apparatus the philosophical assumptions of this modern culture. No one for a minute can suppose that Spencerian sociology is independent of the philosophy of Spencer; nor can anyone suppose that the Comtian sociology has an independence of the Comtian philosophy. The same is true of all the major anthropological and sociological sciences of our modern Western world. Each has developed a set of technical concepts in terms of which the institutions of different cultures are classified and investigated. Thus all the facts of these other cultures are translated into the conceptual framework of a modern Western sociological science and its modern Western culture. Hence, what one obtains often is not the ideology of the native culture that is being investigated but the empirical facts of this culture brought under the ideology of modern Western sociologists and their particular cultural and philosophical assumptions.

There is but one cure for this state of affairs. The methods of the modern logic of systems must be introduced into anthropology and sociology. This method works with a technique which leaves one's postulates indeterminate, through the methodological procedure which one uses, permitting one to approach a given culture and to allow the institutions of that culture and the conceptual interpretation and evaluation put upon those institutions by the people in the culture in question to determine the conceptual framework in terms of which that culture is understood. This permits us to have an anthropology and a sociology in which the different cultures of the world will be understood in terms of the conceptual framework and apparatus of the ideological theories of the people who created those cultures.

It is precisely such a designation of the respective normative theories of the major nations and cultures in the world today which was attempted, in a rough sort of way and in a preliminary fashion, in *The Meeting of East and West*. Despite all the errors of detail inevitable in so extensive a study carried through by one person, which experts in the special fields discussed will undoubtedly correct, this study none the less demonstrates that it is possible at the present time in our universities to inaugurate a course which will acquaint men with the intercultural problem of the world as a whole and bring them to other cultures and the presuppositions of these other cultures in a mood of sympathetic understanding. This alone will go a long way toward removing the dangers of the contemporary world. For if people thus educated should go into the government or into the meetings of the United Nations, they would, at least, give the representatives of other countries the feeling that, even when differences of opinion on ideological matters arise, the ideological assumptions of cultures other than one's own were sympathetically understood. In such an atmosphere of mutual respect and sympathetic understanding, the practical problem of setting up international agreements sufficient to control the technological discoveries of science could be solved.

If education is to be effective, however, an entirely new type of training of both scholars and students is necessary. Both scholars and students must be trained to think deductively, as well as inductively. Only if men learn how to think deductively, can they acquire the tolerant attitude and the openmindedness necessary to comprehend the empirical cultural practices and institutions of a given people from the standpoint of the ideological assumptions of that people themselves. For each culture is a set of empirical social institutions and practices interpreted by a certain set of philosophical premises. To understand a given culture is to know its premises and to put oneself, at least tentatively, both imaginatively and sympathetically into the standpoint of its premises. Training in the usual textual empirical inductive methods of the traditional research of the historians and in the inductive methods of empirical science is quite inadequate for this. In fact, it is not too much of an exaggeration to say that the weakness of much of contemporary education concerning the needs of our world, centers in the curse of the inadequacy of the traditional historical method in scholarship.

This method, because of its excessively inductive character, paying attention to texts and source materials and the words in texts, is continuously misleading the scholar and those who read his conclusions. The inductive character of the traditional historical method brings the historian and the social scientist to the subject matter of history and of a given culture without the technical, theoretical concepts and assumptions of the people in question which are necessary to understand it. Thus, if the traditional scholar really uses his inductive method according to the sound prescriptions of this method, he comes out with nothing more than a lot of neutral, colorless facts. All the ideas and technically grasped theories necessary to comprehend these facts are lost. This is the reason why most of the current anthropological and sociological sciences and practically all of the results of the historical scholarship dealing with the different cultures of the world throw so little light on the perplexing problems of our time, which are so inescapably ideological in their character.

Actually, however, the errors of the present scholarship of our universities in the social sciences and the humanities are even worse than this. It is impossible even to record and classify the facts of history or of the diverse practices and institutions of different peoples without bringing these facts under concepts and theories. The only way to get pure facts, independent of all concepts and theory, is merely to look at them and forthwith to remain perpetually dumb, never uttering a word or describing what one sees, after the manner of a calf looking at the moon. For the moment one reports what one observes, at a meeting of historians or in a book written for sociologists, at that moment one has not pure facts but facts brought under concepts, and hence theory. Thus the social scientist's or the historian's aim at pure fact is a snare and a delusion. What one gets are not facts, but facts

brought under some often uncritically examined, uncon-
scious, theoretical assumptions of the sociologist or historian
in question.   As a rule, these theories are very speculative,
since neither the social scientist nor the historian has the
training or the method necessary to understand the technical,
economic, political, theological and philosophical theories
which are being exemplified in the facts.   Even if his theories
are more critically examined, they are, none the less, his
theories.   Rarely are they the theories used by a people to
conceive and evaluate the empirical facts exhibited in their
social practices and cultural institutions.

Nor is this all.   The followers of the inductive and the
historical method, because of the excessively verbal character
of the texts which they take as sufficient sources, are continually confusing an identity of words used in different
philosophies and different cultures with an identity of meaning.   The fact, for example, that Locke speaks of a law of
nature, even referring to Hooker when he does so, offers little
proof of the thesis that Locke means by a law of nature what
Hooker means or that Locke derived his meaning from
Hooker.   There will be no cure for these errors until people
are trained to think deductively in the social sciences and
history, as they are trained to do in the natural sciences and
in philosophy when these are properly understood.   Whenever one finds Locke talking about reason or about mind or
using any other word used by any previous scholar, one must
immediately ask oneself the question, "What, upon the
premises of Locke's philosophy, must this word mean?"
Only if one learns to think deductively in terms of the
premises of a given philosopher's philosophy, can one learn to
know what he means by the words he uses.

To learn to think deductively, as well as inductively, will
not merely give us a complete and thorough scholarship.   It
is also necessary in order sharply to state the issues and conflicts of our world and thereby to understand precisely the

basic nature of the problems with which we are concerned. To make this explicit, let us examine the classical normative theory of the culture of the United States and that of contemporary communist Russia.

The theory of the United States is made roughly explicit when one designates the postulates of its economic science, its political theory, its predominantly Protestant Christianity, and so on. Its economic science, analyzed in Chapter XIII, was formulated by Jevons, and later modified slightly by the Austrian School. Its traditional political philosophy goes back to John Locke. Its Protestantism, in so far as its doctrine departs from the doctrine of Thomistic medievalism, is a conception of the Christian religion rooted in the assumptions of modern philosophy. When one examines, technically and specifically, each of these doctrines which are deductively formulated theories, one finds that the basic postulates of the traditional cultures of the United States are not three independent sets of postulates but that instead they are interconnected in a single set of basic ideas and postulates. This common set of postulates joining the economic, political, and religious doctrines into one doctrine of a single culture is one's philosophy. This philosophy is, roughly, pre-Kantian British empiricism.

The technical economic theory, political theory, and religious, or anti-religious, doctrines of contemporary communist Russia are similarly rooted in an underlying philosophy, that of Karl Marx. Marxian philosophy, as is well known, is Hegelian in its dialectical theory of history and Feuerbachian in its materialistic conception of the content of history.

To understand the ideologies of the United States and contemporary Russia thus deductively is to be in a position to formulate sharply the ideological problem at the basis of the perpetual impasses which arise between Russian delegates and the delegates of the United States in the United Nations.

The economic, political and underlying philosophical premises defining the idea of the good society in the traditional
cultures of the United States and of contemporary communistic Russia are self-contradictory.   The hedonistic or psychological postulates of the economic science of Jevons and
the Austrian School contradict the labor theory of economic
value of Karl Marx.   The political axioms of the present
constitution of the U.S.S.R. contradict the axioms of the
Declaration of Independence and the Constitution of the
U.S.A.   Similarly, the underlying postulates of pre-Kantian
British empirical philosophy are incompatible with the post-
Kantian philosophical assumptions of Hegel and Marx.

This means that the conflicts between delegates of the
U.S.S.R. and the U.S.A. in the United Nations are truly
serious conflicts, much more serious than most people have
supposed, and that they cannot be resolved either by practical
compromises alone or by a mutual understanding of each
other's position and premises alone.   In fact, the more the
contemporary Russians and Americans come to understand
each other's premises, the more the intensity of the conflict
will exhibit itself.   For when the basic assumptions of two
different faiths contradict each other, reconciliation by practical expedients is unlikely, and reconciliation by mutual
understanding is unequivocally impossible.   Contradictories
cannot be reconciled.

There is, however, a way of resolving such a difficulty.
Only, however, by learning to think deductively and thus
becoming capable of formulating such an international conflict in precise theoretical terms, can the way out be found.
A clue appears, by way of contrast, if one examines certain
other differences in philosophical premises when one applies
the deductive method of inquiry to the diverse major cultures
of the world.   Then a situation other than that illustrated by
the United States and Russia often arises.   For example, in
The Meeting of East and West, it has been shown that the

basic philosophical premises and attendant economic, political and religious doctrines underlying Oriental civilization are different from those at the basis of Western civilization, and yet these differing assumptions do not contradict one another. Thus the problem of reconciling the East and the West presents no serious logical or theoretical difficulty. It entails merely enlarging the ideology of the one to include that of the other. This, to be sure, is by no means an easy task, since it involves far-reaching changes, especially with respect to the all-sufficiency and perfection of the traditional claims of one's own religion and one's own political and economic doctrines.

But where the basic assumptions do not merely differ but contradict each other, as in the case of the social ideals of the Soviet Russians and the Americans, the changes must be even greater and are far more difficult to achieve, not merely practically but also theoretically. For a contradiction cannot be resolved by enlarging the ideological concept of one people to include that of the other. One set of assumptions does not permit the inclusion of its contradictory.

Such a desperately serious ideological conflict can be resolved, nevertheless. Similar problems occur continually in the deductively formulated, experimentally verified theories of the natural sciences, and the technique for resolving them is well known. One must pass from the assumptions of both of the contradictory theories to a new set of philosophical premises which takes care of the facts supporting the two contradictory theories, without contradiction. This means that there can be no real intellectually constructive solution of the conflicts between democracies rooted in pre-Kantian philosophy and communistic Russia rooted in post-Kantian and post-Hegelian Marxism without passing on to a new set of assumptions which can take care of the merits of the communistic and the traditional democratic theories without contradiction.

Hence, the capacity to think about empirical data deductively, as well as inductively, must be made the primary concern of contemporary education. Before this capacity is obtained by both scholar and student, little can be accomplished. More of the present excessively inductive and textually verbal pseudo-scholarship has the effect of merely throwing dust into the eyes of both the scholars and the readers. The more information which they gather by these means, the less use they can make of it, the more overwhelmed intellectually they are by it, and the less capable they are of understanding it.

Nevertheless, the capacity to think theoretically and deductively is by itself of no use, unless one understands the technical content which goes into the deductively formulated theories of the different cultures of the world. For this understanding, one must be a master in the subjects to which these deductively formulated theories refer. To this end a mere mastery of languages and of dictionaries is quite insufficient. It is as absurd to suppose that a Ph.D. degree in philology or linguistics fits one to understand the philosophy of China as it would be to suppose that a Ph.D. in German fits one to understand the German texts of Einstein's theory of relativity. The basic cultural and ideological differences of our world go down to basic philosophical difficulties, and only scholars trained in the problems of philosophy and in the alternative answers to these problems, each one of which is reasoned out deductively, can hope to be competent to convey the standpoints of the cultures of either the East or the West.

But even more than an understanding of philosophy with the training in deductive thinking with respect to the theories of philosophy is required. One must also know technically the specific economic doctrines, such as the Austrian psychological theory of economic value or the Marxian labor theory of economic value, which go with these respective philosophies. The same is true for technical political and theological doctrines.

It will be said immediately that this is impossible for any one scholar or any one mind. There is no answer to this objection if the methodology of scholarship is purely inductive and verbal and textual. To acquiesce in the latter conclusion is to doom our civilization and mankind to extinction under a rain of atomic bombs within the lifetime of the younger generation.

There is no need to acquiesce in this counsel of doom from contemporary scholars. There is nothing whatever to prevent the introduction of a thoroughly adequate course in the methods of thinking, both inductively and deductively, in the freshman year in any college or university. Part of such a course could be very profitably pushed back into the high schools and preparatory schools. During the last semester in Yale College, such a course, within the limits of one-half year, was taught to a class of six hundred, more than 50 per cent of whom were Freshmen. Providing the capacity to think deductively is mastered, there is no reason, so far as the restrictions of time are concerned, why any good student having subsequent year-courses in deductively presented philosophy, economics, politics and religion illustrated with concrete inductive materials, could not be taken to the basic concepts and postulates of the major philosophical, economic, political and religious doctrines of the major cultures of the world with a thoroughness which would permit him sympathetically to understand all of these doctrines and later to master them technically.

This is not achieved at the present time because of the exclusively inductive character of the historical method in the humanities and the traditional methods of the social sciences. The students are so overwhelmed with empirical information which is not theoretically digested, even by the professors who present it to them, that they never find the key concepts and postulates defining the theoretical stand-points and evaluations of the different peoples and ideologies. An early training in the capacity to think deductively will enable both scholars and students to understand the facts they come upon and to distinguish basic notions in any field from secondary, derived notions. Actually, this enlarged kind of training, permitting any person to know technically philosophy, economics, politics and theology, not only for his own culture but also for the major cultures, could be achieved in a shorter time educationally than the present confusing methods and educational procedures require. The result would be that both scholars and students would be able to handle philosophical, economic, political and theological ideas in history and in the diverse cultures of the world more like expert philosophers, economists, political scientists and theologians, with the technical knowledge needed to understand them.

All this, even, is not enough. One people's ideology will, so far as the prescriptions up to this point indicate, be as valid as that of any other people's, even including the Germans', held spellbound by Hitler. Nor will these ideologies be fully appreciated as the people of any one of these ideologies actually feels it and loves it, if one merely grasps it technically.

Properly to understand any culture means not merely to know the basic philosophical premises defining its stand-point but also to be convinced that these philosophical premises are, for the people in question, a reasonable scientific generalization from the empirical data of their limited experience. Never is any culture understood, even when its indigenous ideology is grasped, unless the facts which led to its particular ideology are also ascertained. This means that the philosophy of any specific culture is grounded in its science, even when the people in question may be what we, in the West, have falsely called "primitive," without science in our more sophisticated form. Any people notes the facts of experience and generalizes from these facts to a philosophy. Consequently, no philosophy of culture is completely understood unless the empirical facts behind the generalization are also ascertained.

This means that the present separation of the social sciences and humanities from the natural sciences must be unequivocally repudiated. No humanistic doctrine in any culture is understood unless the underlying philosophy of that culture is understood. No underlying philosophy is sympathetically and emotionally apprehended unless the empirical evidence and the process of generalization, essentially scientific in character, taking the people in question from the empirical facts noted by them to their basic philosophy, are also grasped. In short, as Socrates and Plato noted long ago, one's philosophy of the good in the social sciences and humanities is one's philosophical generalization of the empirically true in the natural sciences.

An education which connects the technical philosophical systems of the differing cultures and ideologies and their attendantly different economic, political, religious and aesthetic ideas of the good with their scientific empirical background will not merely reconcile the humanities and the sciences, so that as the natural sciences produce new technological instruments, the humanistic social ideas necessary for the good control of these instruments will be present; but it will also provide an empirical, scientifically verifiable criterion indicating which set of philosophical premises has the generality and the deductive fertility sufficient to take care of all the facts noted by all the peoples of the differing cultures of the world. Thereby, ideological and cultural relativism, with its attendant demoralization with respect to international norms valid for all nations, can be transcended and escaped.

If the grounding of one's philosophy of culture in an

empirically verified philosophy of natural science is not to be misunderstood, it must be emphasized that natural science must be taken in the broadest sense.   This broad sense must include the empirical generalizations of so-called primitive peoples.   It must also include the more purely empirical, qualitative, natural history type of natural science as well as the more theoretical, quantitative, mathematical type.   Also, it must specify how these two types of scientific knowledge are related.

To this end, purely empirical data in natural science must be clearly distinguished from inferred hypothetically and theoretically designated factors.   Through all cultures, the purely empirical data of nature are the same, for the most part.   It is largely what is scientifically inferred from some of these empirical data which makes the ideology of one culture different from that of another.   A clear understanding of this situation should go far to sustain an attitude of tolerance toward philosophies of culture other than one's own.

What happens is that people are continually identifying inferred factors in their scientific and cultural philosophy with purely empirically given data.   The therapeutic for this prevalent disease is an inquiry, such as Bishop Berkeley pursued in his *Principles* and his *Dialogues between Hylas and Philonous,* concerning the nature of purely empirically given fact.   Such an inquiry, pursued in Chapter III, shows conclusively that pure fact is merely the immediately apprehended continuum of experience, differentiated by the sensuous qualities delivered by the senses.   The latter qualities are not common-sense external objects, unobservable scientific objects, or theistic religious objects; they are, instead, aesthetic objects in the sense of the impressions of early French impressionistic art.

This means that if natural science is to include and convey most effectively the qualitative, purely empirical part of its knowledge, it and our university teachers must use impressionistic art. For impressionistic art, like much of the landscape painting of the Chinese, is the instrument *par excellence* for conveying the purely empirical data from which the theoretical generalizations of science and its attendant philosophy of culture are made.

In other words, an effective education for intercultural understanding must include, in addition to the five subjects previously noted, at least one course in the different types of the world's art. These types must encompass the Chinese intuitive and the modern Western impressionistic forms, both of which are supreme for conveying the purely empirical component of one's philosophy of science and culture. They must also embrace the more symbolical classical types of Western art, which are superb for the conveying of the theoretically inferred component of one's philosophy of science and culture. These diverse types of art can both exhibit literal scientific and philosophical truth known purely empirically and add persuasion to the analogical presentation of scientifically philosophical truth expressed literally only by more theoretical and mathematical means.

Such an education should be able to capture the hearts as well as the minds of men the world over, thereby adding affection to intellect and action in world understanding.

This chapter was read in the Symposium on *The University and Its World Responsibilities* on February 19, 1947, in connection with the Bicentennial Program of Princeton University. It was published in the *Journal of Higher Education* for April, 1947. It is reprinted here with the kind permission of the Princeton Bicentennial Committee and the Editor of the *Journal of Higher Education*.

CHAPTER XXI

THE SCIENTIFIC METHOD FOR DETERMINING THE NORMATIVE SOCIAL THEORY OF THE ENDS OF HUMAN ACTION

Our question is: Can scientific method determine the ends for which the discoveries of science are used? The fact in our world today which makes this question crucial is obvious. This fact is the scientific discovery of the technological means by which atomic energy can be released. It is clear that scientific methods have led to this remarkable discovery. It is equally clear, also, that the effect of this discovery upon civilization will be determined by the end toward which it, as an instrumental means, is directed.

The ends of social action are defined by social doctrines, termed ideologies. Conversely, an ideology is a theory defining the end or aim of social action; in other words, it is a theory designating the kind of society at which we should aim. Since such a social theory defines the social norm not yet realized which is the aim of social action, rather than the *de facto* character of existent social organization, we shall call such a theory a normative social theory, reserving the adjective "factual," as opposed to "normative," for the designation of that type of social theory which correctly designates the character of *de facto* society.

Our question now becomes: Can scientific method determine the correct, or what ordinary parlance calls "the good," normative social theory? In other words, can scientific methods determine ends, or more exactly, the one correct normative end as well as instrumental means? Furthermore, if the answer to the latter question or questions is in the affirmative, then what, specifically, is the scientific method?

That the answers to these questions are not easy or obvious should be evident from the distinctions which have already come out in the foregoing clarification of the initial question. These distinctions have already separated three different kinds of theory. There is the theory of natural science, from which the discovery of technological instruments such as the atomic bomb are derived. There is also the factual theory of social science, designating the *de facto* state of affairs in society. There is, finally, the normative theory of the humanities and social science, designating the humanistic and social ends, the correct or good form of social organization, not yet perfectly actualized in fact, at which we should aim.

The method for determining the first two of these three different theories, which our analysis of the initial question has distinguished, is clear. This method is the empirical, inductive method with its natural history description, followed by deductively formulated theory indirectly verified through its theorems or deductive consequences. The only difference between the theory of natural science and the factual theories of social science is that the former applies this traditional method of the natural sciences to the facts of nature, whereas the latter applies it to the facts of culture and society.

Once this is noted, it becomes evident that the scientific method for verifying normative social theory cannot be that for verifying the theory of natural science or factual social theory. For otherwise normative social theory and factual social theory would be identical, and the distinction which our foregoing analysis has brought out would evaporate. That the distinction exists and cannot be avoided no one who faces the evidence can deny.

Certainly there are many different normative social theo-[1] ries in the world today, as there have been always in the past. There is the communist normative social theory, the classical Anglo-American laissez faire, democratic social theory, the Chinese Confucian social theory, the Roman Catholic Christian social theory, the Mohammedan theistic social theory, the Buddhist non-theistic social theory, and so on. Also, not even in a society where the majority of its human members accept any one of these ideologies or normative social theories does the *de facto* social organization correspond perfectly to the norm in question. No believer in democracy in the United States, whether he conceives of democracy in terms of laissez faire individualism or in any other terms, would maintain that the *de facto* behavior of all citizens of the United States or the *de facto* political or economic practices in the society of the United States perfectly conform to his normative democratic social ideal. Similarly, Premier Stalin would be the first to affirm that the *de facto* state of affairs in Russia today is not in accord completely with his communistic normative social theory of the correct or good end for social action. His fondest hope is that after several five-year plans the *de facto state* of affairs will more and more conform to but never perfectly accord with the communistic normative social theory which defines the ideology of contemporary Soviet Russia. Similarly, nobody regards it as an argument against the validity of the Christian ideal of life that there is in existent society not even one perfect Christian. This discrepancy between the type of social organization which a normative social theory designates and the type of social organization of *de facto* society which a scientifically verified factual social theory would designate, is of the essence of a normative social theory. Of its very nature a normative social theory departs at least in part from the *de facto* state of affairs to which any social theory must conform completely if it is to be verified by the methods of natural science.

Consider another example. The normative social theory of the present British Labor Government is in its economic portion that of socialism. Nevertheless, all the *de facto* economic institutions and practices in Great Britain are not upon a socialistic economic basis. Thus what a factual social theory scientifically verified for Great Britian at the present moment, would designate, only conforms in part at best to the normative social theory of the present British Government.

Such indisputable evidence indicates that the distinction between normative social theory and factual social theory must be maintained. Consequently, the scientific method which gives the one cannot be the scientific method which is appropriate for the other.

There is a second reason, indicated previously in Chapter XVII. The methods of natural science prescribe that no theory can be regarded as confirmed by these methods unless the facts in the subject matter to which the theory purports to refer are completely in accord with what the theory calls for. It follows, therefore, that when the methods of natural science are applied to the facts of society, rather than to the facts of natural science, the only type of social theory which such methods can give is a social theory which is completely in accord with all the facts of society. This is but another way of saying that the methods of natural science can give only factual social theory.

Furthermore, since, as we have noted, normative social theories, by their very nature, as conceptions of society not yet realized fully at which human beings are aiming, differ at least in part from the factual organization of actual society, it follows that they cannot be completely in accord with what is in fact the case. Also, they are often, if not always, in part incompatible with what is in fact the case. For the whole point in passing laws in any legislative body and in drawing up a constitution prescribing a certain normative social theory is that the people know certain facts in existent society which they want to remove. Thus normative social theories are constructed so that, they will be incompatible with these facts. This very incompatibility is the argument of the proponents of a given normative theory for its acceptance.

Nor is the difficulty met by the pragmatist's reference of the verification of a normative social theory to the future rather than the present. Even if the future situation achieves in fact the aim which the normative theory envisaged, this will merely demonstrate that the normative theory, if accepted, can in part at least achieve its norm in fact; it will demonstrate nothing concerning the crucial question as to whether this is the correct or good norm to achieve. Hitler in his invasion of Poland achieved his normative aim. But this pragmatic success proved nothing scientifically or in any other way with respect to the correctness of his aim.

Moreover, if a pragmatic test of a normative social theory by appeal to future consequences is going to define the confirmation of that normative theory with respect to the future state of affairs in terms of the criterion of confirmation as specified by the methods of natural science, then in the future state of society to which appeal is made the normative social theory must designate a form of social organization which conforms not merely in part but completely to that *de facto* social state. But no normative social theory ever achieves completely in *de facto* society, no matter how long it operates, a complete concordance with any *de facto* state of affairs. Yet such a complete concordance is precisely what a normative social theory must achieve if it is to be a theory verified by the methods of natural science. Again, it becomes evident that the distinction between factual social theory and normative social theory must be maintained and that the scientific method for determining the correct factual social theory consequently cannot be that for determining the correct normative social theory.

It does not follow from this, however, that normative social theory cannot be verified by scientific methods. It follows merely that the scientific method for verifying normative social theory must be different from the scientific method for verifying factual social theory or the theory of natural science.

Is there any way of determining this unique scientific method for normative social theory? An examination of specific normative social theories in their relation to factual social theories in society and in comparison with the theories of natural science should throw light upon this question.

In *The Meeting of East and West* the major normative social theories of the major contemporary nations and cultures of the world have been designated. This designation in each instance demonstrates that the normative humanistic or social theories of a culture, the theory which defines its specific aims and values, is made clear and specific when the technical economic science, political doctrine, theological doctrine, aesthetic theory, etc., of the culture in question is determined. Each one of these doctrines of a given culture turns out to be a deductively formulated theory, or can be put in such a form.

A deductively formulated theory, as has been previously indicated, is a body of propositions falling into two groups termed postulates and theorems, where the postulates logically imply the theorems. This means that given the postulates, the theorems follow. Just as all the propositions in a deductively formulated theory fall into two groups, termed postulates and theorems, so all the concepts in these propositions fall also into two groups, termed primitive or undefined concepts and defined concepts. As their names indicate, the defined concepts are derived from the primitive or undefined concepts by the method of definition. Thus when the primitive concepts and the postulates of a deductively formulated theory are known, the heart and the totality of the theory is possessed. For the remainder follows by the logical methods of formal implication and definition. The primitive concepts always involve both entities and relations.

It follows, therefore, that the economic theory in any normative social theory of a given culture rests on certain basic assumptions, those designated by the primitive concepts and the postulates of the deductively formulated theory of the economic science in question. The political doctrine has a similar set of primitive concepts and postulates. The same is true of the theology, and of the art if the art is indigenous to the culture in question.

But the primitive concepts and postulates of the economic doctrine, the political doctrine, the religious doctrine and the aesthetic doctrine are not, in any specific culture, four disconnected sets of assumptions; instead, they are interconnected. In fact, they are the more specialized expression of a single set of primitive concepts and postulates embracing the economic theory, the political theory, the religious doctrine and the aesthetic forms and values in their organic interconnections. This common all-embracing set of primitive concepts and postulates is the philosophy of the culture in question. It is this philosophy which gives the culture its unity, binding its economic ideology, its political ideology, its religious ideology and its aesthetic values into a consistent, harmonious whole.

Thus, as *The Meeting of East and West* shows, different cultures have different normative social theories and values because their institutions and practices are the expression of different philosophies which have captured consciously or unconsciously the sentiments and outlook of the people in question. Also a given society, or for example Mexican society at the present moment, can possess several different cultures with their attendant conflicting normative social theories. When this is the case cultural conflicts are inescapable within the nation as well as between nations.

Any set of assumptions and postulates of a given deductive theory has specific logical consequences designated by the theorems of that deductive theory. These theorems work out in detail the consequences of the postulates of the normative social philosophy. Thus, just as the theorems logically deduced from the postulates of the deductively formulated theory of natural science define the technological instruments which provide society with its instrumental means, so the theorems which are the deductive consequences of the postulates of the normative social philosophy of a given society define the specific economic, political, religious and aesthetic practices and institutions which embody the ends or ideal norms of that society.

The scientific method and procedure for arriving at the deductively formulated theory of natural science, the theorems of which designate the instruments and instrumental means of society, are clear. These methods and procedures are the empirical and deductively formulated methods of natural science applied to the inductively given facts of nature. Since normative social theory, like the theory of natural science, is deductively formulated theory with its postulates and theorems, our basic problem is that of determining how the normative social theory is confirmed or verified. Put more concretely, our problem is that of finding the principle of selection by means of which, out of all the possible normative social theories which exist in our world or which can be imaginatively conceived, the scientifically verified one can be determined.

An examination of the basic assumptions of any philosophy defining the normative theory of a given culture provides the answer to this question. These basic assumptions of a given philosophy of culture do more than prescribe the ideology or ideal form for the institutions and cultural practices of that culture.   They also make certain assertions about the character of nature and man quite apart from the institutions and practices of culture.   Moreover, these assertions concerning nature and the natural man inevitably made by the philosophy defining the ideology of the culture, are always of a character such that they can be empirically verified by an appeal to the facts of nature and to those characteristics of men generally which are quite independent of any particular cultural ideology men may happen to hold.

Confucius, for example, says that the good man and the good society are those in which *jen* is embodied.   But he tells us also that *jen* is a factor in the natural man and in nature; in fact, it is something binding the two together. As *The Meeting of East and West* has shown, this factor is the empirically given, immediately felt continuum of experience.   Clearly this is something which is quite independent of the different ideologies of the different cultures of the world.   Whether it exists or not does not depend on any value judgment of preference or of any other kind.   Immediate empirical inspection of experience either exhibits such a factor or it does not.   Furthermore, it exists in the experience of everyone.   Thus the criterion of the good, *jen,* in Confucian ethics, is an empirically verified factor in nature and the natural man.

As *The Meeting of East and West* has shown also, the philosophy which defines the normative social theory of any of the other major nations or cultures of the world always makes similar assertions concerning the existence of specific factors in nature or the natural man which are either directly observable empirically or connected with the directly observable by standard scientific methods.   The theology of St. Thomas Aquinas, which defines the normative cultural theory of contemporary orthodox Roman Catholicism, for example, is expressed in terms of the metaphysics of Aristotle, and this metaphysics in turn makes certain assertions about nature, the natural man and natural science generally which can be scientifically checked.

As Chapter XVI has shown, recent anthropologists have been forced to the conclusion not merely that the cultural institutions and practices of a given society are not understood until the basic philosophical concepts defining their normative social theory are discovered, but also that even this normative standpoint and its attendant social rituals and institutions will not be grasped unless one finds the particular facts of nature observable by any people anywhere which led the sages who formulated the normative theory in question to that particular philosophical generalization.

The difference between a modern Western society and a society of natives in the South Sea islands is not that the ideology of the former is scientifically grounded, whereas that of the latter is nonsensical hocus pocus and illogical. The ideologies of both express logical thinking, once one discovers the conceptual standpoint of each. Furthermore, both conceptual standpoints are empirically and hence scientifically verified. The difference is that the native South Sea islanders pass to their generalization with a particular group of observable factors in nature and the natural man attracting their attention, whereas modern Westerners have come upon different empirical natural facts and have achieved empirically verified generalizations which perhaps include a larger number of observable facts. Even so, as *The Meeting of East and West* has demonstrated, our traditional modern Western scientific and philosophical theories overlook or neglect certain facts of nature, especially those in the realm of aesthetic immediacy, which the empirically supported philosophies of the Orient and the native South Sea islanders, such as the Balinese, take into account.

All these considerations lead to the following conclusion:

The basic primitive concepts and postulates of the philosophy underlying a given culture have two different references, the one a prescriptive reference by way of the theorems to culture, the other an empirical cognitive reference by way of the postulates to nature and the natural man. It is the former of these two references which gives a normative social theory its normative character; it is the latter of its two references which provides normative social theory with its cognitive, verifiable character as true or false.

The latter empirical connection with nature does more than show how normative social theory can be verified. It also provides the method by which the correct, or most adequate, normative social theory can be picked out from among the possible normative social theories of the contemporary world.

The verification of normative social theory is to be obtained not by checking its basic philosophical postulates, either directly or indirectly, against the facts of society either in the present or in the future but by checking them with the postulates of the philosophy of natural science prescribed by the facts of nature. When the relation between the postulates of the philosophy of culture and the postulates of the philosophy of nature is that of identity, the philosophy of culture is true. When the relation is not that of identity, the philosophy of culture is false or incomplete. See the accompanying diagram.

It is because normative social theories look to nature for their truth that they do not have to conform to the facts of *de facto* society. Were they to look to culture, the humanities and *de facto* society for their justification they could not measure the humanities or have a prescriptive power with respect to *de facto* society.

The philosophy defining a particular normative social theory has the two apparently paradoxical properties of designating both an "ought" for culture which introduces choices,

DIAGRAM OF THE RELATION BETWEEN FACTUAL SOCIAL THEORY, NORMATIVE SOCIAL THEORY AND THE THEORY OF NATURAL SCIENCE

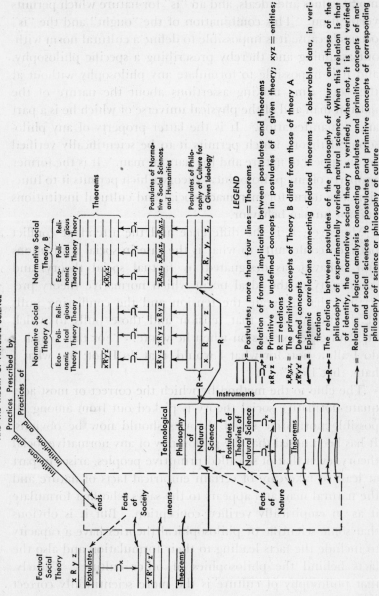

LEGEND

|||| = Postulates; more than four lines = Theorems

$\supset_x$ = Relation of formal implication between postulates and theorems

$xRyz$ = Primitive or undefined concepts in postulates of a given theory; xyz = entities; R = relations

$x_iR_jy_jz_j$ = The primitive concepts of Theory B differ from those of theory A

$x'R'y'z'$ = Defined concepts

= Epistemic correlations connecting deduced theorems to observable data, in verification

$R \longrightarrow$ = The relation between postulates of the philosophy of culture and those of the philosophy of experimentally verified natural science. When this relation is that of identity, the normative social theory is verified; when not, it is not verified

$\longrightarrow$ = Relation of logical analysis connecting postulates and primitive concepts of natural and social sciences to postulates and primitive concepts of corresponding philosophy of science or philosophy of culture

moral values and ideals, and an "is" for nature which permits
verification.   This combination of the "ought" and the "is"
occurs because it is impossible to define a cultural norm without assuming and thereby prescribing a specific philosophy,
and it is impossible to formulate any philosophy without at
the same time making assertions about the nature of the
natural man and of the physical universe of which he is a part
and a manifestation.   It is the latter property of any philosophical theory which permits it to be scientifically verified
by an appeal to nature and the natural man.   It is the former
property of any philosophical theory which permits it to function as a norm for man-made social and cultural institutions
and for human behavior.

Moreover, it is the difference and the attendant conflict
between conformity to what is the case in social institutions
and behavior as designated by factual social theory, and
conformity to the ideal norm which normative theory prescribes, that generate the tension and the conflicting pulls
of the moral life — that tension and those pulls to which
St. Paul gave expression when he wrote: "For that which I
do I allow not; for what I would, that do I not; but what I
hate, that I do."

The clue to the method by which the correct or most adequate normative social theory is picked out from among all
possible normative social theories should now be obvious.
It has been noted that the philosophy of any normative social
theory, even that of so-called primitive peoples, arises in part
at least to take care of certain empirical facts of nature and
the natural man and appears to the sages who first formulate
it as an empirically verified conception.   But it is obvious
that some scientific or philosophical theories have a capacity
to include the facts leading to their formulation and also the
facts behind the philosophies of other cultures.   Clearly,
that philosophy of culture is the more scientifically correct
and adequate one which can take care of the widest range of

facts concerning nature and the natural man. Just as Einstein's theory of mechanics is generally regarded as a more scientific and correct theory than Newton's because it takes care of all the facts for which Newton's theory can account and additional inescapable facts for which Newton's theory cannot account, so that philosophy which can take care of the facts of nature for which the philosophy of one culture accounts and for the facts of nature noted by other cultures also is a more scientifically correct and adequate normative social theory.

It immediately becomes obvious that there are two ways of obtaining this more scientifically correct and adequate cultural ideology for our world. One way is to specify the diverse philosophies of the diverse cultures of the world, noting in each instance the empirical facts of nature and the natural man leading the formulators of each philosophy to regard it as empirically verified, and then to attempt to construct as a generalization, including all these partial philosophies of culture, a new set of philosophical premises which as far as possible consistently combines the different assumptions of all the different ideologies of our world. The other way is to go to the theories arrived at by the experts in the society of the world whose business it is to construct scientifically verified theory which as far as possible includes under a single set of premises all the facts of nature and the natural man. These experts are the natural scientists, supplemented with the analytical philosophers of natural science who bring out into the open the basic methodological, epistemological and ontological premises implicit in the natural scientist's verified theories.

Both of these ways were pursued in *The Meeting of East and West*. They lead to a common conclusion. The philosophy called for by an analysis of the basic philosophical assumptions implicit in and entailed by the verified theory of contemporary natural science is also the philosophy which most universally includes, combines and reconciles the diverse philosophies of culture of the major nations and cultures of the contemporary world.

The results of the entire foregoing analysis can now be summarized. There are three different kinds of deductively formulated scientific theory. There is the deductively formulated theory of natural science. This is verified by applying the empirical and deductive formal methods of natural science to the facts of nature and the natural man. There is the deductively formulated theory of factual social science. This is verified by applying the empirical and formal methods of natural science to the facts of *de facto* society. There is also deductively formulated normative social theory. It is not verified by the methods of natural science applied to social facts. Otherwise factual social theory and normative social theory would be identical; also, the distinction between what is actually the case in society and what ought to be the case in society would not exist. Instead, normative social theory is defined by a set of philosophical premises, and these philosophical premises are verified by way of the philosophy of natural science, that is, by way of the first of the three different deductively formulated theories. Put more explicitly, this means that that philosophy of culture, that normative social theory, is the scientifically verified and the correct one in which the basic philosophical primitive ideas and postulates are identical with the primitive ideas and postulates of the philosophy of natural science arrived at by the analysis of the verified theory of natural science which brings out into the open its basic methodological, epistemological and ontological assumptions. The accompanying graph distinguishes and relates these three types of deductively formulated theory when they are properly understood and pursued with the methods appropriate for each.

The question with which this entire inquiry began can now be answered. The question is: Can the methods of natural science determine the ends for which the discoveries of natural science are, or, more exactly, should be, used? If by an affirmative answer to this question one means what traditional modern moral philosophers such as the pragmatists and the ethical empiricists have meant, namely, the application of the methods of the natural sciences to the facts of society or to the pragmatic consequences in the future of present normative hypotheses, then the answer must be unequivocally in the negative. The methods of natural science applied either to present social facts or to future social consequences, give factual social theory, not normative social theory. And it is only normative social theory which defines ends.

Nonetheless, the basic initial question is to be answered in the affirmative. There are other ways of scientifically verifying normative social theory than that of applying the methods of natural science to the facts of *de facto* society. This other way is to note the role of the deductive method in deductively formulated scientific theory, which exhibits itself both in the verified theory of natural science and in the normative theory of social science. Any deductive theory analyzes into its primitive concepts and basic postulates or assumptions. By making these primitive concepts and postulates identical in both the normative theory of social science and the factual theory of natural science, one thereby obtains normative social theory which is different from factual social theory and at the same time obtains normative social theory which can be verified, since the deductively formulated theory of natural science is scientifically verifiable.

One also solves the basic paradox of moral authority. This paradox is that a normative theory, if we are to claim cognitive value for it, that is, claim that it is true or false, must be at one and the same time both normative and verifiable. To be normative it must, in part at least, prescribe a form for society different from that which is in fact the case, but to be cognitive and verifiable it must, with respect to some subject matter, be completely in accord with what is the case. These two attributes are impossible to achieve if both the normative and the cognitive or verifiable properties of normative social theory are referred to the facts of society. For to be verifiable with respect to these facts the normative social theory must accord completely with them. Then the distinction between factual social theory and normative social theory evaporates. And to be normative with respect to social facts a normative social theory must in part at least differ from the facts of society and attempt to remove or change them. If this condition is satisfied, then the normative social theory cannot be verified by an appeal to the facts of *de facto* society.

This paradox of moral authority can be resolved only if one refers the normative property of normative social theory to the facts of one subject matter and the cognitive or verifiable property of normative social theory to the facts of another subject matter. This is precisely what is done by the method at which we have arrived. Normative theory projects its normative prescriptions upon society; it receives its empirical verification from nature.

This solution has the additional merit of making the philosophy of the humanities and the philosophy of the natural sciences one and the same philosophy. Consequently, not only is scientifically verifiable normative social theory obtainable with the precise scientific methods for obtaining it specified, but also humanistic man and scientific man are reconciled. The gulf between the philosophy of value and the philosophy of science introduced by Immanuel Kant is removed. Also, the culturalistic fallacy of identifying the "ought" for culture with the historical "is," into which Fichte, Hegel and Marx fell in their attempt to remove the latter gulf, is avoided.

Several cautions are to be noted. It does not follow from the conclusion that there is a good or a normative social theory scientifically verifiable in a sense valid for everybody, that everybody actually knows this good and believes this theory; any more than it follows because the geological theory that the earth has a curved surface is scientifically verified in a sense which is valid for everyone, that everybody actually holds this belief. There are still people who believe that the earth is flat. What is meant in the latter case is that if *anyone* analyzes the problem concerning the geometrical character of the earth's surface, pursuing the analysis to all the facts relevant to its solution, and then proposes the two alternative hypotheses of "flat" and "curved," using the method which the nature of a hypothesis in its relation to inspected facts prescribes, the result obtained by one proficient person will be identical with that obtained by any others. Similarly, with respect to normative theory scientifically verified in a sense which is valid for everybody, what is meant is that the analysis of the problem of ideological social conflicts and ethical norms shows that this problem and the data relevant to its solution are such that there is a scientific method, not a matter of arbitrary preference or choice, but called for by the nature of the problem, which, when pursued by those who understand it and who, by practice, have learned how to use it, will give the same verified norm for one person in one society as it gives for another person in any other society.

Nor does it follow from the foregoing conclusion that *all* values or norms are invariant through the relativity of personal and cultural standpoints. It merely follows that there is a scientific method for finding *certain* values and *some* ideological principles which are invariant. There are relative goods, as well as the absolute good which we approximate in a more and more adequate scientifically verified philosophy. Within the invariant good which prescribes normative principles valid for everybody and every society, other things are left open and indeterminate, a matter of psychological preference and environmental circumstance. Thereby richness and variety are added to life. Moreover, because such a philosophy has scientific content it is able to prescribe precisely which normative factors are invariant or absolute and which are relative, a mere matter of preference.

It is the latter preferential element which gives the traditional "naturalistic" theory of ethics its partial truth, just as it is the distinction between the normative and the factual which provides the traditional "idealistic" theory of ethics with its partial insight. Without the invariant norm which the modern "idealists" correctly envisaged to exist, but to which, because of their lack of a scientific method, they could give no content, the empirically existing relative normative preferences emphasized by the "naturalists" so predominate that nothing but moral relativism and ideological conflict remains, as Soviet-American relations at the present writing clearly demonstrate, and mankind is left without even the minimum invariant communal assumptions necessary to carry on an international conference dealing with the world's problems.

A final caution is to be emphasized. The historical fact that not every philosophical or normative theory has been arrived at in the manner which the foregoing analysis prescribes is quite irrelevant so far as the validity of its result is concerned. Many more philosophies and attendant ideologies have been determined by the method indicated than is usually supposed. Nevertheless, historically, people have reached their philosophical theories and ethical norms in valid, invalid and indifferent ways. It is precisely this which has produced the dangerous ideological conflicts and the moral confusion of the contemporary world. Our concern has been not with the question concerning how in historical fact men have reached philosophical and moral judgments but with the question of what method they must use if they want such judgments to be valid for other people as well as for themselves.

Nor does our conclusion imply that purely speculative philosophy is meaningless or useless. Scientific method requires the cultivation of the imagination in order to discover possible hypotheses adequate to all the inductive data. Thus speculative philosophy is a necessary prerequisite for scientifically verified philosophy. But before the norms defined by a given speculative philosophy can be said to express anything more than a preference or an opinion of the speculator, the philosophy in question must be verified by a scientific method giving conclusions valid for everybody in the sense indicated above. It is this scientific method which this chapter has attempted to designate. Thus, speculative philosophy has not been repudiated; instead, it has been provided with the method necessary to make it effective.

This chapter is reprinted from *Social Science* for July 1947, with the kind permission of the Editor. It was presented originally on December 29, 1946, at Boston, Mass., in the Symposium: *Can Scientific Methods Determine the Ends for Which Scientific Discoveries Are Used?* This Symposium was in Section L of the American Association for the Advancement of Science under the joint auspices of the latter Association and the American Philosophical Association.

CHAPTER XXII

THE PHYSICAL SCIENCES, PHILOSOPHY AND HUMAN VALUES

The issue that arises is whether there is going to be any future for nuclear science — whether or not the release of atomic energy may not, because of the uses to which it is turned, lead to the destruction of science and civilization alike.

We had better begin as best we can by trying to translate these words "human values" and "philosophy" into more exact terms and to put some content into them. One of the first mistakes commonly made in talking about human values is to assume that we know what they are. Nothing is more obvious than that this thesis is false. Quite apart from the release of atomic energy and the resulting dangers is the fact of the ideological conflicts of our world. These are far more dangerous than the atomic bomb. If the atomic bomb is ever used to destroy civilization, it will be because men cannot get together sufficiently upon their ideologies to agree upon the social controls that are necessary to meet the situation. This is the fundamental issue confronting the world at the present moment: whether the ideology of the traditional French and Anglo-American democracies and that of Russian communism are so incompatible that we simply cannot get together; whether we mistrust each other's aims and thus cannot find any basis for discussion of the issues that confront us politically.

The issues are difficult enough quite apart from the conflict with respect to differing conceptions of human values.

There is selfish nationalistic pride. There is also the drive for oil and natural resources all over the world. Science intensifies these competitive factors because the nations with scientific knowledge must secure resources to feed their machines, and these economic pressures are hard enough to control even when the situation is not aggravated by ideological conflicts having their sources in the humanities.

It is important to make an analysis of these ideological conflicts and get out into the open the assumptions that underlie them. Let us take as two examples the doctrine of Russian communism and the ideology underlying the classical Anglo-American democracies. The humanistic theory of the ends of human activity in any specific ideology is not clear until one specifies its technical economic doctrine, its specific political doctrine and its precise religious doctrine if it happens to have one. Most doctrine in any subject is not properly understood until its fundamental basic assumptions are exhibited. In any doctrine, whether it be a factual theory in natural science or a normative ideological theory in the social sciences and humanities, there are certain basic assumptions.

Consider first the classical Anglo-American theory. Were one to ask a classical humanist in the United States what kind of society he would set up as the good end at which to aim, he would probably specify the type of society, so far as economics determines that society, which is defined by the classical economic theory that arose in Great Britain with Adam Smith and came to its final form in the economic science of Jevons. In this theory the basic entities are goods associated with pleasure. Jevons tells us frankly at the beginning of his *Principles of Political Economy* that the basic thing governing all economic actions is the quest for pleasure and freedom from pain. Certain economic wants of men have associations of pleasure. Others have associations of pain. Some have associations of a greater amount of pleasure than do others, and it is this greater amount which increases wants for them. The total number of wants as added up in the market place determines the demand, and scarcity due to the limitations of nature determines the supply. The law of supply and demand and the theory of prices generally come out of the relationship between these two factors.

Jevons is perfectly explicit in saying that the person who justifies these assumptions is the philosopher Bentham. Thus Jevons' economic theory presupposes a specific philosophical theory.

Similarly, the political theory of the good society in the traditional United States — the one that went into its Declaration of Independence and into its Constitution — is rooted in a specific philosophy. J. P. Miller in his *Origins of the American Revolution* makes it clear that the whole community mind at that time was literally steeped in the philosophy of John Locke. J. P. Miller writes that Locke functioned in determining the "idea of the good" that went into the Declaration of Independence and the Constitution in precisely the same manner that Marx functioned in determining the ideological assumptions of the Russian Communistic Revolution of 1918. Thus the classical Anglo-American social ideology in both its economic and its political content is rooted in and presupposes for its justification the philosophical assumptions of modern British empirical philosophy.

This British empirical philosophy and in particular the philosophy of Locke was determined in considerable part by Galilean and Newtonian physics, as this physics was first understood and described by Galilei and Newton themselves. The Lockean philosophical theory is that the whole of the universe — both nature and man — is to be understood as an aggregate of physical objects, termed by Locke and Descartes "material substances," which are located in public mathematical space and which act upon observers who project back colors and sounds in sensed space and time as appearances.

This distinction between sensed qualities in private, relative sensed space and time and physical objects or material substances in public mathematical space and time is put quite clearly by Newton in the Scholium at the beginning of his *Principia*. There Newton points out that the sensed space and time in which sense qualities are located must never be confused with the public mathematical space and time within which the public objects of physics are situated.

Immediately, the question arose, not merely for physicists but also for all modern philosophers, concerning what the relation is between the relative sensed space and time, with its sense qualities which we directly observe, and the public mathematical space and time, within which the public objects of physics are located. The answering of this question was the basic task bequeathed to early modern philosophy by Galilean and Newtonian physics.

The answer was specified for Locke and other early modern philosophers by Galilei and Newton themselves. Both Galilei and Newton assert that the sense qualities in relative, private sensed space and time which we directly observe are the way in which the public material objects in public mathematical space and time *appear* to the observer. Put more precisely, this means that sense qualities in private sensed space and time are related to physical masses in public mathematical space and time by a three-termed relation in which the sense qualities in sensed space and time are one term; the physical objects, or material substances, in public mathematical space and time are a second term; and the observer is the intermediary, third term. Without the observer, there would be no sensed qualities and no relative, private, sensed space and time.

All the latter sensuous factors are mere projections from the observer. This is what Newton meant when he called them "appearances." Physical objects in public, mathematical space exist, however, even when no one is looking and no observers are present.   This is what Newton meant by calling them "real."

To say, moreover, as Newton did, that the sense data in sensed space and time are appearances of the public physical masses in public mathematical space and time is to add a further qualifications with respect to the role of the observer in the relationship between the two, the qualification, namely, that the observer does not project the sense qualities in sensed space and time spontaneously, but only does so when he is acted upon by the material substances in public mathematical space and time.   Note, however, that this is precisely the philosophy of man and nature of John Locke, the philosophy which asserts that the whole of reality is to be conceived as material substances in public space, acting upon observers who project back sense qualities in private sensed space and time as appearances.

To appreciate the full philosophical consequences of Galilei's and Newton's physics as made explicit in Locke's philosophy, it is necessary, however, to note what is entailed concerning the nature of the observer.   The observer cannot be conceived as merely an aggregate of the material substances of his body, since the latter type of observer would be quite unable to be conscious of sense qualities in sensed space and time as appearances.   This follows, as both Galilei and Newton emphasize, because material substances have only the properties of moving in a straight line with a constant velocity when no external forces are acting upon them and of moving in an accelerated manner when acted upon by external forces. Material substances, furthermore, have no consciousness and hence no capacity to be aware of ineffable sensuous qualities in sensed space and time as appearances.   Thus Locke saw that the Galilean and Newtonian observer had to be a different kind of substance from the material substances or even the aggregate of material substances in mathematical space and time.   This unique type of observer Locke called a "mental substance." Thus, put more precisely, the Lockean mental substance is simply the kind of entity identified with the observer which has the property such that, when it is acted upon by the material substances of physics in mathematical space and time, it has the consciousness of, and the capacity to project back, sense qualities in sensed space and time as appearances.

The point which led us into these scientific and philosophical distinctions and technicalities has now been demonstrated. This point was that the Lockean philosophy which defined the economic and political ideology of classical Anglo-American culture was not merely a philosophy of economic science and politics but also the philosophy to which Galilean and Newtonian physics first forced modern philosophical thought. Since Lockean philosophy was a necessary consequence of distinctions drawn by Galilei and Newton themselves in the Newtonian physics which was experimentally verified, it followed for Locke and his followers that the Lockean philosophy was not merely an idea of the good for the state and for culture but also a philosophy of the experimentally verified for nature.

Locke had no alternative, therefore, but to identify the human soul or personality in religious discussion and the political person in legal theory and the state with the person as conceived by his philosophy; that is, with the mental substance which functions as the intermediary second term in the three-termed relation joining apparent sensed qualities in apparent sensed space and time to the physical objects in mathematical space and time.

In this Lockean theory of the nature of the person, there are no imaginable relations whatever between one person or mental substance and another. Mental substances are not related spatially. This is what Leibnitz meant when he termed them "windowless monads." It is this lack of any intrinsic social relations between persons which is the Lockean modern foundation of the political philosophy expressed in the American Declaration of Independence to the effect that there is no basis for government, no normative social theory, apart from a social convention.

The significance of the latter point will be grasped if we compare the concept of the person of Galilean and Newtonian physics and the attendant Lockean philosophy with the concept of the person of Aristotelian physics and the attendant Thomistic philosophy or the theological polity of the English Tudor Hooker. According to Aristotelian philosophy and science, personality is embodied soul, where soul is the form of the living body. Aristotle explicitly says in his psychology that the study of the soul falls within the science of nature. This soul or form of the living body is related organically to the forms or final causes of all other living creatures. Consequently, the concept of a person in the Aristotelian sense is one in which the individual person is part of a hierarchical order of species and genera defined by the scientific method of classification in science of the natural history descriptive type.

This conception of a person as involving a position in a hierarchical order which relates his individual nature essentially to the individual natures of other persons and creatures throughout the cosmos is what Aristotle had in mind when he said that man is in his essential nature a "political animal." Man's individual nature is a social nature. He cannot be himself as an individual man except as he is part of a social organization or state which embodies the hierarchical relation of himself to all other creatures and natural objects. Thus in the Aristotelian theory of a person, a person is organically related to other people and must have this relation expressed in society, if society is to give expression to his own individuality. Consequently, a good state is one in which a man cannot be himself except insofar as he operates through an organized social church and through an organized political government.

But in the Lockean theory, in which one cannot even imagine what the relation is between one person or mental substance and another, there are no scientifically and philosophically defined and grounded relations to be used in defining political theory. Consequently, Lockean and classical Anglo-American modern political theory has no alternative but to ground government in nothing more than a convention, that is, in the consent of the governed.

The Marxian theory of a person and of politics is similarly opposed to the Lockean conception and much nearer to that of Aristotle, even though different also from the position of the Greek. According to Marx there is no meaning to the individual human nature apart from the organic structure of society which in turn cannot be conceived apart from a particular stage of the historical process. Furthermore, the key factors in the definition of an understanding of both human nature and any stage of the historical process are economic in character and economic in a materialistic, thermodynamically physiological sense.

All these considerations indicate that differences in ideology in the social sciences and the humanities are rooted in differences in the philosophies underlying these ideologies and that the philosophies in turn are connected with the results of scientific inquiry and are always regarded by the people who hold them as called for by the scientific knowledge which they take into account. Put more concretely, what this means is that any people are impressed by the facts of their experience which fall within their attention. From these facts they derive, consciously or unconsciously, a specific scientific generalization or theory. The analysis of this theory, after the manner in which Locke analyzed the physics of Galilei and Newton, brings out an explicit philosophy.

In terms of this philosophy they define their economic, political, religious and other humanistic doctrines and attendant social institutions. The good state is the state which permits the person to be the kind of person which such a scientifically verified philosophy designates a person to be.

If this analysis be true, we would expect that when for any reason whatever a given philosophy is changed, then the social humanistic ideology and values will also ·change. Many considerations indicates this to be the case. For example, in the Middle Ages human values underwent considerable change in the shift within Roman Catholicism from the definition of its theological doctrine in terms of the philosophy and science of Plato to the formulation in terms of that of Aristotle, a shift which came in the theology of St. Thomas Aquinas. In the transition from the medieval to the modern world a similar reconstruction of ideology took place with the shift from the philosophy of St. Thomas to that of Locke and then to that of Hume, Bentham and Jevons. And even since then, in the movement beyond British empiricism, through Kant to Hegel and Marx, another shift in ideology has occurred, which exhibits itself in the nineteenth and twentieth centuries in Germany and Russia.

Unless the latter shift is kept continuously in mind, we will forget that practically every person east of the Rhine, either a Russian or a German, for at least the last one hundred and fifty years, takes it for granted that the pre-Kantian British empirical philosophy underlying the ideology of the traditional modern French, British and American world is completely outmoded. The intellectual leaders in philosophy and the social sciences in both Germany and Russia since the time of Kant regard it as established that considerations in mathematical physics which Kant, among others, made evident have completely disposed of British empirical philosophy as an adequate theory of scientific knowledge or of political, economic and other humanistic institutions. What

convinced Kant and those following him of the inadequacy
of British empirical philosophy were mathematics and mathematical physics.   It became evident to all competent students
of these subjects that it is impossible to define the technical
concepts of mathematics or the concept of causality as it is
used in mathematical physics in terms of nothing but sense
data and their sequences as the philosophy of Hume requires.
The British empirical philosophy, also, gives one no correct
theory whatever of historical cultural evolution with the
shift and negations between different ideologies noted in the
previous paragraph which the evidence of history unequivocally indicates to be the case.

It was noted at the outset that the problem of establishing
proper social controls of the scientific instruments which the
natural sciences and engineering are now placing at the
disposal of men centers at bottom in the problem of resolving
the ideological conflicts between the different conceptions of
economic and political theory and human values of the different nations and peoples of the world.   The foregoing
analysis has now made it evident that these ideological conflicts center at bottom in philosophical differences and that
the philosophical differences in turn are connected with
scientific theory concerning nature and the methods of scientific verification in natural science.   Any approach to the
resolution of the ideological problems, therefore, must begin
by getting out into the open the differing technical economic,
political and religious doctrines of the different ideologies
and the basic differing philosophical premises from which the
economic, political and religious doctrines stem.   In the case
of classical German culture of the nineteenth century, these
philosophical premises were the post-Kantian premises of the
philosophy of Hegel.   In the case of the contemporary communistic Russian ideology the philosophical premises are
those of the post-Kantian and post-Hegelian philosophy of
Marx.   In the case of classical traditional Anglo-American

political and economic theory they are those of pre-Kantian modern British empirical philosophy.

There are many other ideological conflicts in the world. When all these different ideologies and their underlying differing philosophies are brought out into the open two possibilities are found to be present, as Chapters XVI and XVIII have noted. Two given ideologies may presuppose philosophies which, while different, are nonetheless compatible. This is the case with the ideologies of the traditional East and the traditional West. Certain other ideologies may not merely differ in their basic philosophical premises but these premises may be contradictory. The pre-Kantian British empirical philosophy underlying the Anglo-American economic and political values and the Marxist post-Kantian and post-Hegelian philosophy underlying the ideology of contemporary Russia is an example of the second possibility.

In the former case, where the philosophies at the basis of the differing ideologies, while different, are nonetheless compatible, the reconciliation is easy, comparatively speaking. One needs merely to enlarge the philosophical assumptions and the different values of the one ideology to include those of the other.

The real difficulty arises in the case where the underlying philosophies are not merely different but mutually contradictory. In this instance the manner in which ideological reconciliation is to be achieved is by no means easy or obvious.

It should be clear, however, that one must get some criterion outside the social sciences and humanities which can serve as an objective check or measure of the correctness of one ideology as compared with another. What kind of a criterion is one to obtain? Is there any criterion for an ideology that is objective? Is there any basis for saying that a given ideology is verified for everybody, Russian communists and Anglo-Americans alike?

The answer to all these questions was given by Socrates

and Plato in the *Republic*.   There they say that only those who have passed through the hypotheses of the mathematical physical sciences can arrive at the idea of the good which one has a right to say holds for everybody.

Is it not extraordinary that Socrates and Plato should inform us that if we want to arrive at an idea of the good in the humanities and the social sciences which holds for everybody we have to investigate the hypotheses and basic concepts of the natural sciences?   Perhaps the best way to explain this is to consider the method of the philosophy of science as we noted it to be illustrated in the passage from the physics of Galilei and Newton to the philosophy of Locke.

In this and all other natural sciences there is the aggregate of empirical data of the natural history type from which eventually, as in the case of Newton, a deductively formulated theory is derived. Such a theory has specific postulates which are expressed in terms of basic primitive concepts.   When such a deductive theory is verified by the empirical experimental methods of science, which give the same results for one person who pursues them with understanding as they give for another, we clearly have in such deductive theory a set of propositions which, if they are true or verified for one person are also verified or verifiable for any other person. Providing, therefore, that one can specify methods by which such verified, deductively formulated theory in the natural sciences is shown to entail a philosophy, one will then have verified philosophical theory.   When this verified philosophical theory is used to define one's idea of the good for culture, one can say that this idea of the good for culture holds for everybody, since its basic foundation is a philosophy derived from verified scientific theory of nature in which the verification is of a character such that it is valid for everybody.

It remains, therefore, in order to derive our objective criterion for judging conflicting ideologies, to specify the method of the philosophy of science by means of which the philosophy

of experimentally verified deductively formulated theory in
natural science is made articulate.   This method Plato and
Socrates called "dialectic." Careful analysis shows that
"dialectic" is nothing more than logical analysis.

This analytic method of the philosophy of science has two
parts. The one part consists in analyzing the deductively
formulated empirically verified theory of natural science to
determine the primitive concepts in its postulates.   These
concepts designate the elementary and hence ultimate entities
and relations in terms of which nature and man as part of
nature are at bottom to be conceived.   Such a specification of
ultimate entities and relations is precisely what one means by
a philosophy.   Such philosophy was called by the Greeks
"ontological philosophy," since these elementary entities and
relations designate that which the verified theory indicates
nature to be.

The second task of analysis in the philosophy of natural
science consists in analyzing the method of verifying the
deductively formulated theory in question, and noting the
connection between the concepts of the theory and the
observable data of experience.   This part of the philosophy
of science designates what the Greeks called the "epistemological philosophy" which the scientifically verified theory
exhibits and entails.

An instance of this appeared in the distinction made by
Galilei and Newton between sensed space and time and
mathematical space and time.   This is an epistemological
distinction.   Thus the Newtonian and Galilean physics, as
thus described by Galilei and Newton themselves, clearly
and unspeculatively entailed a specific epistemological
philosophy.

When the ontological results of the analysis of one's scientific theory of nature and the epistemological results of the
analysis of its method of verification are combined, one has a

complete philosophy. The important thing to note is that the epistemological part designates, as we indicated in the case of the relation between Newton and Locke, not merely a scientifically verified theory of nature but also a scientifically verified theory of man as the observer or knower of nature. Thus out of the philosophy of natural science one necessarily and automatically obtains, under analysis, a philosophy of human nature also.

We arrive, therefore, at this very important conclusion, first designated by Socrates and Plato, but still true, nonetheless, as our previous examination of Locke's relation to Galilei and Newton has indicated: That philosophy of the good for the social sciences and the humanities is a publicly valid one which is also the philosophy of the experimentally verified theory of the natural sciences.

In other words, in a properly constructed society the philosophy which underlies the definition of one's economic doctrine, one's political doctrine, one's religious, poetic and artistic theory must be identical with the philosophy of the natural sciences which is determined by nothing more than the logical analysis of the experimentally verified theories of the natural sciences to bring out their primitive, ontological assumptions and their methodological and epistemological assumptions. The philosophy of the good in culture and the humanities, which defines the ends of human action, must be identical with the philosophy of the scientifically verified theory of the natural sciences, which, when pursued with respect to its deductive consequences, provides the instruments for human action. Such a philosophy of the good or the ideal in the social sciences and the humanities may be truly said to be an ideology which holds for everybody since, being at the same time entailed by the experimentally verified, deductively formulated theory of the natural sciences, it is thereby verified by the methods of natural science, which give the same result for one person that they give for another.

This is the answer to the question concerning the proper relation between the natural sciences, philosophy and human values. One tragedy of our civilization is that whereas natural science has gone forward, the separation of the departments of knowledge has obscured the essential connection between ideological or humanistic philosophy and the philosophy of natural science. As a consequence, our ideological philosophies have not changed along with changes in our philosophy of the natural sciences. Thus we find ourselves with sets of normative ideas grounded often in outmoded philosophies or in partial philosophies which get into conflict with each other. Hence the conflict of moral and social ideologies.

The previous considerations do, however, suggest a technique by means of which these ideological conflicts can be resolved. The fact that the criterion derives from natural science means that it is one which should work in our relationship to the Russians. For the Russians, likewise, believe in scientific method and in the natural sciences. They, like us, believe in the values of scientific inquiry applied to the resources of nature to lift the well-being of men in general and applied to the understanding of the dialectical evolution of their social institutions to enlighten the minds of men socially.

There is little likelihood of the Russians and us getting together upon the basis of a purely humanistic philosophy, since in the more ideological humanistic sphere the doctrines unequivocally contradict one another. But there is a real possibility, because of the considerations just noted, of the Russians and the members of the traditional democracies west of the Rhine finding a philosophical basis for agreement, providing this basis is rooted in a philosophy of the natural sciences. It may be that in this manner we can resolve the ideological conflicts which at present prevent the leaders of

the major nations of the world from agreeing upon th
of international social control necessary to direct the
logical discoveries of natural science to good rathe
destructive ends.

This chapter was presented in September, 1946, at the Sympos
The Future of Nuclear Science in connection with the Bicen
Program of Princeton University. It is reprinted here with th
mission of the Princeton University Press.

CHAPTER XXIII

THE METHODS AND GROUNDS OF
RELIGIOUS KNOWLEDGE

The instruments for the control of technology for good ends are morality and religion. Consequently, never before was the need for an effective moral and religious knowledge more pressing than it is today. Unless we can find a social morality and a religion with the power to win men to its ways everywhere throughout the world mankind may be doomed.

The unique character of the recent war points to the same conclusion. Strictly speaking, this war was the first world war. The previous war was a purely European conflict. The recent war, on the other hand, started in the Orient when the Japanese invaded Manchuria. It then spread to Abyssinia, Spain, Poland, Scandinavia and Russia, and encircled the world with the Japanese bombardment of Pearl Harbor.

These facts mean that the issues confronting us now in peace as well as in war are world-wide issues, affecting the Orient as much as they affect the Occident. It becomes evident also that the problem confronting our world now becomes that not merely of reconciling conflicting Western nationalistic and humanistic ideologies, but also of peacefully merging the radically different political, moral and religious values of the East with those of the West. For such an undertaking a truly global, as opposed to a provincially Eastern or a provincially Western, morality and religion are essential.

The question immediately arises: Is our present moral

and religious knowledge adequate for either of these two tasks? An examination of the evidence relevant to this question forces one to reply in the negative.

A morality and religion which would control scientific technology must be one which can connect itself in some way with contemporary science. This, contemporary Western religion in both its Roman Catholic and Protestant forms, is incapable of doing.

Roman Catholicism possesses a moral theory and a religious doctrine which is connected intimately with science. Unfortunately, however, this science is that of Aristotle and the medieval world, not that of Galilei, Newton, Einstein, Planck, and the modern world which has made possible the release of atomic energy. Thus, the ethical and religious humanism or the attendant society which Roman Catholic doctrine would define as good, is not one which can fully comprehend, relate itself to, or control the contemporary scientific technology.

Contemporary Protestant doctrine, on the other hand, can connect itself with no science whatever. This is the case because traditional modern moral idealism and traditional and recent modern Protestantism affirm that moral philosophy and religion are autonomous subjects, standing on their own feet with grounds of justification quite independent of natural science, and having nothing to do with natural science. Such a morality and religion are of no use to control scientific technology, since by definition and their own claims, they have no connection with science and technology. An autonomous morality or religion may perchance give one an egocentric personal ethics and a subjective personal religion, but it is not adequate to generate and provide the objective social and international instruments necessary to control the atomic bomb. For before one thing can hope to control another thing it must connect itself with that other. And this an autonomous morality and religion cannot do.

The reasons for this unfortunate state of contemporary moral philosophy and religion are worthy of note. In the late Greek and Medieval periods, the scientific conception to which the majority of scientists were led by their investigations in mathematics, physics, chemistry, astronomy, biology and psychology was that made articulate in the physics and metaphysics of Aristotle. St. Thomas Aquinas in formulating present Roman Catholic orthodoxy took this Aristotelian scientific conception of man and nature and identified the basic concepts of theology, such as the soul, its immortality and God the Father, with explicit technical scientific elements in this Aristotelian science. God the Father, for example, was identified with the Unmoved Mover or final cause in Aristotelian and medieval physics. The soul of man was identified likewise with the formal or final cause of the living body of Aristotle's psychology. This final cause of nature and man, or God the Father, was not in the world naturally and perfectly, because of the stubbornness of prime matter in the Aristotelian physics in resisting the imposition of the divine formal cause. Thus, for God, or the Unmoved Mover, to be revealed to man in the world, some representative of God the Father had to come into the world. It is precisely in this fact that the divinity of the historical Christ found technical meaning in terms of the accepted scientific knowledge of the medieval world. Thus it is to be noted that Roman Catholic ethics and theology were essentially connected with Greek and Medieval science.

Protestanism began with the Reformation. This Reformation initially did not depart from the medieval conception of man and nature. Luther in his Lutheranism and Calvin in his Presbyterianism held a medieval conception of both. The only thing which these and the other Protestant reformers questioned was the claim of the Roman Catholic Church to be the sole earthly representative of this medieval theology and Christianity.

The decisive departure from the medieval scientific and philosophical foundations for religion came not with the Protestant Reformation but with the development of modern physical science. It was Galilei's analysis of the motion of the projectile which led to the discovery of a new definition of force, that inaugurated the break from Aristotelian science and philosophy to that of Descartes and Newton of the modern world. And it was this new science which made inescapable the construction of a new philosophical theory of man and nature. This new modern philosophy was inaugurated first by Descartes and later for the English-speaking world by John Locke.

As formulated by Descartes this modern philosophical theory of man and nature seemed to provide adequate meaning for the concepts and doctrines of the Christian religion. Descartes began man's knowledge with a demonstration of the existence of the self, moved on to a demonstration of the existence of God, and culminated in a demonstration of the existence of an external world. As the assumptions of modern philosophy developed, however, these demonstrations by Descartes turned out to be unconvincing if not invalid.

With Locke similarly, Christian doctrine seemed initially to be justified. It was not long, however, before certain misgivings arose. According to Locke's philosophy all the facts of experience are accounted for when one assumes that the whole of reality is to be conceived as an aggregate of free and independent mental substances or minds acted on by the material substances or atoms of Newton's physics. The mental substances, or minds, like the physicists' atoms, were conceived of as without parts; hence they were indivisible and indestructible. Thus the modern Lockean man had merely to identify the concept of soul in Christian doctrine with Locke's mental substance to have the doctrine of the immortality of the soul provided with content and validity in terms of modern scientific and philosophical knowledge.

When one turned, however, to the basis for the concept of God, difficulties began to appear. Since every fact in nature was supposedly accounted for by the material atoms of physics and chemistry and their mechanical laws, and all the characteristics of human beings were accounted for by the mental substances, little justification remained for believing in anything more than the mental and material substances alone. God was no longer to be conceived, as in medieval science and philosophy, as the formal causal factor in nature, since nature, according to modern Newtonian physics, is the effect of material entities operating according to purely mechanical laws. This made all the traditional medieval arguments from causality or design in nature to the existence of God untenable. Thus if a meaning for the belief in God was to be justified in terms of modern knowledge, this meaning and justification would have to be found in man alone. But man was accounted for in terms of his independent, completely free, solitary mental substance.

The suggestion was made that God be defined as the creator of the mental and the material substances. This doctrine is deism. Scientists, philosophers and theologians soon concluded, however, that this deistic solution of the problem is quite unsatisfactory.

Also, for scientific and philosophical reasons which space does not permit us to indicate here, Locke was led to define his mental substance or person as an entity which has no ideas in its consciousness except as material substances acted upon it to give rise to sense impressions. Thus Locke called this modern mind or mental substance a *tabula rasa,* a blank tablet. This entailed Locke's theory of ideas, the theory namely, that the only meanings a mind can have in it are meanings referring to sense data or associations of such sense data. Once this is admitted, Bishop Berkeley had no difficulty in showing that Newton's and Locke's concept of a material substance is meaningless and hence non-existent, and Hume had similar ease in demonstrating that Locke's and Berkeley's concept of mental substances is equally meaningless and non-existent. If the only possible sources of meaning and of meaningful objects in man and nature are sense data or associations of sense data, then minds and material objects must be mere sequences and associations of sense data also. In this manner positivism in natural science, and William James' theory of the self in psychology, as nothing but the sequence of the associated sense impressions, arose. Upon this basis there is no soul with a persisting identity to be immortal. The self is merely a certain temporary sequence of associated sense impressions, a "flow of consciousness" as James termed it. With this development of the assumptions of modern science and philosophy, not merely the traditional doctrine of God but also the traditional Christian doctrine of the immortality of the soul became meaningless and untenable. Thus it happened that as the Protestants moved away from Medieval Rome further and further into the modern world, priding themselves upon their freedom of thought and their acceptance of modern knowledge, the more the traditional doctrines of Western religion became mere empty words devoid of philosophical and scientific content and the greater became the discrepancy between what the student learned about man and nature during the six days of the week in his courses in physics, psychology and sociology and what he heard in the University Chapel on Sunday morning.

Such was the state of religion in the modern world when Kant came upon the scene. Immanuel Kant was an expert mathematical physicist before he became a philosopher. He thoroughly understood Newton's physics and used its experimentally verified laws to solve certain astronomical problems and to discover the nebular hypothesis. This intimate knowledge of physics made Kant aware of the inadequacy of Locke's theory of ideas and the attendant philosophy of

Hume. This inadequacy forced Kant to the construction of a new philosophy of science in which sensed factors given empirically after the manner of Hume are combined with a formal systematic theoretical factor given, as Kant supposed, by the knower *a priori*.

That scientific knowledge does involve these two empirical and theoretical factors cannot be denied, as previous chapters have demonstrated. Thus Kant's theory was very important.

Unfortunately, however, this Kantian philosophy of natural science left no meaning, as Kant himself noted, for morality and religion. In fact, the situation was worse than when Kant came upon the scene. In previous modern thought, the problem had been a serious one, since Newton's physics, because of its doctrine of mechanical causation, seemed to make man nothing more than a mere cog in a vast cosmological machine. Upon this basis the moral and the religious life become meaningless since both, for most thinkers, presuppose genuine human freedom of choice, and regard remorse for bad choices and evil conduct as something real. One can hardly, however, be blamed for anything which one does, and have genuine remorse for it, if the decision was really made by the mechanical universe and not by a free act upon one's own part. In Kant's philosophy of science the situation was made even worse. For not only was the object of scientific knowledge completely determined and necessary, but also man's *knowing* of the scientific object was subject to the same absolute necessity. This followed because the *a priori* "forms of sensibility" and "categories of the understanding" which Kant's scientist brought to the knowing of nature were characterized by *"Allgemeinheit und Notwendigheit"*; that is, by universality and necessity. Thus for Kant, and for all German and other modern idealistic philosophers following Kant, not merely nature itself but also man's knowing of nature was characterized by absolute necessity and hence provided no meaning for the freedom necessary for the moral and religious life.

Consequently, Kant seemed to have no alternative but to set up morality and religion as independent autonomous subjects having no connection with science. This occurred in Kant's *Critique of Practical Reason*. This point is tremendously important because it explains why the modern man came to the notion of an autonomous ethics and religion having no basis in science.

The immediate effect was most exhilarating. Man found himself in the happy position of being free to believe anything about morality and religion which the demands of the moral free will suggested. From this belief came the Romantic Movement in Prussian politics, in German militarism and in modern literature. No longer could scientific evidence present any difficulties for ethics or religion since supposedly Kant had shown that science has nothing to do with these subjects.

Unfortunately, the consequences in the long run were not so salutary. The ethics and religion which this gave one turned out to be exceedingly formal and verbal. Thus the empty verbalism which appeared in the Protestantism which followed Locke, Berkeley and Hume returned in a slightly less obvious but nonetheless real form in the later Protestantism which followed the German idealism of Kant and his successors. Furthermore, ethics and religion were robbed of one of their previously most important functions in life, the function, namely, of pulling together every phase of man's knowledge and experience into a single moving triumphant whole. This, an independent and autonomous ethics or religion cannot do. They constitute, even if taken on their own terms, but one item in man's knowledge and experience, standing over against the increasingly important scientific item. Thus the task of putting these two factors together falls inevitably and necessarily upon some other factor in man's experience than his ethics or his religion.

It was precisely this consideration which gave rise to the philosophy of Kant's successor, Fichte. The problem took on the technical philosophical form of the question concerning the relation between the philosophy of science of Kant's *Critique of Pure Reason* and the philosophy of morality and religion of Kant's *Critique of Practical Reason*. Fichte answered this question by reducing the former to the latter. Immediately, however, certain consequences of this reduction arose which transformed the individual, initially free, Kantian moral man into a mere expression of the necessary historical development of the consciousness of the Absolute. Thus this Kantian moral philosophy which began with an emphasis upon the freedom of the individual man ended with the reduction of man to a moral and cultural historical determination which was as rigid as the determination of Kant's philosophy of natural science. Moreover, this Fichtean and Hegelian autonomous moral and religious philosophy identified the divine and the good with the actual historical development of Western cultural institutions, a development which reached its perfection, according to Hegel, in the German *Kultur* of the 19th century, and which was smashed in the defeat of the Kaiser's Germany in the first major war of this country.

Notwithstanding the verbal emptiness of the Kantian theory of an autonomous morality and religion and the *reductio ad absurdum* of the Hegelian theory, this notion of an autonomous morality and religion still persists in contemporary Protestant moral and religious thought. One independent consideration has supported this conclusion. This consideration has to do with the ethical character of technological instruments.

The recent traditional moralists and humanists noted quite correctly that scientific instruments by themselves are ethically neutral.   Considered in isolation, they can be used for good or bad ends.   From this truth the false inference was made that therefore values must have some other basis than science.   Thus again the notion of an autonomous ethics and religion arose.

What this conclusion overlooked is that there is more to science than its technological instruments.   There are also (1) the theory without which the instruments would not have been invented, and (2) the method by which this theory is grounded in or related to immediately apprehended fact. And, as the sequel will show, neither of these two factors is ethically neutral.   Each contains within itself the various factors available for human knowledge in the nature of things which, when pursued in isolation by different peoples, make the ideals and values of the diverse cultures of the world in considerable part what they are.

This brings us to the second fact in the contemporary world which necessitates a conception of morality and religion quite different from the current one.   This fact, it will be recalled, is the global character of the recent war and the international character of the problems of its peace.

It has been noted that the major problem confronting the world is that of merging the differing cultures of the East and the West.   This makes it impossible any longer to conceive of an adequate morality and religion in purely Western terms.   For the problem of merging Oriental and Occidental cultures brings us face to face with the fact that the philosophy and religion of the Far East is different from that of the West in either its Hebrew, Roman Catholic, or Protestant form.

A few considerations will make this clear.   The four major religions of Far Eastern origin are Confucianism, Taoism, Buddhism and Hinduism.   None of these religions is theistic. None has a religious prophet without whom one cannot be saved.   The treatises in terms of which each has been conveyed tend to be poetic, intuitive and aesthetic in character.

The major religions of Western or Middle Eastern origin are Judaism, Christianity and Mohammedanism. All these religions have a divinely inspired prophet without whom one cannot be saved. Each is theistic in form. For this reason Japanese Shintoism is more like a Western religion than it is like the other religions of the Far East. This is not unconnected with the historical fact that the Japanese revived this theistic Shintoism in order as quickly as possible to create a strong nationalistic state of the Western type. The major treatises of the religions and cultures of the West are abstract, technical, logically reasoned and doctrinal in form. This shows itself in the logical methods used by Socrates and Plato in ethical and religious inquiry, in the dry abstract form of the metaphysics of Aristotle, in the technical definitions and syllogistic reasoning of the *Summa Theologica* of St. Thomas Aquinas, in the mathematical character of the *Principia* of Newton, and the equally abstract and technical terminology of the natural and moral philosophy of Kant.

All these differences between the philosophy and religion of the Far East and that of the Middle East and the West have their basis in a more fundamental distinction having to do with the methods to be used in gaining trustworthy knowledge. The Oriental religious sage and philosopher is always insisting that while formal scientific methods and inference may be very important for practical purposes they are of no use whatever to take one to knowledge which is philosophically real or religious. The latter type of knowledge the Oriental always maintains is to be known by intuition or immediate apprehension alone and by contemplation of that which is given in immediate apprehension and intuition. The Oriental sage also maintains that nothing determinate, i.e., definite in character, is immortal. All determinate things are transitory. Thus Nirvana, Tao, Jen and Brahman, the names for the divine factor in man and nature in the Orient, are not describable by any determinate properties whatever. These Far Eastern religions do not affirm the existence of a *determinate* divine factor in things, nor do they believe in the immortality of the unique determinate differentiated personality.

The theistic religions of the West believe in the immortality of the determinate personality and in a divine being with determinate characteristics. This, in fact, is the definition of theism. The divine is a being whose character can be designated by a determinate thesis.

These differences become clear if certain very elemental considerations concerning the nature of human knowledge are noted. All that anyone can possibly know in any field of experience or knowledge whatever must be of one of two kinds or a combination of both: One can know what one immediately apprehends without any theoretical acts of faith or logical inference taking one beyond the immediately apprehended. Or one can know that which, by an act of the mind, one infers from the immediately apprehended. All these distinctions between Oriental philosophy and religion and Western philosophy and religion will become clear if one assumes that the West has tended to identify the scientifically true, the philosophically real, the morally good and the religiously divine with the inferred unseen factor in the nature of things; whereas the Orient has restricted scientific knowledge, philosophical reality, moral goodness and religious divinity to the immediately apprehended portion of our knowledge alone.

To understand the sources of these differences between the East and the West, we may best begin by noting the part of our knowledge which is given by intuition and immediate apprehension with all inference and theory neglected as far as this is humanly possible. Can we not say that it is a continuum differentiated by the colors, sounds, odors, pains and pleasures which our senses convey to us? To distinguish this immediately apprehended continuum, given in intuition, from the unseen space-time continuum of mathematical physics, given by the scientific method of postulation, let us term the immediately apprehended continuum "the differentiated aesthetic continuum". Within this differentiated aesthetic continuum, two immediately apprehended factors can be distinguished. One of these factors is the aggregate of differentiations, i.e., the specific immediately sensed colors, sounds, odors, pains and pleasures with their finite temporal duration and spatial extension. The other factor is the immediately apprehended continuum apart from these differentiations. The latter can be appropriately termed "the undifferentiated aesthetic continuum". Since the Oriental sages tell us that the divine is to be found by intuition or immediate apprehension, it must be identified with one of these two factors. Since they tell us also that the divine is not determinate in character, it becomes evident that it is the indeterminate aesthetic continuum to which the terms Nirvana, Tao, Jen, and Brahman must refer.

The divine object in the West is an unseen God the Father. This means that He cannot be known by the aesthetic intuition after the manner of the divine being of the Orient. Christ tells us that His kingdom is not of this world. St. Paul asserts that the things that are seen are temporal and that it is only the things which are unseen which are eternal. All the theistic religions affirm in addition that the determinate personality is immortal. Certainly this is not true of the self given with immediacy in the aesthetic intuition. As Plato, Hume and Kant in the West and the Hinayanistic Buddhists in the East have noted, and as is evident to common sense, all immediately apprehended personalities pass away. Thus it is obvious that if a religion is going to affirm the doctrine of the immortality of the determinate personality the real in knowledge must be identified not with the self given with immediacy in the aesthetic intuition but with a self inferred from the immediately apprehended self. Similarly, there is no immediately apprehended form in nature as a whole, which is immortal. Thus if the divine is to be a determinate being embracing more than man it is with a determinate factor inferred from the immediately apprehended and not with the immediately apprehended alone that the divine must be identified.

Let us call the immediately apprehended factor in knowledge and reality the aesthetic component, and the unseen inferred factor, the theoretic component. Oriental religion then becomes defined as one which identifies the divine with the timeless factor in the aesthetic component. Western religion becomes similarly defined as one which identifies the divine with the timeless or invariant factor in the theoretic component.

This explains why the Far Eastern religions do not need a religious prophet if the divine is to be revealed to man, and why the Western religions must have one. If the divine is given with immediacy then it is here in the world of immediate intuition already without the mediation of a divinely inspired representative. Thus all that religious sages in the Orient have to do is to direct one's attention to the factor given with immediacy with which the divine is identified. If, however, the divine is identified with an unseen factor in the nature of things, then obviously the only way in which man can know God with the immediacy of the aesthetic intuition is by a divinely inspired being representing God coming into the world of immediacy. Hence the religious prophet without whom man in the theistic religions cannot be saved, becomes essential.

All these considerations indicate that an adequate religion for the contemporary world, one which is to give expression to and combine the moral and religious thought of the East with that of the West, must relate the intuitive emotional type of religion of the aesthetic component of reality with the inferred more doctrinal theistic type of religion of the theoretic component of reality. Such a religion has a chance of gaining the response of the whole world, since it permits each religious group and each portion of the world to preserve its own integrity and self-respect, contributing something to the totality of the good and the divine, instead of forcing one part of the world to give up its traditional morality and religion by being converted to that of another part of the world. The latter type of religion has no hope of practical success. Moreover, it is as erroneous in theory as it is inadequate in practice. Thus the practical and the ideal solution for the humanistic portion of the international problems of our time is the development of a more perfect truly international morality and religion which combines the theistic Western identification of the divine with the theoretic component in things with the Oriental grounding of the good and the divine in the aesthetic component of things.

It must be emphasized, however, that the Western world does not at present possess an adequate religion even of the Western type. This is because the development of modern moral and religious thought has distorted Western religion. This becomes clear when one asks the following question which every religion of the Western theistic type must face: How is it possible to know a factor which cannot be seen? To this question there is only one effective and correct answer: Unseen factors can be known only by inference.

Immediately a second difficulty arises. How is one to distinguish a faulty inference or act of faith from a valid one? Only if there is an answer to this question can truth about unseen factors be distinguished from falsehood, or orthodoxy avoid confusion with heresy.

The only answer to this question is as follows: Trustworthy unseen factors can be distinguished from erroneously inferred ones only by means of the logical and scientific

methods developed by the West for making trustworthy
inferences to the unseen.   Otherwise the fantasies of a
moron or the obsessions of a crank become as trustworthy
conceptions of the divine which is unseen as the doctrines
of a true theistic religion.

This means, however, that nothing corrupts Western
religion as unequivocally and thoroughly as does the current contention in contemporary Western Protestant humanistic circles that religion and morality are things which the
methods of logic and science cannot touch.   Recently these
moralists have turned to the philosophy of intuition of
Bergson, and to the *existence* theory of Kierkegaard and
Heidigger.   This movement toward religion based on intuition rather than on reason is a healthy one, but what it
gives is not the religion of theism of the West but the
religion of intuition of the Orient.   Also none of these
three Western philosophers is content to remain with nothing but the deliverances of intuition, since intuition for
all its merits is quite inadequate to account for Western
knowledge and institutions.   Thus what actually is provided
in these recent religious philosophies is neither a genuine
religion of intuition of the Oriental type nor a genuine
religion of doctrine of the theistic Western type, but a
muddled confusion of both in which an inadequate conception of the intuitive factor is mixed with a false or
immature conception of the theoretic, theistic element in
religion.

Two things are required to restore the integrity of
Christianity or any other religion of the theistic type.   The
first is the pursuit of the emphasis upon intuition in Western
philosophy which has occurred recently.   This pursuit can
be effective only if the intuitive element in human experience is separated from the theoretic element so that it
is gained in its purity.   The methods appropriate for this
are not those of recent Western thinkers, such as Bergson

and Kierkegaard, but those of the Orient, where an art, a philosophy, a religion and a culture grounded in the aesthetic intuition have been pursued for centuries.

There is one factor, however, in the West which will aid in this undertaking. It is the recent painting to be found in the work of the Impressionists, and especially of Paul Gill and Georgia O'Keeffe, who have separated the intuitive element in experience from the inferred external common-sense or theistic theological objects, so that we get the intuitive aesthetic component of experience in its purity. Such developments are purely negative, however, so far as Western religion is concerned. They prevent it from being confused with what it is not.

What are the positive requirements? Because theism goes counter to the deliverances of immediate apprehension by affirming that a determinate factor in man and the nature of things is immortal, when the aesthetic intuition and sense awareness reveal all determinate things to be mortal, the only basis for theism must be in a factor not given with immediacy in the aesthetic intuition but inferred from it. Consequently, the first requirement for the restoration of the integrity of Christianity is the development upon the part of contemporary man of a confidence in the existence of inferred unseen factors in knowledge.

To this end, no department of Western knowledge is more effective than natural science, especially mathematical physics, since the world of man and nature which it reveals to us has characteristics differing radically from what we immediately apprehend. Yet these objects and space-time structures of mathematical physics constitute the most trustworthy knowledge which the Western man possesses at the present moment. Certainly we do not immediately apprehend electrons in the four-dimensional space-time continuum with its metrical properties as defined by Einstein's tensor equation for gravitation, nor the electro-magnetic waves travelling through apparently empty space with a velocity of approximately 186,000 miles a second. Yet we believe in the existence of all these unseen factors and processes, and it is by means of them that the United States Navy was able to destroy the Japanese Navy in the blackness of night in the Battle of the Solomons, when nothing was visible by immediate intuition.

These and all other inferred unseen objects, such as God the Father or the immortal soul of theistic religions, can be known and distinguished from illusory inferred objects only by the empirical and logical scientific methods which science and philosophy and medieval theology developed. Moreover, it is not the business of the theologian to determine whether such an unseen inferred theoretically known component of reality exists or not, or what its character is. This is the business of the scientist.

The reason for this is that it can only be known effectively and in a trustworthy form if all the immediately apprehended data of man and nature are taken into account. The theologian, or the philosopher, by himself is quite incapable of doing this. The immediacy of experience exhibits so many facts that the task of determining them and then inferring the correct unseen factor in the nature of things from them must be divided among a large number of specialists, such as astronomers, physicists, chemists, biologists and psychologists. The philosopher, or the theologian, who is concerned with the theoretic as opposed to the aesthetic component in knowledge, when he proceeds correctly and effectively, therefore, must begin his task, as did Plato, Aristotle, St. Thomas, Descartes, Locke and Kant, after the scientist has completed his inquiry and verified by logical, mathematical, empirical and experimental means, the theory designating the unseen theoretic component in things and its character. A religion of the theistic Western type arises if within the scientifically inferred and verified unseen, theoretically known component in things, timeless, invariant relational factors can be found with which the objects of religion are identified. The justification for this identification is that religion is by definition the subject which is concerned with those factors in man and nature which are invariant with respect to time, or in other words immortal. Once those identifications are made, the meaning of doctrines like God the Father, the immortality of the soul, and the divinity of the prophet take on empirically verified scientific content and meaning.

This is precisely what occurred in medieval times with St. Thomas using the medieval science and its philosophy of science of Aristotle. It is precisely this which needs to be done by contemporary philosophers and theologians using the verified theories of contemporary science.

Thus it is to be emphasized that modern philosophers and theologians have been attempting to provide an understanding of ethics and religion and their content in entirely too cheap and easy a way. They have fallen into the error of supposing either that morality and religion in their existent form are their own justification, or that a religion of the theistic type is given by intuition, thereby on the one hand leaving contemporary religion without any content and without any conception of the way in which it can relate itself to anything else, or on the other hand confusing and corrupting Western religion by identifying it with intuition, which will give only religion of the Oriental, non-theistic type. Or to put the matter positively, before Western religion can take on the content and integrity which are its birthright, leaders in religious thought and ceremonies must undergo a far more technical and rigorous training than they receive at present.

In addition to a knowledge of the Bible after modern biblical criticism has whittled down the statements of Christ to the few words which remain after the contributions of editors are removed, contemporary students must be thoroughly trained in logic and in analysis of scientific method. For only thus will the distinction between the immediately apprehended and the theoretically and logically inferred take on specific content and meaning; only then can the theories of science be understood in those aspects which are relevant to philosophy and religion; and only then will the criteria be known for distinguishing trustworthy knowledge of unseen factors in man and nature from untrustworthy theories of such factors. Secondly, such students must be grounded in the philosophy of Western science, including Greek science first and contemporary science afterward. The philosophy of Greek science is essential because there one sees how science, when its verified hypotheses are analyzed, defines a philosophy, and how such a scientifically meaningful and verified philosophy, when proper identification of its terms with moral and theological concepts are made, provides a definition of the correct moral and religious doctrine. The contemporary philosophy of science must be studied because the scientific theory of the unseen theoretic component in things which was adequate to and verified for the empirical facts known in Greek or even medieval times is no longer adequate for the additional empirical evidence known in our day.

Such a theistic religion, with such content and foundations, has some chance of directing the release of atomic energy to good ends, since being essentially connected with the theory and philosophy of contemporary science it has a way of effectively relating itself to the scientific technology which it would control.

But even when all this is done a final problem will remain: the problem, namely, of relating this scientifically grounded, theoretically known theistic component of divinity to the Oriental aesthetic component known by immediate intuition. This is the basic problem of the philosophy of religion and the philosophy of culture of the present moment. Its solution is already known in principle. It centers in the epistemic correlation between the aesthetic and theoretic components of all things.

In any event, certain things are clear. There is an inferred unseen factor in the nature of things which constitutes trustworthy knowledge. This, Western science, and especially contemporary deductively formulated Western science, has made abundantly clear. Upon the assumption of its existence, all the greatest social, political, religious and technological achievements of Western civilization rest. Furthermore, with the primary and invariant in this unseen scientifically known factor in the nature of things, Western moralists and theologians, when they know their method, identify the good and the divine. Also there is an immediately apprehended factor in the nature of things given by intuition. The existence of this factor, Oriental intuitive philosophy and recent Western painting have made evident. Our task becomes that, therefore, of learning the character and content of the theoretic theistic component and the intuitive aesthetic component and then putting them together.

When this is done our world will possess a moral and religious knowledge which, because of its essential connection with the theory and philosophy of science, should have the means necessary to control the otherwise ethically neutral technological instruments of science. And, because of its roots in the traditional culture of the East as well as the West, this humanism should possess the truly international character necessary to call forth the support of men the world over.

A morality and religion of this character may seem altogether too abstractly philosophical and scientifically technical to win the allegiance of men. Such a conclusion, however, would be erroneous. It arises because the emotional, moving, luminous character of the aesthetic factor given by intuition has not been developed in this chapter; also, because the use of art to convey the theoretic component has not been indicated here. When these two omissions are removed, by the artistic means indicated in Chapter IX, there are ample evidences of appeal to the heart as well as to the mind of men.

This chapter is reprinted from *Et Veritas* with the kind permission of the Editor.

CHAPTER XXIV

LOGIC AND CIVILIZATION

Formal reasoning and deductively formulated science, philosophy and religion are not necessary if only concepts by intuition are used in a given culture. If what science and philosophy attempt to designate is immediately apprehended, then obviously all that one has to do in order to know it is to observe and contemplate it. The methods of intuition and contemplation become the sole trustworthy modes of inquiry. It is precisely this which the East affirms and precisely why its science has never progressed for long beyond the initial natural history stage of development to which concepts by intuition restrict one.

The philosophy of intuition of Bergson and the pure empiricism of William James mark a return in the West to the methods of the East, mixed however with the more formal and technically scientific procedures of the West. The same mixture occurs in the existentialism combined with theism of Kierkegaard. Existentialism, it is to be noted, is the thesis that immediately felt and apprehended reality, which is always a particular rather than a universal, is the real. Hence, only in Heidigger and Sartre does one find a pure existentialism in which reality is restricted to the concrete particularity given by intuition. And with them, as was not the case with William James, only its transitory differentiations have been emphasized. Hence, the English title of Sartre's play, *No Exit*. The more timeless all-embracing field character of the existentially immediate, which the Eastern methods of intuition and contemplation exhibit, has been overlooked by Heidigger and Sartre and also by Kierkegaard.

The traditional Oriental, like William James, has noted the timeless aesthetic continuum in the existential as well as its transitory differentiations. Hence for the existentialist of the traditional Orient, there is an exit. This exit, however, is not as with Kierkegaard, to the determinate God the Father of the Christian, or any other, theistic religion, since the theistic deity belongs to the theoretic component of reality which the Orient rejects. The exit, instead, is from *the mortal, transitory differentiations* of the aesthetic continuum to *the indeterminate timeless aesthetic continuum* of which they are the transitory differentiations. In other words, the exit is from the differentiated transitory factors to the timeless all-embracing indeterminate factor within the purely existential aesthetic component.

Consequently the methods underlying the knowledge and attendant civilization of the traditional Far East are more complicated than their designation as intuition and contemplation at first suggests. This complication arises because the difficult factor to experience existentially is not everything which intuition or immediate apprehension gives but the indeterminateness and continuity of the aesthetic continuum with the differentiations which it contains omitted or neglected.

Although this indeterminate factor is exactly as immediately and empirically apprehended as the determinate items given through the distinctive senses and by introspection, the intuition of it, in and for itself, is not given by a specific sense and is by no means easy. Consequently, it was natural that methods should be devised to facilitate this difficult achievement.

The Yoga is precisely such a practical method. The dialectic of negation of Buddhism by which one rationalistically rejects all determinate factors whether postulated or intuited until only the bare indeterminate manifold remains is another. The practice of the early Indian sages of sitting on their haunches in the heart of an Indian forest, so overwhelmed with the diversity and complexity of its tropical foliage that the mind loses all capacity to distinguish differentiations and is left to contemplate the unfathomable and ineffable intensity and the inexpressible immediacy of indeterminate experience itself, is a third.

If, on the other hand, that which knowledge is attempting to determine is designated by concepts by postulation which propose common sense, scientific, philosophical and theological objects and structures quite other than the ineffable aesthetic material which mere immediate apprehension reveals, it is evident that the Eastern methods of observation, intuition and contemplation, while necessary, are quite insufficient.

The question immediately arises, therefore, in the West, how trustworthy postulated factors can be distinguished from spurious ones. Without logic and deductive reasoning this is impossible. Only by applying formal logic or mathematical computation to what is postulated to deduce from it consequences which can be put to an empirical test in a crucial experiment, or a direct inspection, can the proposal of a crank be distinguished from that of a Newton or an Einstein. This is the reason why the West in its science and philosophy, having introduced concepts by postulation, is necessarily forced to maintain that mathematics and formal logical reasoning, and not merely intuition and empirical apprehension and contemplation, are absolutely necessary to gain trustworthy knowledge.

The precise method involves four parts: (1) The postulational formulation of various hypotheses concerning unobserved entities and structures, (2) the application of formal logic to the postulates stated in terms of concepts by postulation to deduce theorems stated in terms of the same kind of concepts, (3) the designation of epistemic correlations which relate the concepts by postulation in the deduced theorems to corresponding concepts by intuition which are usually concepts by sensation, thereby bridging the gulf between the postulated and the empirically intuited in order to make empirical verification or falsification possible, and (4) the immediate inspection of fact to note whether it is what the concepts by intuition designated in (3) prescribe. When the latter is the case, the postulated entities, for example, electrons, atoms or electromagnetic propagations, are said to exist; when it is not the case, the postulated factors are said not to exist. In this manner false theories in terms of concepts by postulation are distinguished from trustworthy ones.

The important point to note, for our present purposes, is that this distinction between false and trustworthy knowledge is not possible without the deductive formulation of theory involved in steps (1) and (2) and the attendant inescapable use of precise definitions and formal logic. This is the reason why the West has tended to insist on mathematics and logic in its criterion of genuine knowledge, and why even its ethical, philosophical and theological treatises have had the systematic technical, logical form of Spinoza's *Ethics,* Aristotle's *Metaphysics,* Kant's *Critique of Pure Reason,* St. Thomas's *Summa* and Whitehead's *Process and Reality* rather than the intuitive, informal, poetic temper of the Upanishads or the *Analects* of Confucius.

Stages (3) and (4) in the foregoing analysis of Western scientific and philosophic method make it equally evident however, that the West, notwithstanding its insistence upon concepts by postulation as designative of real knowledge, also uses concepts by intuition. Without the latter the bridge cannot be made by the epistemic correlations from the postulated to the positivistically and aesthetically intuited, which is essential if verification or falsification is to be attained. The charge often made by Easteners that the West entirely neglects intuition cannot, therefore, be maintained.

It may be doubted whether anyone in the East has ever intuited and contemplated all the fine distinctions in the different species of observed plants and animals to the degree to which this is true of a Western naturalist such as Linnaeus. The West has its natural history science as well as its more mature deductively formulated science and philosophy, and even in the case of the verification of the latter, as well as almost exclusively in even the statement of the former, concepts by intuition and the Eastern methods appropriate thereto are used.

Consequently, there is a very definite sense in which the dominant philosophy of the West is more inclusive than that of the major systems of the Orient. Whereas the latter tend to rule out logical methods and concepts by postulation as positively designative of anything ultimately real or important in knowledge, the West in its insistence upon concepts by postulation and their attendant formal logical method as essential for real knowledge of what exists nevertheless also uses concepts by intuition.

For this reason the East, if it is to gain an understanding of the aspect of reality grasped by the West, must accept as positive factors the concepts by postulation and the formal methods to which the sages of the Orient have at most given only a negative value. The West, however, in order to include within its outlook the basic insight of the East, needs merely to begin with its present concepts by intuition which tend to be restricted to those which are concepts by inspection and to note their apprehension not as atomic simples, but as transitory differentiations of the equally intuited manifold. When this manifold is considered in abstraction by itself, apart from the differentiations, as indeterminate, the West will have the basic concept by intuition of the East.

Even so the West has much further to go before it has comprehended the full import of this which the East has to teach it. For the tendency of the West when confronted with the immediately apprehended is either to confuse it and corrupt it with the postulated or to use it merely as a sign of the presence of the postulated and forthwith to neglect it, as Plato and the West's other metaphysical philosophers have tended to do. Thus the West, even in its occasional brief intervals of positivism or in the case of those of its philosophers, like Bergson, who have emphasized intuition, has never learned fully to appreciate the immediately apprehended in and for itself. As a consequence, the Westerner has tended to become emotionally and spiritually starved. He has been saved in theory but unsatisfied in spirit. What must be grasped is the fundamental insight of the Orient that the immediately apprehended is quite other than the scientifically, philosophically and theologically postulated and yet is nevertheless an ultimate and essential component of reality worthy of attention and contemplation in and for itself.

Contemporary Western art, which is breaking the immediately apprehended aesthetic materials free from their epistemic correlation with the old postulated common-sense and theological symbolic references, is a development in this new direction, as Chapters III and IX have indicated. There are other evidences that this movement by the East and the West toward an all-inclusive world philosophy is already under way.

One has but to talk to any contemporary leader in China or Japan or to observe what these countries are now doing to realize that the major factor which they propose to learn from the West is its technology. Their contemporary military adventures are making this all the more necessary. With respect to religion, art and humanistic as opposed to scientific philosophy many important Orientals regard the West as having little to teach them.

To use Western technology effectively, the Oriental must master the Western scientific theories from which it stems. These scientific theories have already made the Oriental aware of the positive significance of concepts by postulation and of the necessity of the formal, logical and mathematical methods of the West upon which their trustworthy usage depends.   In this manner the East is being forced to enlarge its concept of the nature of things to include the theoretic component of reality cultivated by the West.   Consequently, the philosophy of tomorrow, even in the more passive, contemplative portion of the Orient, as well as in the busy, active technical West, is going to be a philosophy of natural science.   It is not from mere fancy, but because of a profound understanding of the basic task of his own culture that Junjirō Takakusu, at the age of seventy-two, after spending his entire life upon the study of the Sanskrit and other historical sources of the Buddhist religion, turned the major portion of his thought and time to the study of the philosophy of natural science.

The Easterner's own intuitive philosophy will also be retained.   Such a believer in Western science as Hu Shih has made this clear.   In the Introduction to his *The Development of the Logical Method in Ancient China,* he writes as follows: "It would surely be a great loss to mankind if the acceptance of this new civilization (of the West) should take the form of abrupt displacement instead of organic assimilation."   To this end he proposes a return to the ancient Chinese classics where the beginnings of Western scientific methods were suggested but never pursued.   One result of such a return may well be the rediscovery of the intuitive concept of the indeterminate continuum which is at the basis of Confucianism, as we have previously indicated, and the retention of this along with the concepts by postulation from Western science.   Between these two factors there is no conflict whatever.   In this manner, the basic doctrine of the East and the unique use of concepts by postulation from the West can be combined.

There is a converse movement in the West already taking it to the same position.   This movement has its origin in the intense analysis of the method of deductive, empirical science which is now going on. This analysis centers around the question concerning how theories about unobserved scientific objects designated by concepts by postulation can be verified. The epistemic correlations, referred to previously, answer this question. They also make it evident, however, that any complete and adequate philosophy of science must have an irreducible concept by intuition as well as irreducible concepts by postulation. Otherwise theories formulated in terms of the latter concepts could never be verified, and there would be only the theoretically conceived and no directly apprehended world with all its moving aesthetic immediacy to apprehend and contemplate. In this manner the analysis of the method of verifying scientific objects designated by concepts by postulation is driving the West to the acceptance of a concept by intuition as essential also.

One other development in the West is enforcing the same conclusion. Its modern philosophy began with Descartes' conviction of the indubitable certainty of the existence of his own self as a mental substance. It is significant that Descartes justified this conclusion not on the empirical grounds of intuition and contemplation but on the rationalistic ground that it was logically presupposed in the introspected fact of his own doubting. Only the doubting, not the doubter, was given by immediate apprehension. Thus Descartes' mental substance was a concept by postulation. His concepts of God and matter were of the same kind.

This is true also of Locke's mental and material substances. They arose as a result of the necessary attempt to clarify the relation between the postulated atoms in Newton's physics and the directly inspected colors and sounds and odors given to the senses. As Newton emphasized, only the latter were concepts by intuition.

It was an essential point in the theories of Descartes and Locke that colors, sounds and all other immediately apprehended aesthetic impressions had their basis solely in the action of the material substances on the mental substances. In short, modern Western philosophy has been reared upon the attempt to define the intuited away in terms of an inter-action of the postulated.

The history of modern philosophy is the story of the failure of this attempt. Berkeley and Hume showed that upon such a basis the knower could never get the meanings requisite to formulate even the notion of a substance, whether it be mental or material. Modern psychology and psychobiology have confirmed Berkeley's and Hume's analysis. All attempts to clarify the manner in which the atoms of physics and their emissions of energy act upon the mental substance to cause the latter to project the supposedly phenomenal continuum of colors and sounds have been unproductive. The theory has now turned out to be a deductively futile scientific hy-pothesis. The results in epistemology have been similar. All attempts of modern philosophers subsequent to Descartes and Locke to resolve the epistemological difficulties, into which this modern Western attempt to reduce the intuited to the postulated lands one, have ended in failure.

The reason is very simple. It has been obscured, because of the neglect of the distinction between concepts by intuition and concepts by postulation. Colors and sounds being im-mediately apprehended things are factors denoted by con-cepts by intuition. Persistent mental and material substances being unobserved postulated factors are entities designated by concepts by postulation. Since these two types of concepts get their meanings in different ways they refer to different worlds of discourse. The logical methods of definition and déduction can move within a given world of discourse, but they cannot move from one world of discourse to an entirely different one. This is the reason why no amount of logical manipulation by means of definition or deduction can take one from the wave-length for "blue" which is a concept by postulation to the immediately sensed "blue" which is a concept by intuition. Yet it is precisely this which the modern attempt to derive the aesthetically immediate factors which we directly apprehend from the interaction of postulated mental and material factors has tried to do. Modern philosophy has ended in failure because its basic thesis, that the aesthetically immediate is a secondary, purely phenomenal factor derived from the postulated, attempts what is logically impossible, namely, the logical derivation or deduction of concepts by intuition from concepts by postulation.

Consequently, modern Western epistemologists are being gradually forced to the same position to which modern logicians have been led as a consequence of their analysis of the relation between empirical intuited and postulated theoretical factors in scientific method, the conclusion, namely, that there must be an irreducible concept by intuition as well as irreducible concepts by postulation. But to admit this is to accept the fundamental thesis of the Orient that the aesthetically immediate known solely by intuition and contemplation represents something scientifically and philosophically irreducible and ultimate.

The psychological, epistemological, religious and cultural consequences of this, when its full implications are grasped, will be tremendous. A veritable revolution will have occurred in Western thought. Instead of defining the aesthetically immediate away as a mere phenomenal projection resulting from the interaction of mind and body, body and mind and the medium joining them will be defined, each in turn and all together, in terms of the relation between the aesthetically immediate denoted by concepts by intuition and the theoretically ontological designated by concepts by postulation. In short, instead of defining aesthetics and logic, including mathematics, in terms of a relation between psychology and physics, psychology and physics will be derived from a more primary aesthetics and logic. Put more concisely, this means that instead of regarding consciousness as a faculty or property of a knower by means of which he takes hold of and is aware of purely subjective projected aesthetic materials such as colors and sounds, a knower will be thought of as conscious because he is composed of irreducible, ineffable, aesthetic materials.   It is the primacy of the aesthetic and the ineffability of anything known with immediacy which is the source of the so-called consciousness of the individual and not the consciousness of the individual which is the source of the aesthetic materials.   Thus aesthetics and logic, including a mathematics defined in terms of logic, become the primary subjects, the one as irreducible, fundamental and important as the other, and psychology, physics and even religion will be derived from them — a complete reversal of the basic assumptions of modern Western thought.

Just as his importation of Western technology is forcing the Oriental to supplement his traditional insistence upon the primacy and irreducibility of the empirically immediate with an equal status for the logically inferred, so recent developments in Western empirical logic and epistemology are driving the Occidental to supplement his traditional emphasis upon the primacy of the postulated with a similar recognition of the importance of the immediately apprehended. The theoretic component of reality of the West and the intuited or aesthetic component of the Orient are both ultimate and in part at least irreducible, the one being, as previous chapters have demonstrated, the epistemic correlate of the other.

It appears that by independent developments in the East and in the West a new and more comprehensive philosophy is being made articulate in which the basic aesthetic component discovered long ago in the Orient is being combined with the newly conceived theoretic component of the nature of things, necessitated by the recent revolutionary scientific discoveries of the West.   This new philosophy, by enlarging the outlook and values of each part of the world to include

those of the other, may well serve as a trustworthy criterion
of the good for a truly cosmopolitan and international world
order, in which the diverse basic conceptions and resultant
valuations of two great cultures are combined into a single
world civilization, the richer and better because it includes
in complementary harmony with balanced emphasis the most
mature logical methods and attendantly profound insights of
each.

This chapter, except for its references to existentialism, is reprinted
with the kind permission of the Editor of the Princeton University
Press from pp. 223-234 of *Philosophy — East and West*. Edited by
Charles A. Moore. Princeton University Press. 1944.

Hu Shih. *The Development of the Logical Method in Ancient
    China*. Shanghai, 1928.

F. S. C. Northrop. *Science and First Principles,* pp. 256-261.
    The Macmillan Company, New York, and Cambridge Uni-
    versity Press, England, 1931.
    The Meeting of East and West. The Macmillan Company,
    New York, 1946.
    "The Complementary Emphases of Eastern Intuitive and
    Western Scientific Philosophy" in *Philosophy — East and
    West*. Edited by Charles A. Moore. Princeton University
    Press, 1944.

INDEX